Elements of Operational Research

Elements of
Operational Research

F. M. WILKES
Senior Lecturer in Economics
Faculty of Commerce and Social Science
University of Birmingham

McGRAW-HILL Book Company (UK) Limited

London · New York · St. Louis · San Francisco · Auckland · Bogotá
Guatemala · Hamburg · Johannesburg · Lisbon · Madrid
Mexico · Montreal · New Delhi · Panama · Paris · San Juan
São Paulo · Singapore · Sydney · Tokyo · Toronto

Published by
McGRAW-HILL Book Company (UK) Limited
Maidenhead · Berkshire · England

British Library Cataloguing in Publication Data

Wilkes, Francis Michael
  Elements of operational research.
  1. Operations research
  I. Title
  658.4'034   T57.6   80-40607

  ISBN 0-07-084540-9 SC
  ISBN 0-07-0845468 HC

ELEMENTS OF OPERATIONAL RESEARCH

1 2 3 4 5 CUP 83210

Cover design by Vivienne Wilkes.
Typeset by Advanced Filmsetters (Glasgow) Limited and
printed and bound in Great Britain by Cambridge University Press

As when on some secluded branch in forest far and wide sits perched an owl, who, full of self-conceit and self-created wisdom, explains, comments, condemns, ordains and orders things not understood, yet full of his importance still holds forth to stocks and stones around—so sits and scribbles Mike.

Faraday (Letter)

CONTENTS

PREFACE

Professor Silvanus P. Thompson began the prologue to his immensely successful *Calculus Made Easy* with the following words: 'Considering how many fools can calculate, it is surprising that it should be thought either a difficult or a tedious task for any other fool to learn how to master the same tricks.' In presenting this quotation here, I do not intend to suggest that we are all of us fools—or that Operational Research is merely a bag of tricks. I do imply, however, that the difficulty of OR techniques—in basic form—is frequently exaggerated.

A good example of this phenomenon is the 'simplex' method in linear programming. This is often spoken of in reverential tones as being extremely complicated and for initiates only. One referee of this book suggested that most accounting students would not get past first base (sic) so far as this technique was concerned. This is nonsense! The simplex method involves nothing more than the four operations of simple arithmetic, a few verbal rules, and plenty of practice. In stock control, admittedly, things get more involved: we are required on occasion to take a square root. However, from a distance a rash of square root signs can give a page a 'Greek' appearance and thus render the material instantly inaccessible.

In the transportation and assignment methods only two of the four operations of common arithmetic (adding and subtracting) and some simple verbal rules are called for. Again practice is the key. Indeed nothing could be much simpler, unless it is critical path method. Here one is required to connect circles with straight lines. Queueing theory, with all its formulae, dense in summation signs (Σ) and factorial signs (!) can give the impression of daunting complexity. But once again 'Σ' only involves adding and '!' only involves multiplying. At a basic level most problems here involve substitution in formulae. Similar remarks would apply to the material covered in the chapters on statistical replacement methods and forecasting.

Simulation involves finding out what would (on average!) happen if...; Johnson's method of sequencing requires three verbal rules and the ability to decide which of two numbers is the smaller. A similar skill is required in finding the 'saddle point' in a 'game'. Expected values involve averaging and dynamic programming (stripped of the unhelpful notation) calls for the ability to add and the patience to take one stage at a time. The key to successful understanding is practice.

To this end, worked examples in the text are designed to illustrate all the main technical points and there are numerous exercises at the end of each chapter. Comprehensive worked solutions to the numerical questions are provided at the end of the book. Several of these questions are from past examination papers of the Association of Certified Accountants, the Institute of Chartered Accountants in England and Wales, and the Institute of Cost and Management Accountants. Permission by these bodies to use their questions is gratefully acknowledged. The text of each chapter has been designed to give the coverage necessary to answer these questions. I should point out that the solutions that I have prepared should not be regarded as model answers.

In all of this I am not trying to suggest that having read this modest volume the reader will be equipped to tackle full-blown Industrial Operational Research problems. Nor am I trying to suggest that advanced (i.e., difficult) OR is not difficult. But at a basic level the subject is perfectly manageable for the average, well-motivated student. Operational Research is a stimulating topic with enormous practical utility and provides great insight into structures and immense richness of interpretation. Thus it should be pleasant to learn. I hope that you enjoy this book.

ACKNOWLEDGEMENTS

It always helps to speed things along for editors to have a 'clean' manuscript to work with. I should like to thank Marilyn Mansell for some pristine typing and near miraculour decipherment. I should also like to thank fellow students M. A. Both, M. J. Titmus, D. J. Meek, D. Birtwistle, R. W. T. Apps and G. Powell for the relish with which they debugged the numerical examples. Of course, any errors and ambiguities remaining are fully my own responsibility. I should like to thank Petre Sefton for the efficient and thoroughly professional way that the whole project was managed. Finally, my thanks to Vivienne Wilkes for unflagging support and encouragement and for technical assistance with the design of the book.

F. M. Wilkes
Birmingham
February 1980

ONE

INTRODUCTION

1-1 OVERVIEW OF THE TEXT

This text covers the vast majority of topics that would enter into any Operational Research (OR) syllabus. A special eye has been kept on the contents of, and answers to, professional examination papers. The depth and scope of the content at times go beyond what seem to be current standards. This has been done for two reasons: (a) to allow the better student to give first-rate answers to the kind of questions that currently arise and (b) to allow for 'syllabus development' and shifts of emphasis by the examining bodies. However, not *absolutely* everything can be included. Even H. M. Wagner's massive Principles of Operations Research (Wagner, 1972) leaves some stones unturned. Thus several further references are here written into the text (and listed in the Selected Bibliography). The interested student can follow these trails but the present book alone should be amply sufficient in respect of the OR content of most professional papers. Further, the time pressures on professional students are such that it would be unreasonable to expect every word of every chapter to be understood—this should not be necessary. However, if full familiarity can be attained for *some* topics the opportunity may arise to really 'sparkle'.

It has been the writer's intention to achieve a fairly 'easy' style. This should not give the impression that the arguments are casual. All statements have been thoroughly researched and have rigorous foundations in the subject literature. The writer has tried to pose as many commonly arising questions as possible when discussing the topics. No doubt the users of the book will find many more. However, it is the writer's hope that the reader will find few remaining ambiguities.

As regards the structure of the text, from the Contents you will see that the (linear) programming methods are grouped together in Chapters 2, 3, and 4 and there is considerable interlinkage between them. Critical path, inventory control, queueing theory, and replacement methods are given more or less self-contained presentations in Chapters 5, 6, 7, and 8. Students who want only to revise a topic or two can, for example, go straight into the queueing theory of Chapter 7 without having to read Chapters 1 to 6. The chapter on forecasting is also essentially self-contained, but that on simulation draws examples and exercises from other areas. In Chapter 11 attenuated presentations of the rather less commonly arising topics are given, although each and every one has cropped up in examination questions at some time or another (as did the 'traffic flow' topic of Chapter 10). The presentation bears very much in mind the likely requirements of examiners.

Just a quick word to the instructor. The material *does* go some way beyond what appear, at the time of writing, to be the requirements of most professional bodies. It should not be necessary to cover absolutely every point. Exercise your judgement freely about what to leave out—or what extra to put in. The instructor is the 'agent in the field' and is in close touch with current trends and requirements. The self-instructor can similarly use the text as both manual and resource book. There is no better guide to current requirements than recent examination questions. Sometimes the official and unofficial 'answers' leave something to be desired in respect of both clarity and accuracy. While using these sources as *guides*, it is suggested that you use this book, or some of the references given herein, to elaborate and develop answers and arguments.

1-2 WHAT IS OPERATIONAL RESEARCH?

It is now well known that Operational Research originated in England as a result of the study of military operations during the Second World War. After the war its commercial potential was soon recognized and its development has proceeded fastest in the United States where it is known as 'operations research' or alternatively as 'management science'.

There have been many attempts to pin down operational research with a definition. Here are some.

Definition 1

Operational research is the application of the methods of science to complex problems arising in the direction and management of large systems of men, machines, materials and money in industry, business, government and defence. The distinctive approach is to develop a scientific model of the system, incorporating measurements of factors such as chance and risk, with which to predict and compare the outcomes of alternative decisions, strategies or controls. The purpose is to help management determine its policy and actions scientifically. (Operational Research Society of Great Britain.)

Definition 2

Operations research is concerned with scientifically deciding how to best design and operate man-machine systems, usually requiring the allocation of scarce resources. (Operations Research Society of America.)

These two definitions may be considered to be the most important since they emanate from two of the most important agencies in the subject area. Note that they are not identical. While the UK definition spells things out more fully the US definition contains that vital reference to 'the allocation of scarce resources'. Key words are 'scientific approach', 'model', 'system', 'measurement', 'decide', and 'scarce resources'. Notice that the British definition contains no reference to *optimization* and that the US definition slips the word 'best' in rather quietly. While admitting that some systems cannot be optimized, the 'optimizing style of approach' with an objective or criterion function to be maximized or minimized is an essential feature of many OR models. There is no shortage of other definitions.

Definition 3

Operations research is the systematic application of quantitative methods, techniques and tools to the analysis of problems involving the operation of systems. (Daellenbach and George, 1978.)

Definition 4

Operations research is essentially a collection of mathematical techniques and tools which, in conjunction with a systems approach, are applied to solve practical decision problems of an economic or engineering nature. (Daellenbach and George, 1978.)

Definition 4 refers to the alternative view of OR as a motley assortment of methods and models that have grown up largely independently of one another. There is much to be said for this view. Synthesis and rationalization came later in the development of the subject.

Still other definitions emphasize the growing interdisciplinary nature of the subject. Thierauf and Keklamp (1975) lay considerable emphasis on this aspect.

Definition 5

Operations Research utilizes the planned approach (updated scientific method) and an interdisciplinary team in order to represent complex functional relationships as mathematical models for the purpose of providing a quantitative basis for decision making and uncovering new problems for quantitative analysis.

While Taha (1976) says:

Definition 6

this new decision-making field has been characterized by the use of scientific knowledge through interdisciplinary team effort for the purpose of determining the best utilization of limited resources.

The word 'interdisciplinary' covers a multitude of possibilities, from referring, at one extreme, to a group as diverse as managers, economists, engineers, mathematicians, computer programmers, personnel staff, etc., to the other extreme of a 'team' of two people with slightly different outlooks. Of course there is nothing to prevent *one* person from considering several aspects of the problem. There is an element of *fashion* in the style in which a problem is tackled. One of the best definitions was that given by Churchman, Ackoff, and Arnoff (1957).

Definition 7

OR, in the most general sense, can be characterized as the application of scientific methods, techniques, and tools to problems involving the operations of systems so as to provide those in control of the operations with optimum solutions to the problems.

The reader could easily dig up more definitions as most textbooks make an attempt or two. An interesting exception is S. L. Cook (writing in Littlechild, 1977) who says:

Operational research has been described as a method, an approach, a set of techniques, a team activity; a combination of many disciplines, an extension of particular disciplines (mathematics, engineering, economics), a new discipline; a vocation, even a religion. It is perhaps some of all these things.

Amen to that.

1-3 MODELS IN OR

Models (of the mathematical rather than the iconoclastic variety) are used in the OR problem solving approach. But when does a problem exist? Daellenbach and George (1978) list four conditions:

1. There must be a *decision maker* ('who' may be a company or a single individual) who must have an objective.
2. The decision maker must have at least two alternative courses of action available.
3. There must be some degree of doubt as to which course of action best achieves the objective.

4. There must be an environment to which the problem pertains (e.g., the firm or the economy).

A mathematical model consists of *decision variables* linked by *constraining relationships* and entering into an *objective function*. In the model will be certain fixed factors (*constants, parameters, coefficients*) which are data. There may be uncontrollable factors such as *random variables*. In the linear programming chapter we give a step-by-step procedure for construction of an LP model from a somewhat idealized environment.

Sometimes it is argued that 'the model is not realistic'. Of course it is not. This is the whole point. The model should reflect the *important* factors and relationships in a situation and leave out the trivia. However, it can be very difficult to judge what is important in any particular case. The purpose of building a model is to identify the *best values of the decision variables*, or to *predict* or, less ambitiously, simply to study the system so as to find ways of *improving* its performance.

Sometimes when a model is first built it may still be too complicated. There are various ways in which *simplifications* can be made; for instance:

1. 'Linearize' those relationships which are non-linear.
2. Reduce the number of decision variables or constraints.
3. Change the nature of some variables (e.g., discrete to continuous).
4. Replace many objectives with a single objective.
5. Exclude dynamic elements (make the model static).
6. Assume that random variables take specific values.

Phillips, Ravindran, and Solberg (1976) list ten principles of model building:

1. Do not build a complicated model when a simple one will suffice.
2. Beware of moulding the problem to fit the technique.
3. Exercise great care in 'solving' the model (do not make mathematical slips).
4. Confirm the appropriateness of a model before implementing decisions.
5. A model should not be mistaken for the real thing.
6. Do not try to make a model do that for which it was not intended.
7. Beware of overselling a model.
8. The construction and development of the model itself yields many benefits.
9. GIGO (garbage in, garbage out. A model's value is no better than its data).
10. Models cannot replace decision makers.

There is one absolutely crucial point about the use of a model-building approach. It is this: *to be justified, the model or technique only has to improve on what would otherwise have been done.* It does not have to find the 'global' optimum or be perfect in any other respect. In short, it only has to work.

1-4 THE PHASES OF AN OR STUDY

This brings us to the subject of getting things to work, and what phases are involved in reaching this point. We can list five stages:

1. Define the problem.
2. Construct (or reconstruct) the model. This stage includes data gathering.
3. Obtain a solution.
4. Test the solution for reasonableness ('validation') and if necessary return to step (2).
5. Implement the results.

We have already touched upon the subject of problem definition. Essentially this involves the identification of objectives, variables, and constraints. This generally calls for 'skill', 'experience' or 'flair'. The human element is certainly not lacking at this juncture. The second phase is closely linked with the first and when variables, objectives, and constraints have been identified the picture should have become a lot clearer. It can then be decided whether a standard *mathematical model* (for example, linear programming) would suit. If the situation is too complex then a *simulation* model is indicated. In really vague situations intuitive or *heuristic* 'models' may apply. Of course, some situations may involve hybrids of these types.

Phase (3) is the best defined of all, involving the use of optimization techniques as described in this text, or, if simulation is used, the extraction of measures of effectiveness of the system. The important role of sensitivity analysis should be emphasized at this point. It is very common for there to be a measure of uncertainty about important system parameters.

Phase (4) often involves running the model in parallel with the real system for a while. Better still, if past data for the system can be fed into the model it can then be seen how well its performance corresponded to, or improved on, the actual historical results. Of course, there is no *guarantee* that a good 'historical' performance will be continued in the future. These validation methods do not apply to systems which do not yet exist! In this case a simulation model could be constructed.

Phase (5) implementation is often the most difficult of all. As Taha puts it, implementation 'would basically involve the translation of these results into detailed operating instructions issued in an understandable form to the individual who will administer and operate the system after its execution'. Continuous liaison between the OR team and management staff not on the team is essential so that vital practicalities are not overlooked. Even so, the implementation can cause problems. Obviously it would be nonsense to implement the results in such a fashion that the assumptions of the model were violated. Further, the model structure and results may conflict severely with the existing managerial structure of the organization. In such a case we would talk of 'phasing-in'. Implementation is rarely accomplished overnight. Six months is not an untypical period for sizeable exercises, and on the very largest scale years may be involved. This latter is the case when new capital equipment is required that has a long lead time, and redundancy problems may involve running down a labour force by natural wastage.

There is a good deal more that could be said at these general levels. Consideration of some of the points made here can help to put the models used into perspective. But by far the best way to discover limitations and develop skills is in actual practice.

EXERCISES

The best place for a chapter on the methodology of a subject is two-thirds of the way through the book. At such a stage the essential style of approach to the subject will have been conveyed in the most efficient way—by example. In the remaining one-third of the book the reader would then be in a position critically to evaluate the main ingredients in the style of approach. However, there is an immense historical insistence on locating such a chapter at the front of a book. This has duly been yielded to. Nevertheless the student might consider attempting some of these questions after having read a few more chapters. Indeed, such reading will be essential to questions 1-5, 1-6, 1-7, and 1-8.

1-1 Compare and contrast the definitions of Operational Research given by the British and American Societies.

1-2 Explain the conditions under which an operational research problem exists. Illustrate the points in the context of a firm.

1-3 What are the important principles of OR model building? And how can models be simplified?

1-4 List and describe the various phases of an OR study.

1-5 'Model building is an essential feature of the operational research practitioner's approach to problem solving.' What is meant by 'model building' in the context of operational research? Illustrate your answer with particular reference to inventory control and simulation. (Association of Certified Accountants, Professional Examination: Section 2, paper 12, Management Mathematics, December 1976.)

1-6 The stages in the Operational Research approach to a problem may be listed as follows:

    (a) Problem definition.
    (b) Construction of a model.
    (c) Derivation of a solution from the model.
    (d) Testing the model and its solution.
    (e) Establishment of controls.
    (f) Implementation.

Explain what you understand by these various stages illustrating your answers by referring to a particular problem or problems. (Association of Certified Accountants, Professional Examination: Section 2, paper 12, Management Mathematics, December 1975.)

1-7 'Operational Research attempts to remove the need for experience, imagination and insight from the process of business decision making. Any and every problem, it is hoped, will eventually succumb to a mathematical technique. At that point humanity may as well retire from the scene and concede the machine its final victory. Problem solving will quite simply be a matter of selecting the appropriate formula, plugging in, switching on and meekly awaiting the results.' How does your view of OR, its aims and method, compare with this statement? (Association of Certified Accountants, Professional Examination: Section 2, paper 12, Management Mathematics, December 1978.)

1-8 'The chief failing of operational research is that it gives the appearance of providing simple and definitive answers. In a world where the questions are often ill-defined and important factors are subject to rapid and unpredictable change, this readily leads to dangerous inflexibility. Indeed, fluctuations in price, demand, supply, cost or requirement—to name but a few—may well ensure that a "solution" is obsolete long before it is applied.' In what way can sensitivity analysis guard against obsolescence of this sort? Give specific examples of its use and discuss its value and limitations. (Association of Certified Accounts, Professional Examination: Section 2, paper 12, Management Mathematics, June 1978.)

1-9 (*a*) Model building is a central element in operational research method. Give a description of the following basic types of model.

     (i) Iconic

     (ii) Analogue

     (iii) Mathematical (Symbolic)

    (*b*) Give an account of the information requirements, assumptions and applications of any three of the following different types of mathematical model.

     (i) Allocation

     (ii) Queueing

     (iii) Inventory

     (iv) Replacement

(Institute of Cost and Management Accountants, Professional Stage: Part I, Quantitative Techniques, May 1979.)

1-10 Discuss the methodology of operational research and describe the main stages involved in carrying out an operational research project. (Institute of Cost and Management Accountants, Professional Stage: Part I, Quantitative Techniques, May 1978.)

TWO
LINEAR PROGRAMMING

2-1 BACKGROUND

Linear programming is one of the most widely used and best understood management techniques. Developed mainly since the Second World War, the method first found military use in logistical problems. The commercial potential of the technique was soon recognized with agriculture providing one of the earliest commercial applications. It was seen that the problem of producing (at least cost) an animal-feed mix with given minimum nutrient contents was a linear programming problem. Other early uses were found in the petrochemical industry and the use of the method then spread rapidly. Some industries currently using linear programming (LP) are: oil refining, steel making, food processing, paper making, brick manufacture, electrical goods, and very many others.

A general description of an LP problem sounds very similar to a definition of the static economizing problem, viz., the problem of the optimal allocation of scarce resources between alternative uses within an all-linear framework. Indeed some writers describe LP as the 'general allocation' problem. More specifically some problems usefully addressed by LP are:

1. Production planning (deciding what goods to produce and how much of each).
2. Production scheduling (deciding which jobs should go on which machines in what order).
3. Transportation arrangements.

4. Assignment problems (assigning people to jobs, work to machines or contracts to bidders).
5. Investment planning.
6. Overall corporate planning.

There are many other uses but (5) and (6) above represent increasingly important areas of use.

2-2 A PROBLEM AND ITS FORMULATION

In this context, 'formulation' means writing or 'expressing' a problem in a convenient mathematical form. Consider an example:

Example 2-1 Azed Enterprises can manufacture two products. Relevant financial and resource requirement details are:

	Alpha	Omega
Materials (kg per unit)	4	1
Labour hours (per unit)	2	3
Unit variable cost (£)	18	11
Selling price (£)	24	16
Maximum sales (units)	180	320

The available daily supply of 'materials' (of a uniform type) is limited to 800 kg and labour hours per day are limited to 900. No other resources are in limited supply, but the costs of these factors, along with the materials and labour hours, have been allowed for in the unit variable cost figures. Azed management wish to set production levels so as to maximize the overall 'contribution' secured.

SOLUTION In formulating a problem there are essentially three questions to answer. We shall state these questions and answer them in the context of the Azed Enterprises problem.

What are the decision variables? Decision variables are those elements within a problem over which the decision maker (you!) has at least some control. Sometimes the decision variables are called 'instruments'. For instance, a farmer's decision variables might be the acreages to plant with wheat or barley, an investor's decision variables might be the number of shares to buy in certain companies. Azed's decision variables are the weekly production figures for the two products. Let x_1 and x_2 be the number of units made of the Alpha and Omega models respectively. Of course in reality there are many more decision variables than two (prices in this context) but so long as the problem can be 'linearized' the same principles apply.

What is the objective? Here, we are simply told that this is the maximization of contribution and hence profit. In practice things are not always so clear-cut, particularly in the larger enterprises with separation of ownership and management. Sometimes turnover or growth (defined in some way) are used instead of contribution or profit. In other cases the objective is achieving a target return on capital or just breaking even. The crucial things are to (a) identify the objective and then (b) to express this objective in terms of the decision variables. In Azed's case the unit contributions are given by selling prices less unit variable costs. These are £24 − £18 = 6 (we shall generally omit £ signs in future) per unit on the Alpha model and 16 − 11 = 5 per unit on the Omega. Letting π stand for overall contribution (the letter C will be reserved for Costs) with x_1 Alphas and x_2 Omegas being produced, then

$$\pi = 6x_1 + 5x_2$$

This is the *objective function*, the expression which it is the decision maker's objective to optimize.

What are the constraints? Constraints are limitations or restrictions placed on our choices. Here these relate to the use of the potentially scarce resources: labour and materials. In other contexts the farmer's scarce resource is land; the investor's is cash (or credit). Consider the materials constraint. Obviously as a first step we can write

Total materials used in production $\leqslant$ 800

where the sign $\leqslant$ is read 'less than or equal to'.

From the data given we note that *each* unit of the Alpha product requires 4 kg of material giving a requirement of $4x_1$ kg if x_1 Alphas are made. Also each unit of the Omega product requires 1 kg of material, thus calling for x_2 hours altogether. A production plan is a pair of values of x_1 and x_2 so the amount of materials called for by any plan is $4x_1 + x_2$ in total. Thus we can write

$$4x_1 + x_2 \leqslant 800$$

In a similar fashion each unit of Alpha made requires 2 labour hours while each Omega calls for 3 labour hours. Hence the labour time requirement of a production plan is $2x_1 + 3x_2$ where, clearly,

$$2x_1 + 3x_2 \leqslant 900$$

Now in addition the sales department has put limits to the amounts of the two goods that can be sold at the stated prices. To keep the problem simple we are not considering discounts, special promotions or indeed storage. We simply require that daily production of Alphas does not exceed 180 and for the Omegas daily production must be less than, or equal to, 320 units. Quite simply

$$x_1 \leqslant 180 \quad \text{and} \quad x_2 \leqslant 320$$

We are not quite finished with constraints. Much LP work is done by computer and these rapid but feeble intellects must have it *all* written in—or else nonsense may emerge. In particular we must prohibit negative production. That is (with $\geqslant$ read as 'greater than or equal to'),

$$x_1 \geqslant 0 \quad \text{and} \quad x_2 \geqslant 0$$

These are called the sign requirements. We can now state the problem in full. It is to choose a pair of values of x_1 and x_2 (the daily production levels) such that we:

			Constraint number
Maximize	$\pi = 6x_1 + 5x_2$		
subject to	$4x_1 + x_2 \leqslant 800$		(1)
	$2x_1 + 3x_2 \leqslant 900$		(2)
	$x_1 \leqslant 180$		(3)
	$x_2 \leqslant 320$		(4)
and where	$x_1 \geqslant 0$	and	$x_2 \geqslant 0$

Thus the algebraic formulation of this problem is completed, but once again it should be emphasized that the exercise is not always so simple in practice.

2-3 THE SEMI-GRAPHICAL METHOD

There are a number of solution procedures available for linear programming problems. Small problems (such as the one under consideration here) can be solved graphically or by using diagrams as an aid, which is the main method that is suggested here. Larger problems use an *algorithmic* approach. These are step-by-step repetitive procedures that eventually home in on the optimum. By far the most important of these iterative methods is the simplex method which we shall present later on.

First consider the semi-graphical approach. Here we want to represent all relevant features of the problem in a diagram. Let us start with constraint (1). First draw in the line corresponding to the equation part of the constraint, viz., $4x_1 + x_2 = 800$. This cuts the axes at $x_1 = 200$ and $x_2 = 800$ as shown in Fig. 2-1. Clearly it would be permissible to have $4x_1 + x_2 = 700$ which would give a new line of *the same slope* cutting the axes at 175 and 700 respectively. Thus all points on or below the original line are allowed; we must be on the 'hairy' side of the line.

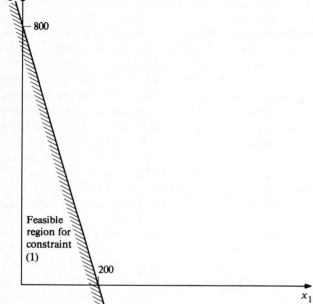

Figure 2-1

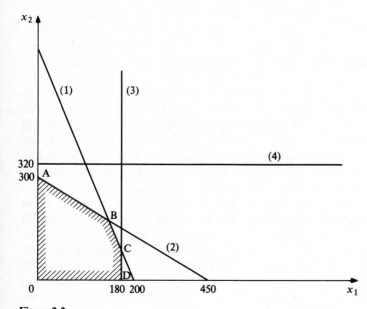

Figure 2-2

Finally, note that as far as constraint (1) is concerned there is nothing wrong with *negative* values of the x's.

Figure 2-2 shows the results of adding the remaining constraints and sign requirements in a similar fashion. In each case take the equality part of the constraint, draw in the straight line that this produces, then identify which side of the line is permitted. The final result is that only points in the polygon OABCD satisfy *all* the constraints and the sign requirements. In the drawing of the figure we have adopted the usual convention of suppressing those parts of the constraint lines that would be outside of the axes. Note that there is nothing different in character about the sign requirements. For $x_1 \geqslant 0$ we could equally well have written $-x_1 + 0x_2 \leqslant 0$ which as an equality identifies the vertical (x_2) axis and we must be on or to the right of this line. Notice also that constraint (4) is *redundant*. At all times one or other of the remaining restrictions sets tighter limits than does constraint (4). Constraint (4) can now safely be left out of the problem (with one caveat which we shall come to later on) although it would not distort the result to leave it in.

The boundary and interior of OABCD is variously called the *feasible region, feasible production set, production possibility set* or *opportunity set*. The coordinates of each point in the feasible region give a pair of production levels for the two products. Even if we did no more than draw the diagram, a good deal has already been accomplished: it is much easier to see the range of alternatives from the diagram than it is from the inequalities. But which point in the set is the best? To find out we need to introduce the objective function into the diagram. This is done in contour form. Consider the point A in the feasible set. At point A, $x_1 = 0$ and $x_2 = 300$, which values, when substituted into the objective function, give $\pi = 6(0) + 5(300) = 1500$ so that 1500 in contributions is made at A. We might ask what other values of x_1 and x_2 would give 1500 contribution? Clearly, if we reduced x_2 by six units this would reduce the total contribution by 30, but this could be made up by raising production of x_1 by five units. Thus the point $x_1 = 5$, $x_2 = 294$ also gives a contribution of 1500. Continuing with this process of substitution at the rate of six units of x_2 for five of x_1 would maintain the contribution at 1500 and bring us eventually to the point $x_1 = 250$, $x_2 = 0$ on the x_1 axis. This is point E shown in Fig. 2-3. All of the points on the line AE represent production levels giving the same (1500) contribution. Such a line is a *contour* of the contribution surface that one can imagine lying above the x_1, x_2 'plane'. It is a contour in just the same sense as the contours of hills (physical surfaces) on an ordnance survey map. Not all points on the contour (shown as a broken line to distinguish it from the constraints) are feasible—E itself is outside the feasible region. The fact is that many of the points along AE *are* feasible. Azed could certainly earn 1500 contribution in a variety of ways. Clearly, we are not especially interested in 1500 contribution; we are seeking the maximum. This first value was a *trial value*,

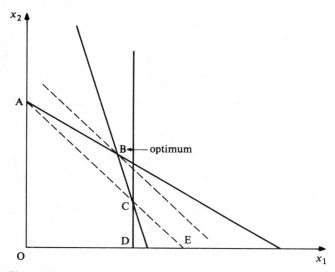

Figure 2-3

the purpose of which was to establish the slope of the objective function contours which we have seen to be 6/5.

Having thus established the slope of the objective function contours, we next note that the further 'out' (upwards and to the right) a contour lies, the greater the contribution to which it corresponds. For instance, £1800 would result from x_1 and x_2 values lying along a line joining 360 on the x_2 axis with 300 on the x_1 axis. Again not all points on such a line would be in the feasible region, but *some* are.

The graphical procedure should now be obvious. Find a point in the feasible region that is on the *highest* contour. This is point B, the coordinates of which are the optimal values of x_1 and x_2. From a well-drawn diagram these values could be read off the axes, but this is not recommended. There is no guarantee that the optimal values will be convenient numbers, and the degree of approximation may not be good enough. Rather we use the diagram to see where the optimum lies and then solve algebraically for the values of x_1 and x_2. In particular we determine from the diagram which constraints *intersect* at the optimum. These particular constraints—and only these—will be satisfied as strict equalities. These equations can then be solved in a simple fashion for the precise values of x_1 and x_2. Thus in the present case we have constraints (1) and (2) intersecting at B so that

$$4x_1 + x_2 = 800 \quad (1)$$
$$2x_1 + 3x_2 = 900 \quad (2)$$

To solve these equations it is perhaps most convenient to multiply (2) by two and subtract (1) from the result. This will eliminate x_1. Doing this

$$(2) \times 2 = 4x_1 + 6x_2 = 1800$$
$$(1) \qquad 4x_1 + x_2 = 800$$

$$5x_2 = 1000$$
$$\therefore \quad x_2 = 200$$

and by substitution of $x_2 = 200$ into either (1) or (2) we obtain $x_1 = 150$. Putting these values of the x's into the objective function gives

$$\pi = 6(150) + 5(200) = 1900$$

In words, the solution is that Azed should manufacture 150 Alphas and 200 Omegas per day and thus secure a maximum daily contribution of £1900. Any other feasible plan will have less contribution. Point B is the *only* point in the feasible region which lies on the 1900 contribution contour. All of the other points in the region lie on lower-valued contours.

To sum up, there are five steps in the semi-graphical method:

1. Express the problem algebraically.
2. On a diagram draw in the constraints and identify the feasible region.
3. Draw in a specimen contour of the objective function.
4. Identify the position of the optimum on the diagram and determine which constraints intersect at this position.
5. Solve these constraints as equalities to obtain the optimal values of the decision variables.

2-4 DUAL VALUES

We shall illustrate the meaning and use of dual values by considering some supplementary questions.

Example 2-2 With the data for Azed Enterprises of Example 2-1:

1. Suppose that more materials were available at a premium of £1 per kg over the price that Azed already pays. Would these materials be worth buying?
2. The men's union is pressing for an overtime wage rate of £1 per hour above the basic rate. Would Azed find this a profitable possibility?
3. Azed has the option of manufacturing a third product which would sell at £26 per unit and cost £19 to make. Each unit made would need 3 kg of material and 4 man hours. Is this a worthwhile proposition?

ANSWER 1. We need to know the changes in production levels that would be brought about by the use of more materials with the same labour hours. Having determined the changed levels of production we

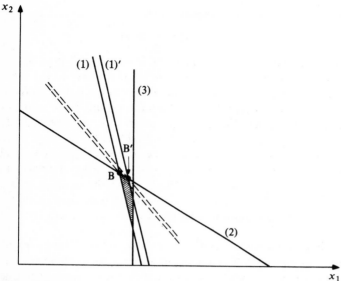

Figure 2-4

can then see what increase in contribution there is. This will enable us to decide whether the premium price is worth paying. First let us see what happens graphically as more material becomes available. The consequence is shown in Fig. 2-4. Constraint line (1) moves outwards to (1)' and the point B 'slides down' constraint (2) to B'. The shaded area is added onto the feasible region. All the old choices are still available to us—in particular the old optimum at B is still feasible—but there are now some additional possibilities as shown by the points in the shaded region. It is evident that the objective function contour through B' is higher than that through B. So that if there had been no change in prices of resources, more contribution would be made at B' than at B. Notice that at B', x_1 has increased while x_2 has decreased relative to B. More is not produced of both products. There has to be a change in balance in the production plan to accommodate the change in the balance of the resources.

Let us now compute the new levels of x_1 and x_2 at B'. We now have

$$
\begin{array}{ll}
(2) \times 2 & 4x_1 + 6x_2 = 1800 \\
(1)' & 4x_1 + x_2 = 801 \\
\hline
& 5x_2 = 999 \\
& \therefore x_2 = 199.8
\end{array}
$$

We shall not worry about the meaning of decimal parts of a unit of production at the moment. Accept that $x_2 = 199.8$. By substitution in

(1)′, $x_1 = 150.3$ so that the new level of profit is

$$\pi' = 6(150.3) + 5(199.8) = 1900.8$$

The extra unit of material *if used in the optimal fashion* will produce an extra £0.8 contribution. This increase is *directly attributable* to the extra unit of material and is called the *dual value* of the resource. The increase of £0.8 in contribution depends upon obtaining the extra unit of material *at the original price*; this charge is included in the unit variable cost figure. So, if we get one more unit of material at the original price contribution rises by 0.8. Also, if we get one more unit of material at the original price *plus* 50p we make an $80 - 50 = 30$p increase in contribution. Now clearly, if we had to pay £1 over the odds to secure the extra unit there would be a *fall* of 20p in contribution. It is therefore *not* worth paying a £1 premium for the first or any subsequent units of material.

The fact that we have dealt with a tiny, impractical change in the constraint level makes no difference to the general result. Perhaps the smallest practical increase would be 10 units. If 810 kg were available then $x_1 = 153$, $x_2 = 198$ and $\pi = 1908$, a *rate* of increase of π of 0.8 per unit of material. Finally suppose that the premium was less than 0.8. How many more units of material would it be worth buying? We note that the level of x_1 is being increased by 0.3 as material availability increases by 1. This increase cannot take x_1 beyond 180 (due to constraint (3)). Thus since x_1 must not increase by more than 30 materials should not increase by more than 100 kg.

2. This is a similar question to (1) and requires the calculation of the dual value of labour. With 901 units the equations to solve become:

$$(2)' \times 2 \quad 4x_1 + 6x_2 = 1802$$
$$4x_1 + x_2 = 800$$

$$5x_2 = 1002$$
$$\therefore \quad x_2 = 200.4 \text{ and so } x_1 = 149.9$$

The new level of π is

$$\pi' = 6(149.9) + 5(200.4) = 1901.4$$

so that the dual value of labour is £1.40. This is the maximum premium that could be paid over the basic rate without depressing total contribution. Thus if the basic rate had been £2 per hour then the maximum overtime wage rate would be £3.40. So the union's claim could be afforded if there were no other increases in costs.

Sometimes the description 'shadow price' is used instead of dual value. There is, unfortunately, no uniformity of interpretation of either term. For instance, in the case of labour hours, the shadow price could be said to be either the marginal increase in contribution of £1.40 or the *full* maximum price of £3.40. Care must therefore be exercised in the reading of different texts and in interpreting examination questions. There would be something to be said for dropping both terms and referring to the £1.40 as the *contribution producing potential* of a further hour at the original price.

3. On the face of it the third product looks attractive since it makes a contribution of £7—higher than either of the existing products. But size of contribution is not the sole deciding factor. In answering (1) and (2) we found that further units of materials and labour would increase contribution by 0.8 and 1.4 respectively. Since the problem is entirely linear, *reducing* the materials availability by one unit would *cut* contribution by 0.8. Similarly one hour less labour would reduce contribution by 1.4. To make one unit of the third product would reduce the materials availability (for Alpha and Omega) by 3 and the labour available by 4. So that the lost contribution from Alpha and Omega production is

$$3(0.8) + 4(1.4) = £8$$

but the third product only replaces this with £7, which is not good enough. Another way of putting it is to say that the contribution-producing potential tied up in the manufacture of one unit of the third product exceeds its own ability to contribute. There would be an *opportunity loss* of £1 on each unit made. Any further product would only increase contribution if the dual value of the resources tied up in its production was less than its per unit contribution.

Notice the dual value of resources in the Alpha and Omega models. We have for the Alpha

$$4(0.8) + 2(1.4) = 6$$

and for the Omega

$$1(0.8) + 3(1.4) = 5$$

The dual values of resources precisely equal the unit contributions. This is always true for products that are produced at the optimum. It is simply re-stating that there is no opportunity loss on producing the products that it is best to produce! If the dual value of resources was *less* than the contribution for some product then the optimum would not have been reached.

2-5 SENSITIVITY ANALYSIS

It would be a poor operational research technique that could say nothing about the consequences of changes in the problem parameters. After all, it is management's *job* to remove bottlenecks (relax constraints) and secure better prices (increase contributions) and changes are all too often being imposed or threatened from other quarters. We have in mind here such questions as: 'Would it still be worth producing the Omega model if contribution fell to £2?'; 'What if the materials availability increased by 10 percent?'; 'A new process cuts the materials requirement for the Alpha product to 2.5 kg per unit. What are the consequences?' All these questions come under the heading of *sensitivity analysis* or as it is sometimes called, *post-optimality analysis*. So we have already performed some sensitivity analysis in the preceding section in answering questions similar to the second. The third question relates to changes in the coefficients of the x's in the constraints. Analysis of such changes is obviously important since it would be concerned with increased efficiency. However, it is rather technical and will be omitted here. The motivated student is referred to Wilkes (1977, pages 111–114 and 121–124) for descriptions of the technique and results. We shall concentrate on questions of the first type: what should be the response to changing profitability of products?

Suppose that contribution on the Omega product *did* fall to £2. Should production be cut back or even stopped altogether and the released resources put to work in making Alphas? The answer in fact is no. There should be no changes at all. The reason for this result can most easily be seen geometrically. Look again at point B in Fig. 2-3. You will see that point B will be on the highest contour, and thus be optimal, provided that the slope of the contours remains between the slopes of constraints (1) and (2). Constraint (1) can be re-written as

$$x_2 = 800 - 4x_1$$

in which the slope is readily seen to be -4. Similarly constraint (2) can be written as

$$x_2 = 300 - \frac{2}{3}x_1$$

in which the slope is clearly seen to be $-2/3$. The slope of the constraint lines is always minus the ratio of the coefficients of x_1 and x_2 in the constraint. In a similar fashion the slope of the objective function contours is minus the ratio of the coefficients of x_1 and x_2 in the objective function, i.e., the slope is the ratio of the contributions of x_1 and x_2 and originally is $-6/5$. We can, in this context, safely ignore the minus signs and write

$$\frac{2}{3} < \frac{6}{5} < 4$$

Now if we call the contribution per unit of Omega made π_2 instead of 5, point B will remain optimal provided that

$$\frac{2}{3} \leqslant \frac{6}{\pi_2} \leqslant 4$$

If π_2 was such that a strict equality held at one end of the range (say $\pi_2 = 9$) then the contours would be parallel to constraint (2) and the optimum would be *non-unique*, anywhere along the line segment AB being just as good as anywhere else. The value of 9 in fact defines the upper bound on π_2. It cannot be more than this (given the original values of the other parameters) if B is to remain optimal. At the other extreme we have

$$\frac{6}{\pi_2} \leqslant 4 \qquad \therefore \quad \pi_2 \geqslant 1.5$$

so that point B will remain optimal provided that π_2 is in the range given by:

$$1.5 \leqslant \pi_2 \leqslant 9$$

Thus there is room for variability in the original contribution figure for Omega. Since £2 falls within this range we conclude that the optimum remains unchanged. Needless to say, the actual contribution made must be less and this in turn will alter the dual values but ideal production levels are unchanged.

In terms of the contribution on the Alpha model (π_1) we can write

$$\frac{2}{3} \leqslant \frac{\pi_1}{5} \leqslant 4$$

so that B is optimal if

$$\frac{10}{3} \leqslant \pi_1 \leqslant 20$$

But what about joint variability in contributions? Underlying forces may affect the profitability of the two products in similar fashions. The first thing to observe is that the slope of the contour depends only on the *relative* sizes of π_1 and π_2 so that equal proportionate changes in both contribution figures make no difference to the optimal plan, although of course the contribution made will be changed by the same proportion. More generally, if we take the slope condition for optimality of B

$$\frac{2}{3} \leqslant \frac{\pi_1}{\pi_2} \leqslant 4$$

the first part of this condition, $2/3 \leqslant \pi_1/\pi_2$, can be re-written as $\pi_2 \leqslant 1.5\pi_1$ and the second part, $\pi_1/\pi_2 \leqslant 4$, can be re-expressed as $\pi_2 \geqslant 0.25\pi_1$. So, for optimality of B all that is required (in terms of the contribution figures that is) is

$$\pi_2 \leqslant 1.5\pi_1 \qquad \text{and} \qquad \pi_2 \geqslant 0.25\pi_1$$

in which it will be observed that insertion of the original value of π_1 gives the individual range of variation (already determined above for π_2). Similarly, the insertion of the original value of π_2 produces the individual range of π_1.

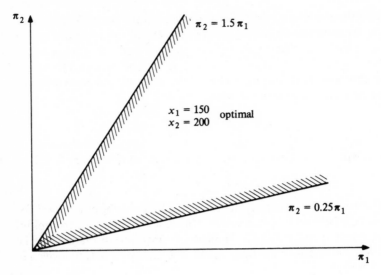

Figure 2-5

Finally, the situation is illustrated in Fig. 2-5. As long as the values of π_1 and π_2 fall within the shaded region the original plan remains optimal.

There is very much more useful work that can be done in the area of sensitivity analysis, but the usefulness of the methods and their general character should now be apparent.

2-6 THE SIMPLEX METHOD

A mystique seems to have grown up around this procedure. It is often presented in hushed and reverential tones preceded by off-putting remarks alluding to the immense difficulty of the method, i.e., you need not bother trying. Nothing could be further from the truth. The simplex method is perfectly straightforward—anyone with a little patience should be able to understand it and use the method successfully. Nothing more than the most elementary arithmetic (adding up, subtracting, dividing and multiplying) is involved. Can you manage these things? Yes? Then you can learn the simplex method.

We do not have space to explain the significance of every step (this can be done, see Wilkes, 1977) so the presentation will have a rote form. Nevertheless it will have interest enough. Let us start straight away and solve the Azed problem using this method.

The first requirement is to turn the inequality constraints into equations.

This is done by the introduction of *slack variables* one for each constraint. In constraint (1), for instance, we introduce s_1 where

$$4x_1 + x_2 + s_1 = 800$$

i.e., s_1 is the shortfall between usage $(4x_1 + x_2)$ and availability of material (800 kg). Similarly unused labour hours are s_2 where

$$2x_1 + 3x_2 + s_2 = 900$$

We shall also need a slack variable in the third constraint; this will be s_3 where

$$x_1 + s_3 = 180$$

and s_3 is simply the amount by which x_1 is below its permitted maximum. For instance in the solution that we already know is optimal, $x_1 = 150$, so that in this solution $s_3 = 30$. The fourth constraint will not be represented as it is redundant. Note that unlike the x's, the slack variables appear only in one constraint each. The slacks *must be non-negative* or the original constraints would be violated. For instance if $s_1 = -10$, this would mean that $4x_1 + x_2 = 810$ which would break the original requirement. In the present context the slack variables do not appear in the objective function (for cases where this is not so, see Wilkes, 1977) or rather the slacks have *zero coefficients in the objective function*. Now write everything out in full. The problem is to:

Maximize $\quad \pi = 6x_1 + 5x_2 + 0s_1 + 0s_2 + 0s_3$

subject to $\quad 4x_1 + 1x_2 + 1s_1 + 0s_2 + 0s_3 = 800$

$\qquad\qquad 2x_1 + 3x_2 + 0s_1 + 1s_2 + 0s_3 = 900$

$\qquad\qquad 1x_1 + 0x_2 + 0s_1 + 0s_2 + 1s_3 = 180$

and $\qquad\quad x_1 \geqslant 0, x_2 \geqslant 0, s_1 \geqslant 0, s_2 \geqslant 0, s_3 \geqslant 0$

Notice that the slack variables have zero coefficients everywhere except in the one constraint to which they are specific. The apparently purposeless inclusion of them in all places will now be justified. What has been done is the first step in building up *a tableau*. The next step is to rearrange the information thus:

6	5	0	0	0
x_1	x_2	s_1	s_2	s_3
4	1	1	0	0
2	3	0	1	0
1	0	0	0	1

in which there is one row which identifies the variables, above which are the coefficients in the objective function. All of the coefficients of x_1 are in the x_1

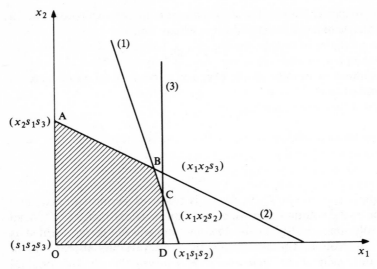

Figure 2-6

column, all of the coefficients of x_2 are in the x_2 column, and so on. Now the logic of the simplex procedure rests on the fact that *only the corner points* (in this case OABCD) of the feasible region can be unique optima. No point in the feasible region can ever be better than all the corner points. Thus we need only concentrate on the corners. Mathematicians, unable to call a corner a corner, term the corners *basic solutions* or, strictly, *basic feasible solutions* (bfs).

A distinguishing feature of bfs is that there are no more positive variables than there are constraints. Except in degenerate solutions (which need not detain us here) there will be precisely the same number of positive variables as there are constraints. Thus each corner of the feasible region should have three variables positive. These are identified in Fig. 2-6 in which the positive variables are shown in brackets. The remaining two variables in each case are zero. Notice something else. Each bfs has two 'neighbours'. For instance B has A and C next door to it; D has O and C and so on. If you move from one bfs to a neighbour the group of positive variables changes by one element, viz., in moving from B to C, s_3 'drops out' of the group and is 'replaced' by s_2. In moving from O to D, s_3 drops out and is replaced by x_1. One last point: the feasible region is *convex*. In everyday terms this simply means that there are no indentations. When a linear function is being maximized over a convex region, to reach the optimum it is only necessary that each 'step' taken from some starting point increases the value of π. In other words one can move from one bfs to a better neighbour and carry on in this short-sighted fashion and be sure of reaching the top. Rather like a walker trying to gain the summit of a dome-shaped hill in a fog. So long as he keeps going up there is only one place that he can finish at—the top (we are ignoring the subtleties of asymptotic increases). This contrasts with the case of a twin-peaked hill, in which case there would be no guarantee of attaining the greater summit by purely myopic progress. LP is exactly comparable to the single-peaked case.

The steps of the simplex method are:

1. Obtain any bfs to start with.
2. Check neighbouring solutions to see if they are better.
3. If there is a better neighbouring solution, move to it.
4. Repeat steps (3) and (3) until no further improvement is possible.

Now back to the tableau. The easiest bfs to find is the origin. The fact that it is usually the worst solution need not concern us; we shall not stay there long—the ease of obtaining this solution outweighs other considerations in general. We want now to add a description of the origin to the tableau so far obtained. This is done thus:

			6	5	0	0	0
			x_1	x_2	s_1	s_2	s_3
0	s_1	800	4	1	1	0	0
0	s_2	900	2	3	0	1	0
0	s_3	180	1	0	0	0	1

In the central column to the left are listed the variables in the solution (i.e., positive) at the origin, adjacent to their appropriate constraints. To the right are shown the levels (magnitudes) of these variables. Obviously, since the slacks equal the right-hand sides of the constraints, all resources would be unused. To the left of the solution variables are their objective function coefficients. All variables not listed in this left-hand (solution) part of the tableau are zero, i.e., at the origin $x_1 = 0, x_2 = 0$.

The next step is to determine the value of the objective function at the origin and to see if any improvement is possible. The value of the objective function will be the sum of the level of each variable multiplied by its objective function coefficient. This is a trivial exercise at the origin. We obtain $\pi = 800(0) + 900(0) + 180(0) = 0$. This value is inserted immediately below the solution column. Next we must ascertain if improvement is possible. This is done by considering the consequences of introducing each non-basic (not-in-the-solution) variable to *unit level*. Suppose we set $x_1 = 1$. Geometrically we move a little way along the x_1 axis away from the origin— towards D in fact. Clearly, if we set $x_1 = 1$ this will affect the levels of the slack variables. In fact the column of coefficients under x_1 (viz., 4, 2, 1) shows by how much each of the variables in the solution will have to be reduced to accommodate one unit of x_1. Thus s_1 must go down by 4, s_2 must go down by 2 and s_3 must go down by 1. If not obviously correct the results may be checked by reference back to the constraints themselves. Now, if at some stage we are cutting back on the levels of variables in the solution the objective function will be affected if these variables have new zero objective function coefficients (ofcs). The effect on the objective function of the adjustments necessary to accommodate one unit of x_1 is the sum of products of 'rates of exchange' in the x_1 column and the ofcs of solution variables. Thus on account of the alterations necessary, the objective function alters by

$$4(0)+2(0)+1(0) = 0$$

but in return we get one unit of x_1 worth (from the head of the x_1 column) 6. The *net* decrease in the objective function is then

$$4(0)+2(0)+1(0)-6 = -6$$

that is, an *increase* of 6. The number -6 is now entered in a new row—the *index row* (or z_j-c_j row as it is sometimes called) under x_1. A negative number in the index row thus represents *improvement* possibility. A decrease of -6 is, of course, an increase of $+6$. This rather backhanded way of going about things has a reason which we shall come to later on. An index row number is now determined for each variable. For x_2, for instance, we obtain

$$1(0)+3(0)+0(0)-5 = -5$$

All basic variables (those already in the solution) have zero index row numbers as may be verified by completing the workings. *Provided* that the slack variables have zero ofcs the first index row will be the negation of the ofcs. The complete picture is:

			6	5	0	0	0	
			x_1	x_2	s_1	s_2	s_3	
0	s_1	800	4	1	1	0	0	
0	s_2	900	2	3	0	1	0	
0	s_3	180	1	0	0	0	1	
Value of $\pi \rightarrow$		0	-6	-5	0	0	0	$\leftarrow$ index row

We now select the variable with 'most negative' index row number to come into the solution. This is the variable showing the greatest *per unit* improvement in π. We now introduce this variable, x_1, to the maximum extent. This will correspond to movement to point D. Notice from Fig. 2-6 that in moving from O to D, x_1 enters the group of positive variables and s_3 drops out. From the simplex tableau the variable to drop out is identified by forming the ratios of solution values to rates of exchange of incoming variable. Thus we have

$$\text{for } s_1: \text{ratio} = 800/4 = 200$$
$$\text{for } s_2: \text{ratio} = 900/2 = 450$$
$$\text{for } s_3: \text{ratio} = 180/1 = 180$$

The one with the smallest ratio represents the variable to leave the basis. The ratios are the maximum extent to which x_1 can be introduced without making the respective basic variable negative. This procedure of selecting the outgoing variable guarantees that no solution variables will ever be negative, i.e., we are confined to basic *feasible* solutions. The row of numbers corresponding to the variable going out is called the *pivotal row*. The column of numbers corresponding to the incoming variable is termed the *pivotal column*. The number at the junction is called the *pivotal element*. It is convenient to 'block in' the pivotal row and column as shown below. The description of the new solution (corresponding to point D) can now begin. We shall produce a new tableau beneath the (now) old one. Start by writing down the variables in this new solution and to the left the three-element column of objective function coefficients. Thus we obtain:

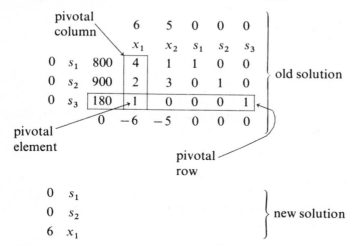

The next step is to provide a full numerical description of this solution—with solution values for s_1, s_2, and x_1 and the rates of exchange. In other words we must now fill in the blanks in the new solution tableau.

There are two rote pieces of arithmetic involved in forming the new tableau. We first form the *main row*. The main row is the row in the new tableau in the *same position* as the pivotal row in the old tableau. All main row numbers are pivotal row numbers divided by the pivotal element. Since the pivotal element is unity (in this case) the main row is the same as the old pivotal row. Thus we write in

$$0 \quad s_1$$
$$0 \quad s_2$$
$$6 \quad x_1 \quad 180 \quad 1 \quad 0 \quad 0 \quad 0 \quad 1$$

Now we must find the remaining numbers, which are all found by the same means. Suppose we start with the new level of s_2. Call this the 'new number'. Call the number in the same position in the old solution (the old level of s_2) the 'old number'. Now use the formula:

new number = old number − corresponding main row number

× corresponding pivotal column number

The 'corresponding main row number' is the number in the main row in the same column as the new number. The 'corresponding pivotal column number' is the number in the pivotal column in the same row as the old number. Thus, using the formula

$$\text{new value of } s_2 = 900 - 180 \times 2 = 540$$

Now find the rate of exchange between s_2 and x_2. This was 3 in the old tableau. Now we have

$$\text{new number} = 3 - 0 \times 2 = 3$$

The new rate of exchange between s_2 and x_1 is

$$\text{new number} = 2 - 1 \times 2 = 0$$

In this case the 'corresponding pivotal column number' is the old number itself. We can now fill in the entire s_2 row. It is

$$0 \quad s_2 \quad 540 \quad 0 \quad 3 \quad 0 \quad 1 \quad -2$$

Note that the rate of exchange between s_2 and s_3 is negative. For each unit of s_3 brought into the solution s_2 would *increase* by two units. For all the numbers in the s_1 row the corresponding pivotal column number is 4. The new level of s_1 itself is given by

$$\text{new level of } s_1 = 800 - 180 \times 4 = 80$$

The rate of exchange between s_1 and x_2 is

$$\text{new number} = 1 - 0 \times 4 = 1$$

The remaining numbers in the new s_1 row are found in similar fashion and the complete s_1 row in the new solution is

$$0 \quad s_1 \quad 80 \quad 0 \quad 1 \quad 1 \quad 0 \quad -4$$

To complete the first iteration we have now only to compute the index row for the new solution. The value of the solution is now 1080 while the full tableau is shown below

			6	5	0	0	0
			x_1	x_2	s_1	s_2	s_3
0	s_1	800	4	1	1	0	0
0	s_2	900	2	3	0	1	0
0	s_3	180	1	0	0	0	1
		0	-6	-5	0	0	0

0	s_1	80	0	1	1	0	-4
0	s_2	540	0	3	0	1	-2
6	x_1	180	1	0	0	0	1
		1080	0	-5	0	0	$+6$

← new index row

The index row elements are formed just as before. To recap on the number for s_3 this will be

$$0(-4)+0(-2)+6(1)-0 = +6$$

The new tableau describes the situation at point D. A contribution of 1080 is made but the presence of a negative number in the index row (under x_2) means that the solution is not optimal. Specifically the variable x_2 must be brought into the solution. This will correspond to a move from D to C. The new pivotal column (determined by the -5) and the new pivotal row (determined by the smallest of the ratios 80/1, 540/3, 180/0) are indicated above. All that now needs to be done is to repeat the procedure until a solution is found with no negative numbers in the index row.

The next solution (point C) is

			6	5	0	0	0
			x_1	x_2	s_1	s_2	s_3
5	x_2	80	0	1	1	0	-4
0	s_2	300	0	0	-3	1	10
6	x_1	180	1	0	0	0	1
		1480	0	0	$+5$	0	-14

← index row

Again this solution is not optimal. This time s_3 must be introduced. For once the pivotal element is not unity so that the main row will be

$$s_2 \quad 30 \quad 0 \quad 0 \quad -0.3 \quad 0.1 \quad 1$$

and the full solution is

			6	5	0	0	0
			x_1	x_2	s_1	s_2	s_3
5	x_2	200	0	1	−0.2	0.4	0
0	s_3	30	0	0	−0.3	0.1	1
6	x_1	150	1	0	0.3	−0.1	0
		1900	0	0	0.8	1.4	0	← index row

This solution is optimal, since there are no negative numbers in the index row. Note that in obtaining the entries in the new x_2 row the corresponding pivotal column element is −4 so that, unless the corresponding main row number is also negative, there will be increases in solution values and rates of exchange.

The optimal solution calls for 200 units of the Omega model ($x_2 = 200$), 150 units of the Alpha model ($x_1 = 150$) and $s_3 = 30$. The value of s_3 is simply the extent to which x_1 is below its maximum permitted level. Any variable that does not appear in the solution part of the tableau is at zero level. Thus since s_1 and s_2 do not appear, $s_1 = 0$ and $s_2 = 0$ at the optimum.

One very useful feature of the simplex method is that the dual values are given free of charge. The dual value of a resource (or of any binding constraint) appears in the final index row under the slack variable corresponding to that resource. Thus in the index row under s_1 we see that the dual value of resource one is 0.8 and under s_2 we have the shadow price of resource two, 1.4. It is seen that the dual value under s_3 is zero. Although s_3 does not correspond to a physical resource, if the upper bound on x_3 had been binding there would have been a positive shadow price. Notice one curious feature of the dual values. If each dual value is multiplied by the total amount of the resource (or upper bound) to which it corresponds, then the number thus achieved is the optimal value of the objective function, viz., $800(0.8) + 900(1.4) + 180(0) = 1900$. This is always the case. The dual values, in a sense, give an *average* valuation of resources as well as a marginal one. We say 'in a sense' because it does *not* follow that a resource with zero dual value is worthless on average and thus can be dispensed with.

One final point on dual values. Linear programming problems go in pairs. For each such problem there is a *dual problem* which uses the same information in a different way. The dual problem to the Azed enterprises case (with the bound on x_2 omitted) is:

$$\text{Minimize} \quad G = 800y_1 + 900y_2 + 180y_3$$
$$\text{subject to} \quad 4y_1 + 2y_2 + y_3 \geq 6$$
$$y_1 + 3y_2 \qquad\quad \geq 5$$
$$y_1 \geq 0, \; y_2 \geq 0, \; y_3 \geq 0$$

in which the variables y are the dual values in the Azed problem. The maximization problem is called the *primal* and the associated minimization problem is called the *dual*, although the two problems are in fact duals of each other. The reader is invited to study the relationship between the primal and dual Azed problems. The dual problem can be solved by the simplex method but further technical devices are needed. Further material can be found in Wilkes (1977, Chapter 4).

2-7 ANOTHER EXAMPLE

A Ltd is drawing up production plans for the coming year. Four products are producible with the following data:

Product	1	2	3	4
Amount per unit:				
selling price	£55	£53	£97	£86
cost of materials	£17	£25	£19	£11
labour hours: grade A	10	6	—	—
grade B	—	—	10	20
grade C	—	—	12	6
other variable costs	£6	£7	£5	£6

Fixed overheads of the firm amount to £35 500 per annum. Each grade of labour is paid £1.50 per hour but skills are specific to a grade so that an employee in one grade cannot be used to undertake the work of another grade. The annual supply of each grade is limited to the following maxima: Grade A, 9000 hours; grade B, 14 500 hours; and grade C, 12 000 hours. There is no effective limitation on the volume of sales of any product. A's objective is profits maximization.

1. Calculate the product mix which will maximize profit for the year and state the amount of the profit.
2. Determine the minimum price at which the sale of product (1) would be worth while.
3. Find the amount by which profit could be increased if the supply of grade A labour was increased by one hour.
4. A possible fifth product would sell for £116, would have materials cost of £29, would require eight hours of each of all types of labour and would have other variable costs of £9. Should the fifth product be produced?

ANSWER The decision variables will be x_1, x_2, x_3, and x_4, the amounts made of each product. The objective is profits maximization and for this we need to know the contribution per unit of each product. This is selling price less unit variable cost. On x_1 the unit variable cost is £17 for materials plus 10 grade A hours at £1.50 plus other variable costs of £6, viz., £38. This results in a contribution of £55 − £38 = £17. For the other products we obtain

unit contribution on $x_2 = 53 − (25 + 6 \times 1.5 + 7) = 12$

unit contribution on $x_3 = 97 − (19 + 10 \times 1.5 + 12 \times 1.5 + 5) = 40$

unit contribution on $x_4 = 86 − (11 + 20 \times 1.5 + 6 \times 1.5 + 6) = 30$

so that the total contribution made will be

$$\pi = 17x_1 + 12x_2 + 40x_3 + 30x_4$$

This can be taken to be the objective function since profits will be $\pi − £35\,500$.

There are three constraints; these can be written as

$$10x_1 + 6x_2 \qquad\qquad \leqslant \quad 9000$$
$$10x_3 + 20x_4 \leqslant 14\,500$$
$$12x_3 + 6x_4 \leqslant 12\,000$$

To which sign requirements must be added. The problem is one in four structural (x) variables but it *can* be solved graphically. This is because of the special structure of the constraints. The scarce resources needed by x_1 and x_2 (i.e., grade A labour) are quite separate from those needed by x_3 and x_4 (grades B and C labour). There is no overlap at all. Products (1) and (2) do not 'compete' for scarce resources with products three and four. In technical language the constraint set is *partitioned*. All this means that the whole problem should be split into two *sub-problems*; the first sub-problem involves x_1 and x_2 only and the second involves x_3 and x_4 only. These problems can be considered quite separately. So first of all

Maximize $\quad \pi(1, 2) = 17x_1 + 12x_2$

subject to $\qquad\qquad\quad 10x_1 + 6x_2 \leqslant 9000$

$\qquad\qquad\qquad\qquad\quad x_1 \geqslant 0, x_2 \geqslant 0$

This is a one-constraint problem which is graphed in Fig. 2-7. The feasible region is the shaded OAB for which A is optimal. At A $x_1 = 0$, $x_2 = 1500$ and $\pi(1, 2) = £18\,000$, so that x_1 should not at present be produced, but all labour of grade A should be used on the second product to yield maximum contribution of £18 000. Now for the second sub-problem. This is

Maximize $\quad \pi(3, 4) = 40x_3 + 30x_4$

subject to $\qquad\qquad\quad 10x_3 + 20x_4 \leqslant 14\,500$

$\qquad\qquad\qquad\quad 12x_3 + 6x_4 \leqslant 12\,000$

$\qquad\qquad\qquad\qquad\quad x_3 \geqslant 0, x_4 \geqslant 0$

Now a graph may be saved here. The slope of the objective function contours, 40/30, falls between the slopes of the two constraints (10/20 and

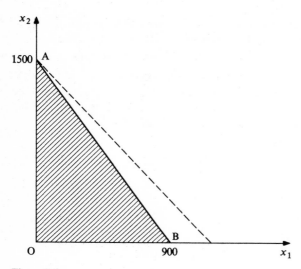

Figure 2-7

12/6) so that the point of intersection of the constraint lines is optimal. Solving the constraints as equations gives $x_3 = 850$ and $x_4 = 300$; so that $\pi(3, 4) = 40 \times 850 + 30 \times 300 = 43\,000$. Thus total profit made is:

$$\pi = 18\,000 + 43\,000 - 35\,500 = 25\,500$$

Now in answering part (2) the manufacture of product one will be *just* worth while when as much profit can be made as from the manufacture of product (2), i.e., £18 000. This would correspond to the objective function contours in Fig. 2-7 being parallel to the constraint line. Clearly for point B to be as good as point A, 900 units of x_1 must give 18 000 contribution, i.e., the unit contribution must be £20. Given the same costs this will result from a price of £58.

In part (3) we are required to determine the dual value of grade A labour. If one more hour was available *at the going rate of* £1.50 then an extra 1/6 of a unit of x_2 could be produced giving an increased contribution of $12 \times 1/6 = £2$. In other words, if an extra hour of grade A labour was available at the original price profit would increase by £2. Evidently if the extra hour can be obtained for less than £1.50 + £2 = £3.50 some extra profit will remain. The maximum overtime wage rate for grade A labour is thus £3.50. The reader may wish to verify that the maximum overtime wage rates for labour of types B and C are £2.16 and £4.27 respectively.

Now consider the possible fifth product. The unit contribution is

$$116 - (29 + 8 \times 1.5 + 8 \times 1.5 + 8 \times 1.5 + 9) = £42$$

However, consider the dual value (profit producing power) of resources tied up in the manufacture of one unit of product (5). This will be

$$8 \times 2 + 8 \times \frac{2}{3} + 8 \times \frac{25}{9} = \text{£43.56}$$

so that there would be an *opportunity loss* of £43.56 − £42 = £1.56 on the production of each unit of product (5). The reader should verify that there is no opportunity loss on the manufacture of x_2, x_3 and x_4 and that the opportunity loss on x_1 is £3. (How does this latter figure compare with the price rise necessary to make manufacture worth while?)

2-8 A FURTHER SIMPLEX PROBLEM

Use the simplex method to solve the problem:

$$\text{Maximize} \quad x_1 + x_2$$
$$\text{subject to} \quad x_1 + 2x_2 \leqslant 100$$
$$2x_1 + x_2 \leqslant 110$$
$$x_1 \geqslant 0, x_2 \geqslant 0$$

and state the dual values for the two constraints. Having introduced slack variables s_1 and s_2, the full solution in tableau form is

			1	1	0	0	
			x_1	x_2	s_1	s_2	
0	s_1	100	1	2	1	0	
0	s_2	110	2	1	0	1	← pivotal row (no. 1)
		0	−1	−1	0	0	
0	s_1	45	0	3/2	1	−1/2	← pivotal row (no. 2)
1	x_1	55	1	1/2	0	1/2	← main row (no. 1)
		55	0	−1/2	0	1/2	
1	x_2	30	0	1	2/3	−1/3	← main row (no. 2)
1	x_1	40	1	0	−1/3	2/3	
		70	0	0	1/3	1/3	← index row

Thus, at the optimum $x_1 = 40$, $x_2 = 30$, $s_1 = 0$, $s_2 = 0$ and the dual values are 1/3 for each constraint. A general point is that only when a constraint is satisfied as a strict equality (there are no unused units of the resource) will the corresponding dual value be positive.

2-9 A MINIMIZATION PROBLEM

Many practical LP problems involve minimization. Finding the 'least-cost method' is a recurrent problem. Some of the earliest applications of LP were minimization problems in the area of least cost feed mix and other variants of the 'diet' problem. Consider the following manufacturing exercise.

QUESTION A firm can produce a single product in either or both of two processes. Two resources are needed and the amounts of each resource needed to produce each unit of the product via each process are as follows:

Unit production in:

process one	process two	
3	2	resource one
2	3	resource two

The firm can buy up to 26 units of resource one at £2 per unit and up to 30 units of resource two at £1 per unit. All other costs are fixed. The firm has an order for 11 units of the product.

1. How much should the firm produce in each process to fulfil the order at minimum cost?
2. If the price of resource two went up to £3 a unit, how much should be produced in each process (to minimize cost)?
3. If (with the original resource prices) 28 units of each resource were available, how much should be produced in each process (to minimize cost)?

ANSWER The decision variables are the production levels in the two processes—x_1 and x_2. The objective is a least-cost allocation of production between the two processes. First we must determine the unit variable costs in each process. For process one each unit made requires three units of resource one at £2 and two units of resource two at £1. Thus, since all other costs are fixed, the unit variable cost for x_1 is

$$c_1 = 3 \times 2 + 2 \times 1 = 8$$

and c_2, the unit variable cost on x_2, is similarly obtained as

$$c_2 = 2 \times 2 + 3 \times 1 = 7$$

Thus the objective will be to

$$\text{minimize } c = c_1 x_1 + c_2 x_2 = 8x_1 + 7x_2$$

Now there are *three* constraints. From the resource limits we have

$$3x_1 + 2x_2 \leqslant 26 \quad (1)$$

and

$$2x_1 + 3x_2 \leqslant 30 \quad (2)$$

but there is also the requirement that (at least) 11 units be made overall.

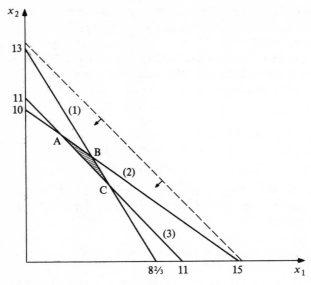

Figure 2-8

Thus

$$x_1 + x_2 \geqslant 11 \qquad (3)$$

and

$$x_1 \geqslant 0, x_2 \geqslant 0$$

A full constraint set is the thin triangular region ABC of Fig. 2-8. We must be *on or above* the constraint (3) line. A specimen contour is drawn through the point $x_1 = 15$, $x_2 = 0$. Since we are minimizing, it is desired to get on to the *lowest* objective function contour, i.e., to be as *near* the origin as possible. Clearly, point B is out of contention and the choice is between A and C. Since the contours are slightly steeper than constraint (3) the lowest goes through point A. Having identified the optimum, solve for the values of x_1 and x_2. At point A only

$$
\begin{array}{llll}
(3) \times 3 & 3x_1 + 3x_2 & = & 33 \\
(2) & 2x_1 + 3x_2 & = & 30 \\
\hline
& x_1 & = & 3 \\
\therefore & x_2 & = & 8
\end{array}
$$

The cheapest way of securing 11 units, given the constraints on resources, is to make 3 units in process one and 8 in the slightly cheaper process two. This gives overall variable cost of $8 \times 3 + 7 \times 8 = 80$. Note that this leaves one unit of resource one unused. It is only because of the constraints that all production is not in the cheaper process two. As it is, we succeed in being as process-two *intensive* as possible.

If the price of resource two changes, this will affect the unit costs and so may change the position of the optimum. Recalculating the unit costs gives

$$c_1 = 3 \times 2 + 2 \times 3 = 12$$
$$c_2 = 2 \times 2 + 3 \times 3 = 13$$

So that now process one is slightly cheaper. The new objective function contours will slope (slightly) less steeply than constraint (3) so that C becomes the lowest obtainable point. All that has now happened is that the firm is as *process-one intensive* as possible—as common sense would suggest.

In part (3) we are concerned with a simultaneous alteration of the availabilities of resources one and two. The constraints now are

$$3x_1 + 2x_2 \leqslant 28 \qquad (1)$$
$$2x_1 + 3x_2 \leqslant 28 \qquad (2)$$
$$x_1 + x_2 \geqslant 11 \qquad (3)$$

It is obvious that the third constraint must be satisfied as a strict equality. This being the case we can write

$$x_2 = 11 - x_1$$

and substitute into the revised constraint (1). This gives

$$3x_1 + 2(11 - x_1) \leqslant 28$$
$$\therefore \quad x_1 \leqslant 6 \quad \text{and} \quad x_2 \geqslant 5$$

Substitution into the second restriction gives

$$2x_1 + 3(11 - x_1) \leqslant 28$$
$$\therefore \quad x_1 \geqslant 5 \quad \text{and} \quad x_2 \leqslant 6$$

And since we are minimizing $8x_1 + 7x_2$ it will be optimal to make x_2 as large as possible. Thus the optimum is $x_1 = 5$, $x_2 = 6$.

2-10 ASSUMPTIONS UNDERLYING LP

There is no workable management technique that takes nothing for granted. Every device that is used from advanced mathematical programming or statistics at one extreme, to business experience and raw hunch at the other, will make assumptions. A model is supposed to simplify reality. If it does not simplify it is not a model. However, when using a technique it is wise to be aware of the main assumptions that are made. In the case of linear programming these are:

1. *All data known and constant.* This means that there are no unknowns, no random variables, and no dynamic variables (values changing with time). It means that prices of outputs and factors are constant and unaffected by output or usage. It means that the firm knows its objective and can measure it. There can be no interdependencies between prices themselves or prices and outputs. The firm operates in a 'fixprice' situation, but the specific, strong assumption of 'perfect competition' in factor and product markets is *not* made.

   It further means that technical coefficients are fixed—the amounts of resources needed per unit of each x are given. Thus economies or diseconomies of scale are not allowed in the basic model.

   Finally the assumption means that management has predetermined the possible range of activities.
2. *No fixed charges.* A 'fixed charge' is a *set-up cost*; it is only incurred if an activity is used. For instance, to start a production run of a product, machinery may have to be re-set. The re-set costs are not incurred if the product is not made.
3. *Divisibility.* It is assumed that fractional values of the x's are meaningful.
4. *Boundedness.* There must be linear restrictions on the choice of values of the x's such that the objective function cannot become infinite. In practice these restrictions take the form of linear inequality constraints, each involving some or all of the x's and sign requirements. In fact sign requirements are not necessary mathematically, but the x's must be bounded from below and from above.

2-11 ADVANCED PROGRAMMING METHODS

Many of the above assumptions can be relaxed—at a price. The price is computational difficulty or outright intractability. Broadly speaking, the most important generalizations are *non-linear programming, integer programming, dynamic programming* and *stochastic programming*. These are not mutually exclusive or exhaustive categories but are intended to give the general flavour.

In the vast range of possible non-linear programming problems, the most important are those with *quadratic* objective functions and linear constraints. This allows a firm to face a demand curve for its products.

In integer programming devices are introduced to ensure that the solution is stated in terms of whole numbers (for requisite variables). Integer programming algorithms are nowhere near as efficient as the simplex method and it is better to approximate (e.g., round off or round down) if possible.

In dynamic programming multi-stage decision processes are considered.

Special techniques have been developed of which the 'backwards algorithm' is the most important.

In stochastic programming various random elements are allowed. Perhaps prices are random variables or constraints have only to be satisfied in a probabilistic sense.

There are numerous technical devices which allow the retention of the LP framework but relax the assumptions of Sec. 2-10. Generally it is best to do this if at all possible as the efficiency of the simplex method is hard to match. In practice none of the advanced methods is used with anywhere near the frequency of LP. A sound knowledge of LP methods will be enough for almost all situations. Remember that a technique does not require guaranteed exactitude to be justified. It only has to improve on what would otherwise have been done. Further material on the advanced methods can be found in Wilkes (1977).

2-12 CONCLUSIONS

LP is a most important, possibly the single most important, quantitative management technique. It has been of surpassing value in manufacturing industry particularly. All computer companies offer a range of LP 'packages' suitable for a wide range of problems from shop-floor production to overall corporate modelling. Many of the non-linearities of the real world can be satisfactorily approximated by linear functions. Sensitivity analysis is most important and is a practical way of taking uncertainties into account. *Any* problem which has the character of maximization subject to constraint is a programming problem of some sort. All significant economic problems involve constraints and in most cases best, rather than merely adequate arrangements are sought. Try to think of business problems that do *not* involve restrictions of some kind. Think what the shareholders meeting will say if no attempt is made to optimize!

EXERCISES

2-1 In what areas of a firm's activity might linear programming prove to be a useful technique? Cite some industries that currently use linear programming.

2-2 What essential questions need to be answered when setting a problem in linear programming form?

2-3 Outline the 'semi-graphical' method for solving linear programming problems. What are the advantages and limitations of the method?

2-4 In what circumstances is sensitivity analysis likely to prove useful in linear programming problems?

2-5 What assumptions underlie the linear programming method? Do all of them always have to hold for the technique to be of any use?

2-6 The Latin Manufacturing Company can make two products. Each of the products requires time on a 'cutting' machine and a 'finishing' machine. Relevant data are:

	Product	
	Prima	Seconda
Cutting hours (per unit)	2	1
Finishing hours (per unit)	3	3
Unit cost (£)	28	25
Selling price (£)	34	29
Maximum sales (units per week)	200	200

The number of cutting hours available per week is 390 and the number of finishing hours available per week is 810. No other resources are in limited supply, but the costs of these resources have been allowed for in the unit cost figures.

    (a) How much should be produced of each product in order to achieve Latin's objective of maximization of profit?

    (b) Find the dual values (shadow prices) of the scarce resources at the optimum.

    (c) A possible third product has a unit profit of £5 and would require two hours cutting and two hours finishing. Should Latin make this product?

    (d) Determine the maximum range of variation in the unit profit figure on the Prima product for the original solution to remain optimal.

2-7 Solve the following linear programming problem first by the semi-graphical method and then by the simplex method.

$$\text{Maximize } F =, \quad 35x_1 + 25x_2$$
$$4x_1 + 3x_2 \leqslant 92$$
$$x_1 + x_2 \leqslant 38$$
$$x_1 \qquad \leqslant 20$$
$$x_2 \leqslant 20$$
$$x_1 \geqslant 0, x_2 \geqslant 0$$

2-8 Acme Ltd currently manufacture two products, the De Luxe and the Grande. Relevant financial and sales data and consumption of scarce resources are:

	De Luxe	Grande
Machine hours (per unit)	1	2.5
Labour hours (per unit)	4	3
Selling price (£)	30	39
Unit cost (£)	26	27
Maximum sales (units per day)	40	30

Each day there are up to 85 machine hours and 200 labour hours available. Acme's objective is the maximization of profit.

    (a) What should be the daily production of each good?

(b) An extra one hour per day of machine time could be made available at a premium of £5 above the current price. Would this be worth having?

(c) Within what range of values must the unit profit figure for the De Luxe model lie for the original solution to remain optimal?

2-9 Excell Ltd can manufacture four products. Only three resources are limited in supply. Each product does not require every type of scarce resource. Resource consumption (per unit produced) and financial details for the products are:

	Product			
	A	B	C	D
Packaging labour (hours per unit)	2	5	—	—
Machine time (hours per unit)	4	1	—	—
Skilled labour (hours per unit)	—	—	3	4
Selling price (£)	25	27	25	24
Unit cost	22	18	20	16

Each month, the resource availabilities are:

Resource	Hours available
Packaging labour	8000
Machine time	4000
Skilled labour	6000

(a) Determine the monthly production levels that would maximize profits.

(b) *Ceteris paribus*, what is the minimum selling price at which the sale of product B would be worth while?

(c) If the current skilled wage rate is £3 per hour, what is the maximum *overtime* wage rate that the company would find it worth while to pay?

2-10 Jewel Enterprises at present manufacture a range of four products. Relevant data are:

	Product			
	A	B	C	D
Current production	1000	900	750	250
Selling price (£)	40	38	35	32
Unit cost (£)	26	14	20	12
Machine hours (per unit)	1	1	1.5	0.5
Materials (per unit)	1.5	2.5	1	2

The two resources, machine hours and materials, are the only ones in limited supply and are currently fully used. A linear programming study revealed that the dual values of the scarce resources were £4 and £9 respectively.

(a) Determine the profits maximizing production levels and the opportunity loss on the present arrangement.

(b) Other data unchanged, at what selling prices would the unattractive products become worth while?

2-11 Peter Ley, who runs a small independent engineering company, has bought a job lot of 350 positronic circuits for £1500. Naturally, he wants to put these circuits to the most profitable use so he is exploring all possible applications. First he considers using them for a small car vacuum cleaner (one circuit per cleaner). From his experience he knows that he can sell at least 350 cleaners at a price of £45 each. The other necessary components are available at £15 a set for each cleaner. The time to assemble each vacuum cleaner is one hour. Alternatively he can use the circuits in making de luxe house vacuum cleaners (one circuit per cleaner) which will sell at £120 each, other necessary components costing £80 per set (one set per cleaner). The time to assemble each cleaner is two hours. However, the maximum estimate of sales is only 10 such cleaners. Recently several people have enquired about a slightly cheaper house vacuum cleaner. On investigation Peter finds that he can produce a standard cleaner still using one circuit for each cleaner, which he can sell at £110, extra components costing £60 per cleaner. Assembly time, however, is higher at three hours per cleaner and he estimates sales would be, at maximum, not more than 20. Assembly workers are paid £1 per hour and a fixed amount of 380 hours of assembly time will be available during the period.

Required:

(a) Formulate a linear programming model to help Peter decide on the best mix of products.

(11 marks)

(b) The following is a computer printout of the final tableau in solving Peter's problem:

	X_1	X_2	X_3	S_1	S_2	S_3	S_4	
X_1	1	0	$\frac{1}{2}$	$1\frac{1}{2}$	$-\frac{1}{2}$	0	0	335
X_2	0	1	$\frac{1}{2}$	$-\frac{1}{2}$	$\frac{1}{2}$	0	0	15
S_3	0	0	$-\frac{1}{2}$	$\frac{1}{2}$	$-\frac{1}{2}$	1	0	5
S_4	0	0	1	0	0	0	1	10
	0	0	0	-20	-10	0	0	10 800

where X_1 = number of car vacuum cleaners,
$\quad\ X_2$ = number of standard vacuum cleaners,
$\quad\ X_3$ = number of de luxe vacuum cleaners,
$\quad\ S_1$ = number of electronic circuits not used,
$\quad\ S_2$ = number of assembly hours not used,
$\quad\ S_3$ = demand not met for standard vacuum cleaners,
$\quad\ S_4$ = demand not met for de luxe vacuum cleaners.

Using the tableau, explain to Peter what his production plan should be and the implications of adopting it.

(c) If assembly labour were willing to work overtime at a cost of £3 per hour, would it be worth employing it and what would be the maximum additional profit attainable?

(d) If it were possible to sell all or some of the positronic circuits at £28 each instead of using them to make vacuum cleaners, how should the linear programming model be adapted? (Association of Certified Accountants Professional Examination: Section 2, paper 12, Management Mathematics, June 1978.)

2-12 The Management Accountant of Fenton Enterprises Ltd has suggested that a linear programming model might be used for selecting the best mix of the possible products A, B, C, D, and E. The following information is available:

(i)

| | Per unit of product | | | | |
	A £	B £	C £	D £	E £
Selling price	48	42	38	31	27
Costs:					
Materials	15	14	16	15	16
Direct labour	18	16	6	4	4
Fixed overheads*	9	8	3	2	2
Total costs	42	38	25	21	22
Net profit	6	4	13	10	5

* Based on 50 per cent of direct labour cost.

(ii) Expected maximum unit demand per week for each product at the prices indicated:

A	B	C	D	E
1500	1200	900	600	600

(iii) Cost of materials includes a special component which is in short supply; it costs £3 a unit. Only 5800 units will be available to the company during the year. The number of units of the special component needed for a unit of each product is:

A	B	C	D	E
1	1	3	4	5

(iv) Labour is paid at a rate of £1.50 per hour and only 20 000 hours will be available in a week.

(v) The management of Fenton Enterprises Ltd has ruled that expenditure on materials must not exceed a sum of £30 000.

(vi) All other resources are freely available in sufficient quantities for planned needs.

Required:

(a) Formulate a linear programming model stating clearly the criterion you use. (You are not expected to produce a numerical solution to your model.)

(16 marks)

(b) Describe the problems likely to be encountered in the application of linear programming to determine the 'best' product mix for Fenton Enterprises Ltd.

(9 marks)

(Association of Certified Accountants, Professional Examination: Section 2, paper 12, Management Mathematics, December 1976.)

2-13 A company has an assured market for any quantities of two products, which are processed on one machine and then finished by hand. The products are not complementary and may be produced independently in varying quantities. Planned output is 600 units per week of each product, a combination chosen because it fully utilizes machine and labour capacities. Maximum utilization is the rule-of-thumb strategy used by the management as most likely to yield maximum profit. Machine capacity is 1200 units per week of either product or a combination of the two; no time is lost in changing over from one product to the other. Machine operators cannot be discharged and their wages are included in fixed overheads. Finishing-labour supply is limited to 2400 direct hours per week. Finishing labour is a fixed cost in the short run as no other work is available if machine output is delayed for any reason. Standard product costs and selling prices are as follows:

	Product A £	Product B £
Standard product costs:		
Materials	2	2
Finishing labour: £3 per hour	9	3
Fixed overhead: 1/3 labour cost	3	1
	14	6
Selling price	16	8

Last week the factory manager scheduled production of only 500 units of each product, as an overhaul of the machine, which would reduce available machine capacity to 1000 units, was unavoidable. As a result, the finishing staff was idle for most of one day while the operators carried out the overhaul.

You are required:

(a) using graphical methods, to show

(i) whether the normal rule-of-thumb strategy optimizes contribution to profit, and if not what strategy would do this;

(ii) how many units of each product would have optimized contribution to profit during the overhaul; and

(b) to calculate

(i) standard net profit under the optimum strategy you recommend in (a) (i);

(ii) how much, if any, contribution to profit was lost by the factory manager's decision on product mix during the overhaul.

(Institute of Chartered Accountants in England and Wales, Professional Examination: II Management Accountancy, July 1975.)

2-14 (a) The following details are taken from the forecasts for 1979 of XYZ Limited:

Sales demand:		Thousands of units per annum, maximum
Super de luxe model	(x_1)	500
De luxe model	(x_2)	750
Export model	(x_3)	400

Production: two production facilities are required, machining and assembly, and these are common to each model. Capacity in each facility is limited by the number of direct labour hours available.

	Direct labour total hours available in millions	Direct labour hours per unit for each model		
		x_1	x_2	x_3
Machining (x_4)	1.4	0.5	0.5	1.0
Assembly (x_5)	1.2	0.5	0.5	2.0

Contribution, estimated to be

Model	Amount per thousand units in £
x_1	1500
x_2	1300
x_3	2500

You are required, using the above information, to set up the first tableau of a linear programme to determine the product mix which will maximize total contribution and then to complete the first iteration only.

(b) Interpret the following tableau, given that it is the final solution to the above problem. The S variables (S_1, S_2, S_3, S_4, S_5) relate to the constraints in the same sequence as presented in (a) above.

x_1	x_2	x_3	S_1	S_2	S_3	S_4	S_5	b_{ij}
1	0	0	1	0	0	0	0	500
0	0	0	0.25	0.25	1	0	−0.5	112.5
0	0	1	−0.25	−0.25	0	0	0.5	287.5
0	0	0	−0.25	−0.25	0	1	−0.5	487.5
0	1	0	0	1	0	0	0	750
0	0	0	−875	−675	0	0	−1250	−2 443 750

(Institute of Cost and Management Accountants, Professional Stage: Part I, Quantitative Techniques, May 1979.)

THREE

TRANSPORTATION PROBLEMS

3-1 INTRODUCTION

Transportation problems were originally known as Hitchcock distribution problems. The 'transportation' tag that has stuck relates to one particular application of the model. The same method finds usage in other areas—for instance, purchasing, cash management, and inventory models. In the case of cash, money has to be 'transported' from one period or usage to another. In stock control we can think of January's production being 'transported' to July via inventory. However, we shall stick within the physical transportation context in this presentation but it is important to remember that this is not the only area of application of the technique

Transportation problems are linear programming problems, but with a special structure. The simplex method *could* be used to solve them but there is a purpose-built algorithm that is much better.

3-2 THE VAM METHOD

The logic of the solution procedure is similar to that of the simplex method. First, a basic feasible solution is found. Secondly, we check for improvement possibility. Thirdly, we implement improvement and continue until no further improvements are possible. The first thing then is to find a bfs to start with. We shall use Vogel's Approximation Method (VAM) to do this. The VAM initial solution is much better than the origin that we had to make do with in LP proper. Not infrequently the VAM solution is optimal! Consider a typical problem.

A wholesaling company has three warehouses from which supplies are drawn for four retail customers. The company deals in a single product, the supplies of which at each warehouse are:

Warehouse no.	Supply (units)
1	20
2	28
3	17
	65 = total supply

The customer demands are:

Customer no.	Demand (units)
1	15
2	19
3	13
4	18
	65 = total demand

Conveniently, total supply at the warehouses is equal to total demand from the customers. The table gives the transportation costs *per unit* shipped from each warehouse to each customer. Thus it costs £3 for each unit shipped from warehouse no. 1 to customer no. 1. It costs £5 for each unit shipped from warehouse no. 2 to customer no. 4. The operative word here is *each*. This implies linearity and the absence of any economies or diseconomies of scale.

It is convenient to represent all of the data as shown in Fig. 3-1. The supplies and demands are grafted onto the cost table around the perimeter and are known as *rim conditions*. The method that we shall explain works

		Customer					Row VAM nos
		1	2	3	4		
	1	3	6	8	4	20	1
Warehouse	2	6	1	2	5	28	1
	3	7	8	3	9	17	4
		15	19	13	18		

Column VAM nos: 3   5   1   1

Figure 3-1

	1	2	3	4		VAM nos
1	3	× 6	8	4	20	̸1 1
2	6	⑲ 1	2	5	28	̸1 3
3	7	× 8	3	9	17	̸4 4
	15	19	13	18		

VAM nos: ̸3   ̸5   ̸1   ̸1

3   1   1

Figure 3-2

with problems in which there are *balanced rim conditions* (i.e., supply = demand).

The object of the exercise is to find out what supplies to dispatch from each of the warehouses to each customer so as to minimize transportation costs overall.

The VAM starting solution requires the determination of a *VAM number* for each row and column. This number is simply the *difference* in cost between the two most economical routes in that row or column. The first set of VAM numbers are shown in Fig. 3-1. So for row (1), the two best routes from warehouse no. 1 are to customer no. 1 (cost £3) and to customer no. 4 (cost £4) thus the VAM difference = £4 − £3 = £1. For column (2), the two best routes to customer no. 2 are from warehouse no. 2 (cost £1) and from warehouse no. 1 (cost £6). Thus the VAM number for this column is 6 − 1 = 5. And so on for all the remaining rows and columns. Now select the row or column with the *largest* VAM number and dispatch as much as possible along the cheapest route in the row or column selected. Thus we select column (2) and send 19 units from warehouse no. 2. This is shown as 19 in square 2, 2. The maximum dispatch or assignment will be given by the smaller of the supply and demand figures corresponding to the cheapest square in the row or column selected. Thus customer no. 2 is completely supplied and no further entries (for the moment at least) may be made in column (2). This fact is indicated with (pencilled) crosses in that column. The column is said to be *deleted*. The second set of VAM numbers are now calculated ignoring the deleted column (or row). These are shown in Fig. 3-2. Row (3) now has the largest VAM difference so that 13 (the smaller of 13 and 17) is assigned to the best undeleted square in the row. This is square 3, 3. Once again this deletes a column (it will not always be a column that is deleted) and VAM numbers are recomputed. The results are shown in Fig. 3-3. Now column (1) is indicated with a VAM difference of 3; 15 units may be inserted in square 1, 1 which deletes column (1). After making this entry, the remaining entries are forced. There *must* be 5 units sent from 1 to 4; there

	1	2	3	4	
1	3	× 6	× 8	4	20
2	6	⑲ 1	× 2	5	28
3	7	× 8	⑬ 3	9	17
	15	19	13	18	

VAM nos:
3 8 X̶ X̶
3 X̶ X̶
3 1

VAM nos
X̶ X̶ 1
X̶ 3̶ 1
4̶ 4̶ 2

Figure 3-3

must be 4 units dispatched from 3 to 4; and there *must* be 9 units sent from 2 to 4. Only in this way can supplies be exhausted at the warehouses and demand met for customer no. 4. We have now arrived at the *VAM initial solution*. This is shown in Fig. 3-4.

First let us find the total cost of this arrangement. This will be the sum of the products of the 'assignments' and their corresponding unit costs, viz.:

$$\text{Cost} = 3(15) + 4(5) + 1(19) + 5(9) + 3(13) + 9(4) = 204$$

3-3 CLOSED PATHS AND MODI

The question now is whether or not this figure of £204 can be improved upon. The eye is drawn to the route warehouse no. 2 to customer no. 3 which has a unit cost of only £2 but is unused in the VAM-determined arrangement. Would it be worth dispatching something along this route? The situation here is just as it was in straight LP. We have found a basic feasible solution (more of this later) and we shall now consider the consequences of introducing a new variable (x_{23} if you like, a shipment from warehouse no. 2 to customer no. 3) *at unit level*. Just as in the simplex method, when a new

	1	2	3	4	
1	⑮ 3	× 6	× 8	⑤ 4	20
2	× 6	⑲ 1	× 2	⑨ 5	28
3	× 7	× 8	⑬ 3	④ 9	17
	15	19	13	18	

Figure 3-4

	1	2	3	4	
1	3 (15)	6	8	4 (5)	20
2	6	1 (19)	2 start ↑+1	5 (9) −1	28
3	7	8	3 (13) −1←	9 (4) +1↓	17
	15	19	13	18	

Figure 3-5

variable comes into the solution it will be necessary to adjust the levels of existing variables to accommodate it. What adjustments need to be made to allow a shipment of one unit of square $2,3$? The necessary changes are shown in Fig. 3-5.

If $+1$ is sent from 2 to 3 then one less must be sent from 2 to somewhere else. Less can only be sent to customers no. 2 or no. 4. If less were sent to customer no. 2 then more would have to be sent to customer no. 2 from somewhere else. This could only be done by introducing another new assignment, but as in the simplex method we consider only *one* new square (in this case $2,3$) at a time. So, one less must be sent to customer no. 4—hence the -1 in this square. The remaining changes—one *more* unit to customer no. 4 from warehouse no. 3 and one less from warehouse no. 3 to customer no. 3—follow from similar arguments. The pattern of changes shown is the *only* pattern of alterations that involves no new assignments other than square $2,3$. The $+1$ and -1 entries in each row and column must cancel and the changes can be linked by arrows (here shown going clockwise) forming a *closed path* starting and finishing at $2,3$.

Once a closed path has been formed (rules will be given shortly) the cost effects of the changes can be determined. Adding up the costs at squares where one less is being sent $(3 + 5 = 8)$ and at places where more will be sent $(2 + 9 = 11)$ gives a net *worsening* of £3 in cost. This is represented by $8 - 11 = -3$ which is the *evaluation* of the square $2,3$ in the current solution. In contrast to the simplex method negative numbers here mean that currently no improvement is possible via the square in question. As an aside, if the problem were being solved by the simplex method the index row number under x_{23} in the current solution would be $+3$. The closed-path evaluations that we shall obtain will in fact be *minus* the index row numbers.

The rules for establishing the closed path for a square are simple. The only turns allowed are $90°$, turns can *only* be made at 'assignment' squares (although some may be passed over), the path must finish at the 'vacant' square it started at (i.e., it must be 'closed'). The pattern of adjustments is

Left tableau:

	1	2	3	4	
1	⑮ 3	6 +	8	⑤ 4 −	20
2	6 −	⑲ 1	2	⑨ 5 +	28
3	7	8	⑬ 3	④ 9	17
	15	19	13	18	

Right tableau:

	1	2	3	4	
1	⑮ 3	6	8 +	⑤ 4 −	20
2	6	⑲ 1	2	⑨ 5	28
3	7	8	⑬ 3 −	④ 9 +	17
	15	19	13	18	

Figure 3-6

easily found by putting alternate plus and minus signs *at turning points* in the path, starting with a plus sign at the vacant square being evaluated. The evaluation is then found by adding up costs at 'negative' (*minus* one) places in the closed path and subtracting the sum of costs at 'positive' places in the path. *Positive* evaluations will represent improvement possibility. Thus square 2, 3 although it is the cheapest unused route will not in the present context show improvement.

All the closed paths for the vacant squares in this case are simple rectangular paths. Those for squares 1, 2 and 1, 3 are shown in Fig. 3-6. The reader should identify the closed paths for the remaining vacant squares and confirm the following table of evaluations:

Square	Evaluation
1, 2	− 6
1, 3	− 10
2, 1	− 2
2, 3	− 3
3, 1	+ 1
3, 2	− 3

Evidently, the only square showing improvement potential is 3, 1 even though it is itself one of the more expensive unused routes. The reason is that using this square enables less to be sent along the even more expensive route 3, 4 which is at a negative place in the closed path.

Thus we decide to 'introduce' square 3, 1. Since the problem is an LP problem *every* unit shipped via 3, 1 will save £1. The most that can be sent is determined by the *smallest assignment at a negative place in the closed path*. The closed path consists of the four corner squares. Assignment levels will increase at 3, 1 and 1, 4 and decrease at 1, 1 and 3, 4. So by the time *four* units have been 'shipped round the path' the assignment in 3, 4 has gone down to zero. This is as far as we can go. This procedure for determining the level of

	$v_1 = 3$	$v_2 = 0$	$v_3 = -1$	$v_4 = 4$	
$u_1 = 0$	⑪ 3	6	8	⑨ 4	20
$u_2 = 1$	6 ⑲	1	2 ⑨	5	28
$u_3 = 4$	④ 7	8	⑬ 3	9	17
	15	19	13	18	

Figure 3-7

the new assignment is equivalent to the procedure for selection of the pivotal row in the simplex method. The new solution is shown in Fig. 3-7.

What has been done so far constitutes a complete solution procedure that need only be repeated to produce the optimum. Closed paths could be established for each vacant square and an evaluation conducted. The closed path for square 2,3 is shown. This is a non-rectangular path, but as always it is unique. The reader may verify that the path for square 3,2 is also non-rectangular. Incidentally closed paths do not *have* to turn when an assignment square is reached (they may have to pass over) and the path may cross itself. There is no significance in either of these events.

Although we shall still need closed paths, there is a quicker way of doing the vacant-square evaluations. We shall have space here only to present the method in rote fashion. Numbers (call them u_i) are assigned to each row and numbers (call them v_j) are attached to each column in such a way that *if* square i,j is an assignment square $u_i + v_j = cost$ *for that square*. It turns out that it is necessary to determine one of these values arbitrarily and the convention is to set $u_1 = 0$ (see if it makes any difference to the subsequent *evaluations* if v_2 is first set $= 7$ *or* $u_3 = -22$). Now, if $u_1 = 0$ and, by the rule $u_1 + v_1 = $ cost in square 1,1 (since there is an assignment here) then $u_1 + v_1 = 1$ so that $v_1 = 1$. Next, since there is also an assignment in square 1,4 then $u_1 + v_4 = $ cost in square 1,4 $= 4$ so that $v_4 = 4$. Note that there is no necessity for $u_1 + v_2 = 6$ since there is no assignment in square 1,2. Continuing, if $v_4 = 4$ then $v_4 + u_2 = 5$, so $u_2 = 1$. If $u_2 = 1$ and $u_2 + v_2 = 1$, $v_2 = 0$. Now, we found earlier that $v_1 = 3$. If $v_1 = 3$ and $u_3 + v_1 = 7$, then $u_3 = 4$. If $u_3 = 4$ and $u_3 + v_3 = 3$, then $v_3 = -1$. This completes the row and column numbering. Negative numbers, as we have seen, are allowed although most will be positive. There is no connection between u and v numbers (fictitious costs) and VAM numbers. Vacant squares are now quickly evaluated. The evaluation of any square i, j is:

$$\text{evaluation} = u_i + v_j - c_{ij}$$

so that the following results are produced:

Square	u_i	v_j	c_{ij}	Evaluation
1, 2	0	0	6	−6
1, 3	0	−1	8	−9
2, 1	1	3	6	−2
2, 3	1	−1	2	−2
3, 2	4	0	8	−4
3, 4	4	4	9	−1

These evaluations may be checked by the closed-path method if desired. All evaluations are negative; which fact indicates that the solution is optimal. Had it *not* been optimal, we should have picked the square with the largest positive evaluation, established the closed path for the square, shipped as much round the path as possible, recalculated new u_i and v_j (they change when the solution does), and re-evaluated vacant squares. The procedure stops when there are no positive evaluations. If a vacant square has a *zero* evaluation this means that there is another basic solution of the same cost; the solution would be *non-unique*. As an exercise the reader should use the u_i and v_j method to check the evaluations obtained for the VAM initial solution. The use of row and column numbers and closed paths has been called the *modified distribution method* or MODI. This method is spelt out in a number of OR books, but one of the earliest presentations is still the best (Metzger, 1963). Financial applications can be found in Wilkes (1977, chapter 9). Let us apply the method to some more problems.

3-4 FURTHER EXAMPLES

In Fig. 3-8 is shown the workings for a case in which the VAM solution gives the optimum straight off. The reader should verify the workings and confirm that the vacant-square evaluations are all negative. The u_i and v_j that we have used are, in fact, *dual values*. However, in a transportation problem an individual dual value is meaningless; it has meaning only in relation to the other values. Try setting u_1 at some value other than zero (positive or negative); you can make any one of the other numbers come to any value you please, but you will note that: (a) the *sum of* any particular pair of u_i and v_j is constant; (b) the *difference between* any pair of u_i's or any pair of v_j's is constant.

Just as in the simplex method, we can use the dual values for *sensitivity analysis*. Here we shall briefly consider changes in the supplies (row availabilities 24, 23, 13) and demands. Suppose that it were possible, if desired, to stock less at warehouse B and more at C for the same total

	1 $v_1 = 0$	2 $v_2 = 5$	3 $v_3 = 3$	4 $v_4 = 5$		VAM nos			
$u_1 = 0$ A	11	5 ⑨	6	5 ⑮	24	0	0	0	0
$u_2 = 2$ B	2 ⑫	10	5 ⑪	9	23	3	4		
$u_3 = -1$ C	7	4 ⑦	2 ⑥	7	13	2	2	2	3
	12	16	17	15					

VAM nos: ~~5~~   ~~1~~   ~~3~~   ~~2~~
                ~~1~~   ~~3~~   ~~2~~
                ~~1~~   ~~4~~   ~~2~~
                1   2

Figure 3-8

overall. Would there be any advantage in this change? The answer is 'yes'. For every unit less at B we save $u_2 = £2$. For every unit more at C we add $u_3 = £-1$. So that the net saving in cost is no less than £3 for every unit thus transferred (up to a certain limit: 11 units). Try and see why this is so by considering the costs on the routes B3 and C3. Thus, within limits, capacity at C should be built up and B run down in the longer term. It would also be worth ($£(u_1 - u_3) = £1$) building up C at the expense of A up to a point (9 units 'transferred'. Why?).

We can also consider *balanced* changes in supplies and demands. Suppose customer no. 4 wanted one more unit (i.e., demand from 4 of 16) and depot B had an extra unit available (i.e., supply at B of 24). The extra cost of this would be $u_2 + v_4 = £7$ (it is best to alter several supplies than for B to supply 4 directly at a cost of 9). Notice what would happen if customer no. 1 wanted one more unit and depot C had it. Total cost would actually *decrease* by £1. All the old demands to be satisfied *and* one more unit and cost goes down! This possibility is called the *paradox of transportation*. Of course, it is only an apparent paradox. The reader may verify that the extra demand may be met by setting B1 at 13, B3 at 10, and C3 at 7. The slightly changed pattern of demands and supplies allows more use to be made of the very cheap routes B1 and C3 (costing £4 in total) and less use to be made of B3 (saving £5). Thus there is a net saving of £1. Sensitivity analysis can be extended to unbalanced changes in rim conditions and to the transport costs. The reader is referred to Wilkes (1977, Chapter 9) for illustrations.

Now consider a case where total supply and total demand are unequal

	1	2	3	4	dummy	
A	㉑ 8	13	9	⑫ 7	0	33
B	④ 15	13	㉖ 11	16	⑪ 0	41
C	13	⑳ 8	12	⑩ 11	0	30
	25	20	26	22	11	

Real demands   Balancing demand

Figure 3-9

to begin with. In Fig. 3-9 the demand from customers totals 93 but supply at warehouses adds up to 104. The transportation method works only with balanced rim conditions (supply = demand). All that we need to do is to 'fudge' things so as to impart a balance. This is done by inserting an imaginary customer with the missing demand! Somewhat unflatteringly this extra customer is called a *dummy*. All dummy costs are zero. Any warehouse that ships to a dummy has that many units left in stock. In this case (only the optimum is shown here) it should be warehouse B. Obviously if demand had exceeded supply we should have inserted a balancing, *dummy row*. Whichever customers received 'supplies' from the imaginary source would be short on their orders.

A problem that sometimes occurs in transportation is *degeneracy*. A degenerate solution is one in which there is an insufficient number of assignments to establish closed paths for all vacant squares. Equivalently, not all u_i and v_j can be determined. A degenerate solution is shown in Fig. 3-10.

The only square for which a closed path can be found is B3. A simple

	1	2	3	
A	8	⑮ 10	7	15
B	⑧ 6	10	9	8
C	② 10	8	⑳ 4	22
	10	15	20	

Figure 3-10

(a)

	$v_1 = 8$	$v_2 = 10$	$v_3 = 2$	
$u_1 = 0$	⑧ 8 (ε)	⑩ 10 (15)	7	15
$u_2 = -2$	6 (8)	10	9	8
$u_3 = 2$	(2) 10	8	4 (20)	22
	10	15	20	

(b)

	$v_1 = 8$	$v_2 = 10$	$v_3 = 6$	
$u_1 = 0$	8 (2)	10 (13)	7	15
$u_2 = -2$	6 (8)	10	9	8
$u_3 = -2$	10	8 (2)	4 (20)	22
	10	15	20	

Figure 3-11

trick solves the problem. Invent another assignment! The new *very small* assignment (so as not to disturb anything really) is called *epsilon, ε*. This can be placed in any vacant square for which a closed path cannot already be found. These are called *independent locations*. In this case only B3 is *not* independent. In Fig. 3-11(a), ε is placed in square A1. There was no particular reason for this choice rather than another independent location; u_i and v_j can now be determined and the optimum follows in one iteration. Note that the optimum is not degenerate (ε has been set $=0$, i.e., removed). Sometimes an unlucky choice of location results in only ε being relocated (ε is always the smallest number). One of two things must then result. *Either* a position for ε can be found such that a real amount may be shipped round a worthwhile path *or* a location for ε can be found for which there are no positive vacant square evaluations, i.e., the solution was the optimum in disguise!

3-5 TWO NON-TRANSPORT APPLICATIONS

In Sec. 3-1 it was mentioned that the transportation model is useful in many problems that need not centre around physical movement of goods. There is space here to offer two examples. First a procurement application. Consider the following problem:

A department store requires the following annual quantities of five types of clothing items:

Type	A	B	C	D	E
Quantity required ('000s of units)	18	9	12	20	16

The firm has received quotations from four manufacturers who have undertaken to supply not more than the quantities below (of all types combined).

Manufacturer	1	2	3	4
Total quantity ('000s of units)	20	18	25	19

The store estimates that its profits per item will vary with the type and manufacturer as shown in the following table:

		A	B	Type C	D	E
	1	2.0	1.9	2.3	1.5	3.2
	2	1.8	1.9	2.1	1.6	2.8
Manufacturer	3	2.5	2.4	2.2	1.7	3.6
	4	2.2	1.4	2.1	1.8	2.8

Profit per unit in £s

(i) How should the orders be optimally placed? Is this optimal allocation unique?

(ii) Suppose that the store was already contracted to purchase 8000 units of type C from manufacturer 2 (these 8000 units being included in the demand for C and the maximum supply from 2 given above). What is the maximum amount it ought to be prepared to pay to be released from this contract?

The distinctive feature here is that the problem is one of *maximization*. In terms of VAM, the VAM numbers will now be the difference between the two *best* squares, viz., for row (1) the first VAM number will be $3.2 - 2.3 = 0.9$. In fact VAM numbers are always the difference between the two best squares — these will be the least-cost squares in a cost minimization problem. Incidentally, VAM gives good results since in contrast to the 'least cost first' (LCF) method which simply makes the next assignment to the best square (cost-wise or profit-wise) remaining, VAM looks ahead. The VAM number is a sort of opportunity cost figure. It is the *least* penalty (at some stage in the problem) per unit that will be incurred if an assignment is not placed in the best available square in the row or column concerned. In other words VAM

	$v_1 = 2.0$ A	$v_2 = 2.0$ B	$v_3 = 2.3$ C	$v_4 = 1.6$ D	$v_5 = 3.2$ E	$v_6 = 0$ dummy	
$u_1 = 0$ 1	⑧ 2.0	1.9	⑫ 2.3	1.5	ⓔ 3.2	0	20
$u_2 = 0.0$ 2	1.8	1.9	2.1	⑪ 1.6	2.8	⑦ 0	18
$u_3 = 0.4$ 3	2.5	⑨ 2.4	2.2	1.7	⑯ 3.6	0	25
$u_4 = 0.2$ 4	⑩ 2.2	1.4	2.1	⑨ 1.8	2.8	0	19
	18	9	12	20	16	7	

Figure 3-12

considers some of the *consequences* of choices, whereas LCF inspection does not.

The VAM initial solution is shown in Fig. 3-12. It will be seen that (a) a dummy column was needed, and (b) the solution is degenerate. The degeneracy has been resolved by location of ε in square 1, E. The solution is not optimal. Even though the problem is one of maximization the u_i and v_j numbers can be determined just as before, viz., $u_i + v_j = $ profit in square i, j. The difference is that, as regards the evaluations, it is *negative* evaluations that now represent improvement. Thus for square 1, B the evaluation is $u_1 + v_2 - $ profit $1, 2 = 0 + 2 - 1.9 = +0.1$ which means that less profit will be made (check this by establishing the closed path, and bear in mind that the method does not 'know' what the financial entries in the cells represent).

Square 3, A has a negative evaluation of $0.4 + 2.0 - 2.5 = -0.1$ and eight (thousand) units can be shipped round the corresponding path. This, coincidentally, removes the degeneracy and the solution produced is optimal. It is shown in Fig. 3-13. The total profit made is £179 400. The solution, however, is *non-unique*. Square 2, B has a zero evaluation and the solution resulting from shipment around the corresponding closed path will produce an equally good arrangement.

As regards any existing contract to purchase 8000 of type C from manufacturer 2, this would reduce profit by $£800 = 8 \times 1000(-0.1 + 2.3 - 2.1)$. The result of keeping to the contract would be to make an assignment of 8 in square 2, C, so that if the release costs less than £800 it would be worth while.

Transportation methods, as has been suggested, can have direct financial application. An example in the area of short-term investment and cash management is given in Wilkes (1977, Chapter 9). Space permits here only the presentation of a much simplified schematic example.

	$v_1 = 2.1$ A	$v_2 = 2.0$ B	$v_3 = 2.3$ C	$v_4 = 1.7$ D	$v_5 = 3.2$ E	$v_6 = 0.1$ dummy	
$u_1 = 0$ 1	2.0	1.9	⑫ 2.3	1.5	⑧ 3.2	0	20
$u_2 = -0.1$ 2	1.8	1.9	2.1	⑪ 1.6	2.8	⑦ 0	18
$u_3 = 0.4$ 3	⑧ 2.5	⑨ 2.4	2.2	1.7	⑧ 3.6	0	25
$u_4 = 0.1$ 4	⑩ 2.2	1.4	2.1	⑨ 1.8	2.8	0	19
	18	9	12	20	16	7	

Figure 3-13

A holding company owns three firms, A, B, and C. Each firm is at the point of requiring capital inputs of amounts 140, 70, and 90 capital units respectively. The holding company can obtain funds from three sources. It can issue shares in each of the companies held which will represent differing costs to existing shareholders in the holding company, depending on the risk class of the individual firm. Suppose that there is an overall limit (imposed by the holding company) of 100 units of finance raised by equity issue. In addition debt may be increased by up to 80 units and the holding company has 120 units of retained earnings available. Figure 3-14 shows this financing problem and its solution in a distributional format.

In Fig. 3-14 the cost entries are the costs to the holding company of finance for the three firms from the different sources, and 'assignments' represent the amounts to be raised from each source for each firm. This example is one of a rather simple financing problem. Typically, financing

	Firm A	Firm B	Firm C	Sums available
Equity	⑨⓪ 15	20	⑩ 14	100
Debt	12	15	⑧⓪ 10	80
R.E.	⑤⓪ 8	⑦⓪ 8	8	120
Requirements	140	70	90	300 / 300

Figure 3-14

problems will have the structure of more complicated programming problems and ideally the problems of optimal sources and uses of funds should be examined simultaneously. This will not always be possible, but occasionally computational techniques originally designed for quite different management applications can suit the structure of simplified financing problems.

3-6 ADVANCED WORK

There are numerous changes that can be rung on the basic model. In *trans-shipment problems* there are intermediate locations through which goods may pass (see Wilkes, 1977). In *capacitated* problems there are limits on the amounts that may be sent along some or all routes. *Diseconomies of scale* can be allowed for (a discrete increase in unit cost along a route if used above a certain level). Unfortunately, *economies* of scale, which are perhaps more frequent, are much more troublesome computationally. Some models allow for 'losses in transit'—for instance electrical power losses in transmission or deterioration in storage—not to mention pilfering. The US Navy used this kind of model to minimize transportation and overhaul costs at naval shipyards. And so the list could go on. It should by this stage be evident both that the range of uses of the method is very considerable and that the basic model is very adaptable.

EXERCISES

3-1 Outline the logic of the MODI solution procedure for transportation problems and give some instances of problems not involving physical transport for which the method might be useful.

3-2 Obtain the VAM starting solution for the following transportation problem:

Customer

		1	2	3	4	
	1	18	16	8	13	100
	2	14	14	6	10	125
Depot	3	20	15	17	15	70
	4	8	12	19	11	80
		55	130	95	95	

3-3 Using Vogel's approximation method for the initial solution, solve the following problem:

	1	2	3	
A	10	16	12	25
B	7	11	11	20
C	7	9	8	15
	20	27	13	

3-4 The following is a transportation problem from three warehouses (A, B, and C) to four customers (1, 2, 3, and 4). The capacities at the warehouses and the demands from the customers are shown around the perimeter. Per unit transport costs are shown in the cells. Cost minimization is the objective.

	1	2	3	4	
A	7	8	11	10	30
B	10	12	5	4	45
C	6	10	11	9	35
	20	28	17	33	

(i) Find the cost of the VAM initial solution.

(ii) Find the optimal solution and total cost.

(iii) By how much would the BI cost need to be reduced in order to make shipments along this route worth while?

(iv) Now suppose that demand from customer one and capacity at warehouse B both increase by five units. What is the extra cost of satisfying this increased demand? What is special about the solution so produced? What problems does this type of solution pose?

3-5 Explain what is meant by the 'paradox of transportation'. Why is the paradox only apparent?

3-6 A discount store requires the following monthly quantities of five different sizes of refrigerator:

Size	A	B	C	D	E
Number required	16	24	20	22	15

The store has received quotations from four manufacturers who are able to supply not more than the quantities below (of all sizes combined):

Manufacturer	1	2	3	4
Maximum supply	24	30	23	25

The store estimates that its profits per refrigerator will vary with the size and manufacturer as shown in the following table:

Manufacturer	Size				
	A	B	C	D	E
1	20	15	23	25	13
2	19	12	25	27	21
3	17	13	22	21	18
4	22	12	27	23	18

(i) How should the orders be optimally placed and what is the maximum monthly profit for the store?

(ii) Suppose that the store was already contracted to manufacturer 1 to buy seven units monthly of size E. What is the maximum sum the store would be willing to pay (per month) to be released from this obligation?

(iii) Total supplies from manufacturers 2 and 3 are fixed but the amounts obtained from 1 and 4 can be varied (for the same overall total). How would this flexibility be best employed?

(iv) Suppose that demand for size B increases to 30 units monthly and only manufacturer 2 can increase supply (to 36 units maximum). By how much could maximum profit increase?

3-7 Newton Company Ltd specializes in the manufacture of certain electronic components for local industry. The three main demand areas for these components are Sidmouth, Liverbourne, and Centapool and the company has a warehouse in each of these towns. The company's three factories are separate from its warehouses and are at East-Sidmouth, West-Liverbourne, and Martrent. Due to the present economic climate the company is suffering from an extreme shortage of business, as indicated in the following table:

Factory	Maximum output of factory per annum (units)	Warehouse	Expected demand in area served by warehouse for coming year (units)
East-Sidmouth	210 000	Sidmouth	80 000
West-Liverbourne	140 000	Liverbourne	200 000
Martrent	290 000	Centapool	200 000

The nearest warehouses to the East-Sidmouth and West-Liverbourne factories are Sidmouth and Liverbourne respectively. The Centapool warehouse is roughly equidistant from all three factories. The variable cost of distribution (£ per unit) from the factories to the warehouses are as follows:

	Sidmouth	Liverbourne	Centapool
East-Sidmouth	2	4	4
West-Liverbourne	4	3	4
Martrent	3	6	4

The variable costs of production at each factory are:

	£ per unit
East-Sidmouth	11
West-Liverbourne	14
Martrent	12

The present distribution policy of the company is as follows:

All Sidmouth warehouse requirements are supplied from East Sidmouth. All West-Liverbourne production is transported to the Liverbourne warehouse, the remaining demand at Liverbourne being supplied from the East Sidmouth factory. All Centapool requirements are supplied from Martrent.

Required:

(a) Evaluate the cost of applying the present distribution policy in the coming year. Why do you think the company adopted this particular policy?

(5 marks)

(b) Determine the policy which is expected to achieve the minimum total cost of production and distribution for the coming year. What cost saving does this involve? Is this solution unique? If not give any alternative solution you find.

(15 marks)

(c) Assume now that the company is considering the closure of the West-Liverbourne factory. What increase in the total variable cost of production and distribution will this cause assuming that the company operates in a minimum cost manner?

(5 marks)

(Association of Certified Accountants, Professional Examination: Section 2, paper 12, Management Mathematics, June 1976.)

3-8 The Management Services section of Mech International Ltd is planning to expand. Two of the eleven posts currently being advertised within the section require special knowledge of accounting practice and carry a basic annual salary of £5000, a further three need basic training in data processing and are worth at least £4700, while the remainder can be filled by anyone with general experience of management services and pay £4400 at minimum. It has been agreed, however, that any appointee should be paid a salary equal to the greater of his current salary and the company's minimum for the job he is to do.

Of the 14 short listed applicants, all possess adequate general experience. Two are amply qualified in both accounting and data processing, 4 in accounting only and 5 in data processing only. The present salaries of the last 3 groups of applicants are respectively £4800, £4600, and

£4500, whereas those with no knowledge of either specialism are currently earning £4200 or less.
Required:
The Head of Management Services has been asked to produce an estimate of total additional expenditure incurred in his section, for the coming year, on employee salaries.

(i) By defining 'sources' and 'destinations', use the transportation technique to determine the current figure he may reasonably submit. (If your allocation is not unique, detail *all* other possible solutions.)

(20 marks)

(ii) Show by means of a simple algebraic example that transportation is a special case of linear programming.
(Association of Certified Accountants, Professional Examination: Section 2, paper 12, Management Mathematics, December 1977.)

3-9 The following problem should be solved by the transportation method. XW Limited has four production plants and four wholesale warehouse outlets. The warehouses are situated away from the production plants. The production and transportation costs, the selling prices, production capacities, and sales quantities are given below:

							Per unit	
Production plants	Warehouses				Production capacity in units	Materials	Labour and overhead £	
	1	2	3	4				
A	10	14	7	10	140	4	6	
B	8	12	5	10	100	5	8	
C	3	7	11	8	150	4	9	
D	9	12	6	13	160	3	8	
Warehouse requirements in units	80	120	130	110				
Selling price (ex warehouse) per unit	£ 26	£ 32	£ 30	£ 25				

The cost of transporting a unit from a given plant to a warehouse is shown in the body of the matrix in £'s per unit.
You are required to:

(a) compute a plan for production and distribution which will achieve maximum profit for the company;

(b) state the profit achieved by the plan you have given in answer to (a) above.
Your workings should be shown and the steps in the calculations clearly described: answers not supported in this way will be regarded as inadequate.
(Institute of Cost and Management Accountants; Part IV Examination, Management Information and Quantitative Techniques, November 1975.)

FOUR

ASSIGNMENT PROBLEMS

4-1 INTRODUCTION

Just as transportation problems are special cases of linear programming problems so assignment problems are special cases of transportation problems. In fact they are transportation problems of *maximal degeneracy*. Here is one in Fig. 4-1. You can see the special features involved. All of the supplies and demands are *unity*. This being the case the problem must be square (same number of rows and columns, although dummies may be involved). Otherwise the features of a transportation problem remain.

Assignment problems are, however, not just awkward transportation problems. They represent a useful class of problems in themselves. For the problem in Fig. 4-1 suppose that the 'supplies' in each row represent the

28	11	30	15	1
12	30	28	21	1
13	23	28	10	1
17	24	21	40	1
1	1	1	1	

Figure 4-1

availability of *one man* (a different individual in each case). Now suppose that the 'demands' in each column represent different *jobs*, for each of which one man is required. Finally instead of the entries in the squares being costs suppose that they are the *times*, in minutes, that each man would take to do each job. Now you have the essential character of the assignment problem: *m* men are to be assigned to *m* jobs such that each man is allocated precisely one job and each job is performed by one man only. *The allocation is to be such as to minimize the total time taken for the jobs.*

There are numerous other instances where this kind of situation occurs. For example:

1. Assigning offices to staff members.
2. Assigning salesmen to areas.
3. Assigning vehicles to routes.
4. Assigning products to factories.
5. Assigning contracts to bidders.

4-2 COMPUTATION: (i) A CONVENIENT PROBLEM

A slightly different tabular form (than that of transportation problems proper) will be convenient for handling assignment problems. Since we know that the rim conditions are ones all round these can be left out. The time (in this case) data—or in general *effectiveness* data—can then be concentrated upon, as in Fig. 4-2. This form of presentation of data is called an effectiveness matrix.

In trying to decide to which man each job should go, a commonsense idea is to examine the columns for their minimum entries, i.e., see which man is the fastest at each job. In Fig. 4-3 the minimum entry in each column has been subtracted from all entries in that column. Each resulting column is a list of excess times (or reductions in effectiveness) for each job if not allocated to the fastest man. The zero entries (squared off) indicate the fastest man at

	Jobs			
	1	2	3	4
1	28	11	30	15
2	12	30	28	21
Men 3	13	23	28	10
4	17	24	21	40

Figure 4-2

	Jobs			
	1	2	3	4
1	16	[0]	9	5
2	[0]	19	7	11
Men 3	1	12	7	[0]
4	5	13	[0]	30

Figure 4-3

each job. As luck would have it not only is there at least one zero in each column (guaranteed by our procedure so far) but each zero is in a different row. Thus a complete assignment with zeros can be made. The optimum has been reached straight away although things are not always so convenient— as we shall see.

The fact that we were able to make a complete assignment (every man, each to a different job) with zeros means that there is *zero opportunity 'cost'* to the solution. The extra or opportunity 'cost' of other assignment patterns can be found readily from the data of Fig. 4-3. For instance the extra time taken by giving man 1 job 1, man 2 job 2, and so on down the main diagonal, is the sum of the elements on that diagonal, i.e., $16 + 19 + 7 + 30 = 72$. This result can be checked by 'costing' the two solutions from the original data of Fig. 4-2. The extra time taken by any other arrangement can be found by summing the appropriate elements of Fig. 4-3, which is frequently described as the *opportunity cost matrix*.

Some care is required here. In the first place, as in transportation problems generally, *individual* 'opportunity cost' figures are meaningless. It is quite wrong to say that the opportunity cost of giving man 1 job 1 is 16. If man 1 gets job 1, man 2 will have to do something else—there are many possible rearrangements. Secondly, there are many alternative 'opportunity cost matrices' which also work correctly. A rather different looking picture is given in Fig. 4-4. If you care to check, you will see that this set of numbers works equally well. *It is only meaningful to cost out complete alternative solutions.* Any arrangement of numbers which correctly costs the alternative complete solutions is as good as any other (there may be literally hundreds for any one problem). The method that we have begun to demonstrate always gives a valid set of numbers.

We started off working with the columns. What if we had begun with the rows? In Fig. 4-5(a) the row minima are taken away from other entries in the row; in Fig. 4-5(b) the *columns so produced* are operated on. Only column (3)

17	0	19	4
0	18	16	9
3	13	18	0
0	7	4	23

23	0	21	1
0	12	12	0
12	16	23	0
0	1	0	14

Figure 4-4

17	[0]	15	4
[0]	18	12	9
3	13	14	[0]
0	7	[0]	23

Figure 4-5

is affected since it does not contain a zero after the row subtractions. After this process it is again possible to mark out the optimal solution. Note that we have produced yet another opportunity cost matrix.

4-3 COMPUTATION: (ii) THE FULL PROCEDURE

Not all assignment problems are so easily solved. The source of the trouble is that the row and column subtractions do not necessarily produce a complete set of independent zones—one in each row and each in a different column. Where this is the case further operations on the matrix are required. We shall first present a complete set of instructions for solution (after Sasieni et al.) and then apply them to an example.

1. Form the effectiveness matrix.
2. Subtract the minimum element in each row from each element in the row.
3. For the matrix formed by (2) subtract the minimum element in each column from each element in the column.

A complete assignment with all zeros may or may not exist at this stage. If it cannot be spotted quickly by casual inspection then:

4. Examine *rows* successively until a *row* with only one zero is found. Make that square the assignment square (mark with a □) and delete all other zeros in that *column*. Proceed until all rows have been examined and the appropriate assignments and deletions made.
5. Now examine *columns* for single unmarked zeros, mark them □ and delete any other zeros in the same *row*.
6. Repeat (4) and (5) until there are no single unmarked zeros in any row or column.

In outcome (a) we have a maximal assignment, but this may or may not be a *complete* solution to the problem. It *will* be a complete solution if it has an assignment in every *row* (the procedure adopted guarantees that there can be no more than one assignment per column). A method exists to deal with situation (b) but it is rather involved so that inspection is best employed for small problems. Returning to outcome (a), we must further modify the effectiveness matrix by:

7. Marking all rows for which assignments have *not* been made.
8. Mark columns not already marked which have *zeros* in marked rows.
9. Mark rows not already marked which have assignments in marked columns.

10. Repeat (8) and (9) until the chain of marking ends.
11. Draw lines through all *unmarked* rows and through all *marked* columns.
12. Select the smallest of the elements that do *not* have a line through them and subtract it from *all* elements that do not have a line through them. *Add* this smallest element to every element that lies at the *intersection of two lines.* Leave remaining elements unchanged.
13. Repeat steps (4)–(6) to find the maximal assignment to the matrix given by (12).
14. If a complete solution is not given by (13), re-apply (7)–(13) until a complete solution is obtained.

This 14-step procedure may seem rather long but it is extremely easy to apply. Also after a little practice it is surprising how the solving of an example jogs the memory into the next step. Now for the example itself.

Acme Enterprises has five contracts to be distributed among five possible firms. Each firm will be given one contract and the cost estimates (in £1000 units) for each firm on the contracts that it could handle are given below.

		Contract				
		1	2	3	4	5
	A	35	15	—	30	30
	B	25	20	15	25	40
Firm	C	20	—	30	20	50
	D	15	40	35	15	40
	E	10	50	40	30	35

Firm A cannot take contract (3) and firm C cannot take contract (2). How should the contracts be assigned to the firms so as to minimize total cost?

The first step is to complete the effectiveness matrix by putting a large figure in the A3 and C2 position. We *could* put 1000, but to be perfectly sure put a cost figure of M in here where M, unspecified, is large enough to dominate any other number in the problem. Then proceed. The first two stages are shown in Fig. 4-6 on page 70. Column minima are then subtracted giving the numbers in Fig. 4-6(b). This completes (1) to (3). In applying (4) the middle element in row (2) is first made an assignment square (□). We then come to the first element in row (5). This is 'assigned' and the two zeros above it crossed out (X). That completes the first run through the rows. Step (5) picks out the zero at the top of column (2) and the zero at the end of the first row is crossed out. Now back to Step (4). Row (3) now has an unmarked (i.e., neither □ or X) zero. This is duly assigned and the zero below it crossed out. Going into step (7) we first mark (−) row (4). Step (8) then marks

20	0	M–15	15	15	⟵ Result of row subtractions
10	5	0	10	25	
0	M–20	10	0	30	
0	25	20	0	25	
0	40	30	20	25	

20	0	M–15	15	8	
10	5	0	10	10	
•	M–20	10	0	15	–
•	25	20	•	10	–
0	40	30	20	10	–

Figure 4-6

columns (1) and (4). Step (9) then marks rows (3) and (5). An attempt at step (10) produces no further changes. Then comes the simple line-drawing stage of Step (11). Step (12) then produces the numbers of Fig. 4-7 and Step (13) produces a complete, optimal assignment. In this case it was not necessary to re-apply (7)–(13) though this may have to be done in general. In obtaining the solution Step (6) produces only the assignments in the first two rows. There then remain at least two zeros in the rows and columns without assignments. The last three assignments were picked out by inspection. The reader may produce other arrangements. All that this means is that there is a *non-unique* optimum—there is more than one least-cost distribution of contracts.

30	0	M–15	25	8	
20	5	0	20	10	
0	M–30	8	0	5	
0	15	10	0	0	
0	30	20	20	0	**Figure 4-7**

4-4 A FURTHER EXAMPLE

The Aphid car hire company has one car at each of five locations. Aphid has a customer in each of five other locations requiring a vehicle. The mileages between the car locations and the customers are:

Vehicle locations

		1	2	3	4	5
	1	16	10	14	24	14
	2	21	26	15	20	19
Customer locations	3	20	18	20	21	19
	4	25	15	18	24	19
	5	25	12	20	27	14

How should cars be assigned to customers so as to minimize overall mileage?

The answer is obtained in Fig. 4-8. The first matrix shown (a) is the result of the row and column subtractions; (b) and (c) are intermediate stages, and (d) is the optimum. The reader should perform the workings separately as a check. Notice that between the (b) and (c) stages no further assignment is made.

The solution procedure described here is known as the *Hungarian* or *reduced matrix* method. The procedure of covering the zero with lines was first developed by H. W. Kuhn in 1955 and is based on a theorem proved by the Hungarian mathematician König in 1916. The version of the method shown here was originally due to Flood. The reader will have noted that the lines are drawn in such a way as to 'cover' all the zeros: none is left out. By experiment with the examples already shown the reader may verify that there are other patterns of lines that will cover the zeros. However, *none* of these alternatives (which may be found by inspection) will have *fewer* lines than those produced by our systematic method. The optimal assignment will eventually be obtained by alternative coverings but a different (though equally valid) version of the opportunity cost matrix may result.

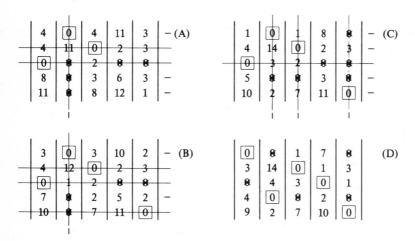

Figure 4-8

Space does not allow an extensive explanation of why the method works, but one point is well worth mentioning. All of the alterations of numbers in the original matrix, including those performed after the line-covering stage, can be reduced to additions or subtractions from entire rows or columns. As is the case in transportation problems more generally, this will not affect the optimal solution.

4-5 MAXIMIZATION PROBLEMS

In some cases the elements of the effectiveness matrix may represent revenues or profits so that the objective will be to maximize. The method presented is a minimization-geared algorithm but only a minor adjustment is necessary to use it on maximization problems. All that is strictly necessary is to multiply all entries by −1 and proceed to minimize. However, for the convenience of working with positive numbers we may simply add to all elements (after negation!) the same positive number. The smallest such number that will eliminate all negative entries is the largest element in the original matrix. So, negate all numbers and then add back the largest one to all entries. Obviously the effect of this is to replace an original entry with the entry subtracted from the largest number. Here is an example.

Beta Corporation has four plants each of which can manufacture any one of four products. Production costs differ from one plant to another as do sales revenues (slightly different output levels and product quality). Given the revenue and cost data below, ascertain which product each plant should produce to maximize profit.

| | Sales revenues (£'000s) | | | | | Production costs (£'00s) | | | |
| | Product | | | | | Product | | | |
Plant	1	2	3	4	Plant	1	2	3	4
A	50	68	49	62	A	49	60	45	61
B	60	70	51	74	B	55	63	45	69
C	55	67	53	70	C	52	62	49	68
D	58	65	54	69	D	55	64	48	66

The first step is to deduct the production cost matrix from the sales revenue matrix. This will give a suitable measure of profit in each case and the result is the first array in Fig. 4-9. The resulting maximization problem is then solved.

Thus the optimal arrangement is for plant A to produce product (2); plant B produces product (4); plant C produces produce (1) and plant D produces product (3). The overall profit resulting is found (by reference back to the profits matrix) to be £22 000.

1	8	4	1
5	7	6	5
3	5	4	2
3	1	6	3

Profits matrix, assignments to maximize.
Subtraction of each element from 8
produces the matrix for minimization:

7	0	4	7
3	1	2	3
5	3	4	6
5	7	2	5

Subtract row minima:

7	0	4	7
2	0	1	2
2	0	1	3
3	5	0	3

Subtract resulting column minima

5	[0]	4	5
8	8	1	[0]
[0]	8	1	1
1	5	[0]	1

Optimal solution

Figure 4-9

The minimization procedure can be applied to the original profits matrix as it stands to find the *worst* possible arrangement. Alternatively, the opportunity cost matrix given in the optimal solution can be inspected to show that the worst arrangement would produce a profit of £10 000.

4-6 UNEQUAL DIMENSIONS

Consider the following question. A company has six men available for work on four jobs. The costs resulting from the assignment of each man to each job are:

		\multicolumn{4}{c}{Job}			
		1	2	3	4
	A	13	15	11	14
	B	12	7	13	13
Man	C	14	19	17	17
	D	9	17	12	15
	E	11	14	16	12
	F	15	18	18	16

	1	2	3	4	D_1	D_2
A	13	15	11	14	0	0
B	12	7	13	13	0	0
C	14	19	17	17	0	0
D	9	17	12	15	0	0
E	11	14	16	12	0	0
F	15	18	18	16	0	0

4	8	[0]	2	0	0
3	[0]	2	1	0	0
5	12	6	5	[0]	0
[0]	10	1	3	0	0
2	7	5	[0]	0	0
6	11	7	4	0	[0]

Figure 4-10   **Figure 4-11**

1. Obtain an optimal assignment of men to jobs.
2. Is the solution unique?
3. What peculiarity of the effectiveness matrix could be exploited to reduce the problem size initially?

In order to answer the question a square effectiveness matrix must be formed. This is done as in Fig. 4-10 by the addition of two dummy columns. Clearly row subtraction will make no difference but column subtraction produces the result shown in Fig. 4-11. There appears at first glance to be an alternative solution in which man C is assigned to D_2 and man F is assigned to D_1. But of course the 'real' assignments are unchanged. Thus there is only one solution involving the real men and jobs. The peculiarity referred to in part (3) of the question is that men C and F can be ruled out of consideration *a priori*. Each has higher 'costs' than all of A, B, D, and E on every job and so could not be assigned to a real job in any optimal solution. Thus the C and F rows could have been ruled out to start with and the problem size thus reduced.

4-7 SENSITIVITY ANALYSIS

The structure of the assignment problem is such as to allow very little scope for sensitivity analysis. Very modest alterations in the rim conditions—such as one man being able to do two jobs—can be dealt with by repeating the man's row and adding in a dummy column to square up the matrix. However, few statements of general interest can be made in these cases. The technical coefficients (the coefficients of the x's in the constraints when formulated algebraically) are fixed at zero or one as in transportation problems. Any changes here would render the problem no longer an assignment problem.

Such analysis as is possible concentrates on the elements of the effectiveness matrix, which are the coefficients in the objective function. Equal proportionate changes in all entries leave the optimum unchanged— as in any LP problem. Addition of a constant throughout any row or column also makes no difference to the position of the optimal assignments. However, we must be careful to note that equi-proportionate changes throughout a row or column *can* make a difference unless all rows and columns are similarly affected. Increasing the cost of a non-assignment square or reducing the cost in an assignment square cannot alter the optimal pattern. This is a stronger result than in transportation or LP, and it can be said because in the assignment context there is no scope for altering the level of an assignment: it is either present or absent. Finally, reducing non-assignment costs or increasing costs at assignment squares *can*, of course, force the solution to change (though not necessarily so).

4-8 CONCLUSIONS

Although assignment problems are special cases of transportation problems, most applications and contexts do not involve actual transportation! The structure is so special that a different, much more efficient solution procedure can be derived.

EXERCISES

4-1 Show that an assignment problem can be set up as a transportation problem. Viewed in this way what special features does the problem have?

4-2 Give seven examples of areas in which assignment problems may arise in practice.

4-3 Construct a three row, three column effectiveness matrix and produce two alternative versions of the opportunity cost matrix.

4-4 Detail the 14 steps of the assignment problem solution technique (the Hungarian or reduced matrix method).

4-5 Find the least cost complete assignment for the following effectiveness data:

3	5	10	15	8
4	7	15	18	8
8	12	20	20	12
5	5	8	10	6
10	10	15	25	10

4-6 A local authority has six contracts to be allocated to six firms that have submitted tenders. Each firm will be awarded exactly one contract. Details of the tenders submitted (in units of £10 000) are:

		Contract				
	1	2	3	4	5	6
A	7	7	3	6	10	11
B	8	9	No bid	5	8	10
C	9	10	11	13	13	8
D	6	6	8	No bid	12	13
E	5	5	9	10	10	12
F	8	4	10	12	9	No bid

Firm (label for rows A–F)

Which contract should go to each firm in order to minimize cost overall?

4-7 A time study is conducted on the performance of four jobs by four men. Expressed in terms of departures from a standard time allowance for each job the results were:

		Jobs			
		1	2	3	4
Men	1	9	4	15	2
	2	4	−1	10	−3
	3	3	−2	9	−4
	4	7	2	13	0

Comment on the results.

4-8 A company presently operates five plants each of which makes a single product. Recently one of the products has become unprofitable and is being dropped from the range. The firm wishes to maintain its one-product-per-plant policy and has now to decide which plant is to be closed. The revenues (in £0000's) from the sale of each of the products (regardless of plant) are:

		Revenue
	1	80
Product no.	2	90
	3	100
	4	85

Production costs however, *do* vary between plants. The cost data (also in £0000's) are:

		Product			
		1	2	3	4
Plant	1	71	78	93	76
	2	69	78	87	74
	3	72	80	89	76
	4	73	80	86	78
	5	65	84	92	72

Closure costs are the same for each plant. Advise the firm on which plant to shut down.

4-9 What scope is there for sensitivity analysis in assignment problems?

CHAPTER
FIVE
CRITICAL PATH METHOD

5-1 INTRODUCTION

Critical path method is one of the most widely used and best understood management techniques. A thorough grasp of this basically simple procedure is essential to the effective control and financial management of large projects. In this chapter, bar charts, critical path method (CPM) and PERT are examined. After being introduced in terms of time as the main consideration, cost and resources problems are then taken into account.

5-2 BAR CHARTS

Sometimes known as Gantt project planning charts, bar charts of one form or another have been part of the decor of production controllers' offices for over half a century. Until the advent of critical path and programming methods they were, allied to much experience, the major tools of project control. While they still find widespread use for viewing things in the large (the 'macro' aspect of control) they have been largely superseded by network methods where complicated projects are concerned. Packages offering three-dimensional, multi-colour 'charts' are available but much of the attractive simplicity is then lost. We shall only describe here the basic form of charts, their requirements, the benefits, and uses to which the charts may be put.

Consider the example of Fig. 5-1. A project has been divided into eight

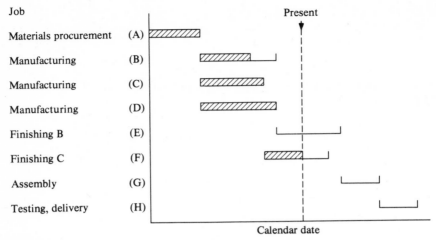

Figure 5-1

phases or jobs. These are represented on the vertical 'axis' (no measure is employed here). On the horizontal axis 'calendar time' is measured. Calendar time is usually used in preference to 'abstract time' ($t = 0, 1$, etc.) since breaks in work such as holidays can more easily be allowed for. The arrow indicates the present. The beginning and end of each bar mark the anticipated starting and finishing date of each task. Shading shows the progress of jobs. Thus A, C, and D have been finished as scheduled while F is on schedule. Job B, however, is running well behind schedule which has caused the start of E to be delayed. This will cause more delays further down the line unless there is some speeding up or rearrangement of schedules.

Requirements for the use of Gantt charts are:

1. Identification of distinct jobs.
2. Job orderings.
3. Job time estimates.
4. Regular reviews.

Benefits to be obtained are:

1. A systematic setting down of the stages of work.
2. Actual progress can be compared with planned progress.
3. Easily understandable.
4. Resources scheduling can be conducted.

Gantt charts cannot (systematically at least) do much more than macro monitoring. Although they can be used in conjunction with trial and error and that elusive factor 'experience' to perform certain *control* functions (such as the resources scheduling of (4)), there are superior methods now available for these purposes.

5-3 THE DEPENDENCY TABLE AND NETWORK DIAGRAM

Up until the mid-fifties Gantt charts and other bar charts were one of the most important tools of project planning. Although they continue to be useful in various guises their place in modern project analysis and control has been largely taken by critical path and similar methods. The concept of a critical sequence of tasks which determine the minimum completion time of a project was known in England by 1955 and shortly afterwards was developed, publicized and oversold in the United States.

There are numerous techniques more or less similar to CPM, most being conceived at around the same time (1957–8), differences between the methods arising primarily as consequences of the particular characteristics of the problems which the methods were originally developed to address. PERT (programme evaluation and review technique) is the best known of these but some others are PEP, PRISM, IMPACT, SCANS, and RAMPS.

In the earliest applications of CPM, time was the only relevant consideration, lateness penalties were very great. In most commercial applications nowadays cost is an equally important factor. Some of the typical objectives are: to arrange jobs and allocate resources to jobs to secure a required completion time subject to a cost resource constraint or to minimize project cost subject to a time constraint. First consider time alone.

The best way to explain CPM is to examine a problem. Consider the manufacturing and assembly process presented in tabular form (the *dependency table*) in Table 5-1. Column (1) describes each task of which the project is comprised and the jobs (sometimes called 'activities') are identified

Table 5-1

Job	Job label	Immediate predecessor	Job time (days)
Procure materials	A		30
Manufacture component one	B	A	40
Manufacture component two	C	A	30
Manufacture component three	D	A	35
Finish component one	E	B	25
Finish component two	F	C, D	30
Assemble components	G	E	15
Test and deliver	H	G, F	20

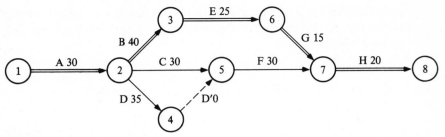

Figure 5-2

by alphabetical label in column (2). The sequence in which the jobs are to be performed is given in the immediate predecessor column and the initial estimates of job times are given in column (4). Although we shall take the project table as a starting point we should note that it presupposes that a good deal of work has already been done in data gathering and determining sequences. The task is now to represent the information of the dependency table in the form of a network. The resulting network diagram is shown in Fig. 5-2. The network contains no more and no less information than the project table but the sequencing can be seen at once.

In this form of diagram the jobs are represented by arrows (technically known as *directed edges*) which connect *nodes* which are shown as circles and numbered. Alongside each line is shown the job label and job time estimate. The 'dashed' job D' with completion time zero is a 'dummy' and is inserted solely to preserve the ordering (F cannot be started until both C *and* D are completed).

There is another tabular form in which the information of Table 5-1 and Fig. 5-2 can be presented. This identifies jobs as the links between events and

Table 5-2

Job	Beginning and end events	Job time (days)
A	1–2	30
B	2–3	40
C	2–5	30
D	2–4	35
D'	4–5	0
E	3–6	25
F	5–7	30
G	6–7	15
H	7–8	20

is shown in Table 5-2. The reader may gain some practice by reconstructing the network from Table 5-2. We shall use the dependency table format in this presentation as it is the form in which information is most naturally put. There is also another form of diagram called the 'activity on the node' form. This has certain advantages (dummies are not required) but has so far been much less popular than the 'arc-node' form of Fig. 5-2. We shall thus stick with the arc-node variety.

The project illustrated in Fig. 5-2 is the same one that was shown in the Gantt chart, but the predecessor–successor relationships stand out more clearly in the network diagram. Each possible path through the network represents a series of jobs that must be done in strict sequence. The longest path (in terms of time) through the network determines the length of time taken in completing the project. This is the *critical path* marked as a double arrow in Fig. 5-2, and is seen to pass through nodes ① ② ③ ⑥ ⑦ and ⑧. Put equivalently, the critical path consists of jobs A B E G and H.

The critical path is sometimes referred to as the 'bottleneck route'—the sequence of jobs which determines the minimum completion time for the project as a whole. If any effective time savings are to be made on the whole project, attention must first be focused on jobs on the critical path—there is no point in trying to speed up or rearrange other jobs; project completion time cannot be reduced this way. This latter pointer, telling us where *not* to expend effort is most important for in large networks there are many more non-critical jobs than critical ones.

At this stage the critical path is found by taking each possible route through the system and summing job times thereon. We shall develop an alternative method of finding the critical path which yields valuable additional information. Before proceeding, however, let us summarize the work done so far.

Information and Work Required

1. Define jobs.
2. Determine sequencing.
3. Estimate job times.
4. Form project table.
5. Form project network.
6. Find critical path.

The benefits that are obtained by this work result from seeing:

1. which jobs are critical to project time;
2. where time savings can be effective;
3. what *not* to do: in the first instance, there is no point in speeding up non-critical jobs.

5-4 EVENT TIMES

The alternative method of finding the critical path requires some further work. The reaching of each node in the network represents a happening or *event*, marking the completion of the immediately preceding job (or jobs in the case of nodes 7 and 5) and the simultaneous commencement of the immediately succeeding job (or jobs in the case of node 2).

For each node we shall now determine the *early event time* (EET); the earliest time by which that node can be reached. Obviously the EET for a node will depend upon all nodes that are strictly in sequence before it being reached at their EETs. This observation suggests the way in which EETs are determined.

Assume that the project may be started right away. The EET for node 1 will then be $t = 0$. Job A takes 30 days so that node 2 has an EET of $t = 30$. Node 2 marks the start of jobs B, C, and D. Thus since job B takes 40 days, the EET for node 3 is 70. Continuing along the upper path, the EET for event 6 is 95. This is as far as we can go along this path at the moment since event 7 marks the completion of both job G and job F. Thus the EET for event 7 will be given by whichever of these two jobs finishes the later.

Although it is fairly obvious that since A B E G is part of the critical path, the completion of G will set the EET of event 7, we shall 'play dumb' and not notice this. For a node which is on the critical path the critical route *must* represent the longest (in terms of time) way of reaching the node, otherwise the path would not be critical.

Node 4 can be reached only by one route—A D—so that its EET is the EET for node 2 plus job time for D, giving 65. Now, node 5 can be reached from node 2 by going via C or D and D'. The longer of these paths sets the EET. Thus via job C, node 5 could be reached by $t = 60$, but via D and D' it is not reached until $t = 65$. This then is the EET.

Now we can return to node 7. This can be reached from nodes 5 or 6. Via job F node 7 could be reached by $t = 95$, but via job G it is not reached until $t = 110$; this becomes the EET. The EET for node 8 is $t = 130$ which marks

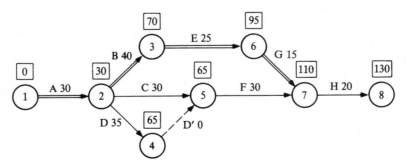

Figure 5-3

the *early finish* time for the entire project. In general, call this F. The EETs are entered in squares above each node in Fig. 5-3. In addition to the EET for each node the early finish (EF) time for each job can be determined. EF for any job is the EET of the immediately preceding node plus job time. Thus EF for critical jobs will always be the EET of the succeeding node, but this will not always be the case for non-critical jobs. For example, EF for job C is 60 and EF for job F is 95. The EET of the immediately preceding node is called the *early start* time (ES) of a job. The subsequent analysis that we shall do with event time could also be conducted in terms of job start and finish times.

Now as well as the early finish time for the project (F = 130 here) there will often be some deadline or *target time* for completion, T. For feasibility in the first instance, of course, we must have T ⩾ F. Suppose here that T = 140; the whole project must be completed in 140 days. This is the *late finish* time for the whole project. We are now to determine the latest time by which each node must be reached in order that the entire project is not pushed beyond the late finish time 140. These will be the *latest event times* (LETs).

The LETs are found by working back from the final node 8 which we know to have an LET of 140. Clearly, in order that node 8 is reached by this time and since job H takes 20 days then node 7 must have been reached by $t = 120$. By a similar argument, since G takes 15 days node 6 must be reached by $t = 105$. This is the LET for node 6. Continuing this process we find that the LETs for nodes 3, 4, and 5 are 80, 90, and 90 respectively. Now node 2 marks the start of the three jobs which lead directly to these nodes. If node 5 is to be reached by $t = 90$, then since job C takes 30 days, node 2 must have been reached by $t = 60$; but if node 4 is to be reached by $t = 90$ since job D takes 35 days then node 2 must be reached by $t = 55$. It is evident that these times are too late, however, since node 3 must be reached by $t = 80$ and job B takes 40 days then node 2 must be reached by $t = 40$ at the latest. This is the LET of node 2. It follows that the LET of node 1, the *late start* of the project, is $t = 10$. The LETs for each node are entered in triangles in Fig. 5-4.

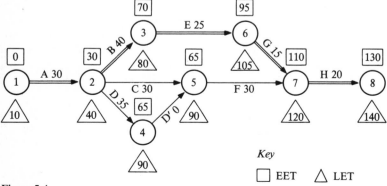

Figure 5-4

Late start (LS) and late finish (LF) times can be computed for each job. LS for a job is the LET of the immediately succeeding node minus job time. LF is the LET of the immediately succeeding node.

The formal rules for obtaining EET and LET can now be stated:

1. The EET for a node is the *greatest* of the times arrived at by summing EETs and corresponding job times for all immediately preceding nodes.
2. The LET for a node is the *least* of the times arrived at by subtracting the corresponding job times from the LETs of all immediately succeeding nodes.

The critical path is identified as passing through *all* those nodes for which LET *minus* EET equals T minus F. In this case critical jobs join nodes for which the LET exceeds the EET by 10 days. Notice that there are no other nodes with just this difference. All the other nodes (which of course will not lie on the critical path) have a greater difference. In a problem in which T = F the critical path would join all events where LET = EET.

5-5 FLOAT AND THE CRITICAL PATH

The EETs and LETs enable us to determine the maximum delays that are possible, individually, for each job in the project such that the target time, T, is not exceeded. Consider job G. If node 6 has been reached by its EET then the start of job G could be delayed by up to 10 days and node 7 could still be reached by its LET of 120. Alternatively, provided that a prompt start is made on job G, it could be slowed down to take 25 days and still node 7 could be reached by $t = 120$. This maximum possible delay in the completion of job G, 10 days, is called its *total float* (TF) or sometimes *total slack*.

It is clear that the total float in each job on the critical path is just 10 days. Of course, the critical jobs cannot be delayed by 10 days in every case. What of the non-critical jobs? Consider job F. Assuming node 5 is reached by its EET time of 65, a maximum of 55 days may be taken for the completion of this job; an increase of 25 days over the original duration of 30 days. 25 is the TF of job F. By a similar commonsense process the reader may verify that the total floats in the remaining non-critical jobs are 25, 25, and 30 for jobs D', D, and C respectively.

A formal procedure by which TF is calculated can now be stated:

1. For critical jobs $TF = T - F$.
2. For non-critical jobs TF = LET of immediately succeeding node minus the sum of the EET of the immediately preceding node and the job time.

If no separate target time is given, F is used instead of T. The critical jobs would then have precisely zero total float.

Total float is not the only concept of spare time in a job. Consider job F again. If node 5 is reached by the EET of 65 then provided that job F does not take longer than 45 days, node 7 can still be reached by its EET of 110. This delay of 15 days $(45 - 30)$ is called the *free float* (FF) in the job. It will be seen that the only other job in the project with positive FF is job C with 5 days. Free float is the maximum delay that is possible in a job without affecting the EET of the immediately succeeding node. This is in contrast to TF which is the maximum delay possible in a job such that the LET of the immediately succeeding node is not affected.

The formal procedure for determining FF is:

1. FF in all critical jobs is zero.
2. FF in non-critical jobs is the EET of immediately succeeding node minus the sum of the EET of the immediately preceding node and the job time.

So long as the project is time-feasible $(T \geqslant F)$ free float can never exceed total float. We can now present some definitions and results concerning 'criticalness' and float.

1. A job is called critical if, when delayed by *any* amount of time $\Delta t \geqslant 0$, the whole project is delayed by Δt.
2. A critical job is a job having *minimum total float*, i.e., critical jobs have total float $= T - F$. This will be zero if $T = F$.
3. All non-critical jobs have total float $> T - F$.
4. A critical path consists entirely of critical jobs.
5. All critical jobs lie on a critical path (i.e., there can be no 'isolated' critical jobs).
6. In any project network there will be at least one path from start to finish that contains only critical jobs, i.e., there will always be at least one critical path.

Result (6) above may require that we insert imaginary jobs 'start' and 'finish' (taking zero time) such that the job 'start' precedes all other jobs and 'finish' succeeds all other jobs. Where there are no real jobs fulfilling these roles it may be convenient in hand-solved problems to insert them, although this is not strictly necessary. Some computer routines require the insertion of such jobs.

5-6 REDUCING PROJECT TIME (i)

We have mentioned in passing the consequences of slowing down of critical jobs—there will be the same delay in the project as a whole. But what if critical jobs are speeded up? How may time savings in general be effected? There are two ways in which F may be reduced:

1. Critical jobs may be speeded up.
2. The ordering of jobs may be changed.

Consider speedings up first of all. If it is our object to reduce F then clearly, in the first instance, *there is no point in speeding up non-critical jobs*. If a critical job is speeded up, then the consequent reduction in F *cannot exceed* the time saved in the critical job and may be less. When a critical job is speeded up it is possible that the CP may change. In formal terms if a critical job is shortened by an amount Δt the reduction in F will be Δt *if the CP does not change* and will be $< \Delta t$ if a new path becomes uniquely critical.

Consider this point with reference to the example problem. Critical jobs are A B E G H. First note that jobs A and H are on any path through the network. Suppose 1 day is saved in job A so that only 29 days are now required. The reader will quickly verify that the EETs for node 2 and in fact all subsequent nodes are reduced by one. Thus the EET for node 8, which is the early finish time for the project as a whole, F is now 129. Each day saved in A will be fully reflected in F. Note what happens to TF in each job when 1 day is saved in A. Minimum TF (recall that this is $T - F$) now becomes 11 days and TF in all of the non-critical jobs goes up by one day also. Therefore, the jobs which were critical before the time saving (had minimum TF) remain critical afterwards. TF in job A itself becomes 11 days (although LET of node 2 remains at 40 and EET of node 1 remains at 0). This is because job time is now 29. Note that the LET of node 1 is now 11 days.

If 1 day is saved on job H, this too will be fully reflected in F. LETs for node 7 and all preceding nodes are increased by 1 day thus increasing TF in each job preceding node 7 by one day. Thus jobs which had the least TF before still have the least TF and the original path remains critical. In job H itself TF increases to 11 since it now takes 19 days.

Jobs A and H were common to any path which may be critical. What if time is saved on B, E, or G? Consider the effects of 1 day saved on job E. If this job is now done in 24 days the effects will be to reduce EET on nodes 6, 7, and 8 by 1 day and to increase LET on nodes 1, 2, and 3 by 1 day. Thus TF throughout the critical path is now 11 days. Note, however, that the nature of these changes in event times is such as to leave TF on jobs C, D, D', and F unchanged. Total float in D and D' remains at 25 and in C it remains at 30.

Bearing this in mind, consider now *substantial* time savings in the section B E G. So long as the amount saved *in total* does not exceed 15 days (say 5 days in each of these jobs for the sake of argument) then the path A B E G H remains critical and the total saving is fully reflected in early finish time, F. If total savings amount to exactly 15 days, then the path A D D' F H becomes critical also and any further savings in B E and G will leave A D D' F H uniquely critical and will not be reflected in F at all. Unless time is saved in F and/or D the LET of node 2 cannot be increased beyond 55 since we are not at the moment considering a reduction in job H time.

Thus if time savings are ruled out in jobs A and H (just to make things awkward) once 15 days have been saved in section B E G additional reduction in early finish time can only be effected by cuts in time in at least two jobs; one in section B E G *and* either D or F. If D is the job that is reduced then once 5 days have been saved here (and in B E F) then further reductions in the early finish time would involve reducing job C if savings in F are ruled out.

Let us review the picture. Time savings beyond certain amounts involved the 'picking up' of new critical paths when we ruled out savings on 'common' jobs. Thus it became necessary to work on several jobs to keep paths jointly critical. When one path becomes uniquely critical time savings elsewhere in the network will not be effective in reducing the early finish time overall. The results may be stated formally as:

1. When an amount of time Δt is saved in a critical job the EETs of subsequent nodes in strict sequence with the job are all reduced by Δt provided that the original CP remains critical.
2. When Δt is saved in a critical job the LETs of preceding nodes in strict sequence with the job are all increased by Δt provided that the original CP remains critical.
3. When Δt is saved in a critical job, the TF in all critical jobs increases by Δt provided that the original CP remains critical.
4. When Δt is saved in a critical job, the TF in other sections of the network not in sequence with the job (i.e., not lying on the original CP) remains unchanged.

5-7 TIME REDUCTIONS (ii)

In some projects there is a certain amount of discretion as to the ordering of jobs. The order relationships between certain of the jobs may indeed be immutable but where some changes are allowed it may be possible to reduce F by varying the 'network logic'.

To the extent that there is discretion in network logic, a combinatorial element is introduced. This can rapidly assume formidable proportions. For instance if a project consists of 100 jobs (small by practical standards) 95 of which have a predetermined sequential relationship, while the remaining 5 can be fitted in anywhere, then in fact there are over eight thousand million possible arrangements of jobs! The rescheduling problem can therefore be formidable and some approximation approaches are discussed in the context of resource problems below. However, a few points relevant to small degrees of discretion in small networks are appropriate here.

First, in order to be worth while, any rearrangement of jobs must affect the critical path. No time can be saved by rescheduling among non-critical jobs only. Secondly, some jobs must be taken *out* of the present CP. Now if any job is introduced into the CP then F is increased by the duration of that job. But if a job is removed from the CP then F will be reduced by the job time only if the original path (minus the one job) remains critical. Without study of a particular network all that can definitely be said (if the path is uniquely critical) is that the EET of all succeeding nodes is reduced and the LET of all preceding nodes is raised. In other words, TF in the CP is increased. The concept of TF in fact can be of value in a rescheduling context. If the position of a job is changed then the saving in project time will be the difference between the old value of minimum TF and the new value. More specifically, if the job is re-located in an 'independent' position—one that does not decrease the TF on any other branch—then the total time saved is the difference between the minimum TF and the next lowest level of TF or time on the re-positioned job, whichever is the smaller.

5-8 PERT/TIME

The original PERT/time system was developed by the United States Navy at around the same time the CPM was developed by the Du Pont Company. PERT/time has as its central feature the notion of a critical path, but differs from the CPM in respect of job time estimates. PERT is concerned with situations in which job times are *random variables*. It may be that job time is simply unknown in the case of an entirely new project or that the job times are influenced by uncontrollable variables (e.g., the weather).

Ideally, we should like to know the *probability distribution* of job times. Roughly speaking this is a list of possible job times and the associated chances of occurrence of each time. Table 5-3 details an instance where there are just four possible durations for a job. These times are listed in column (1). Probability of occurrence is given in column (2), and column (3) elements are summed to give the expected duration of the job. Things are rarely as convenient as this. The underlying probability distribution of job times will be more complicated in most instances. All is not lost, however, if we know

Table 5-3

Time (t)	Probability (p)	$t \times p$
22	0.2	4.4
32	0.2	6.4
46	0.3	13.8
56	0.3	16.8
		expected time = 41.4

the *type* of probability distribution (e.g., discrete (as above), normal, gamma, or beta) and the mean and variance of the distribution. It is rather unlikely that these parameters will be known in advance and PERT/time gives a simple and practicable means of obtaining reasonable estimates of mean and variance.

The person in charge of each job is asked to provide three estimates of job time: a 'pessimistic' estimate, an 'optimistic' estimate, and a 'most likely' estimate. The investigator may quantify 'optimistic' and 'pessimistic', for example, by defining the pessimistic time as one for which there are 95 chances out of 100 of getting the job done within this time. This statistic may be based on past experience with the job or may be an 'a priori subjective estimate' (i.e., a guess) if the job has never been done before. 'Optimistic' would then be that time such that there were only 5 chances out of 100 of completing the job by this time. In non-quantitative terms, 'pessimistic' would be: 'the time taken to complete the job if everything goes wrong short of total disaster', and 'optimistic': 'everything goes well short of a miracle'. Figure 5-5 places these estimates and the most likely figure (m) on the graph of a possible underlying distribution of times.

The arithmetic mean time (expected time), e, can be approximated as a function of a, b, and m given the underlying distribution. For example, if the probability distribution is a beta distribution then e is given by $e \simeq \frac{1}{6}(a+b)+\frac{2}{3}m$. The coefficients $\frac{1}{6}$ and $\frac{2}{3}$ are weights derived from the particular beta distribution which is usually more appropriate than the normal distribution because it has maximum and minimum limits. Once the mean time has been determined this is used as in the CPM diagrams and analysis proceeds as for the CPM.

The job time variance can also be estimated from a, b, and m. In fact variance, σ^2, is given by $\sigma^2 \simeq \frac{1}{36}(b-a)^2$ where a beta distribution is appropriate.

Having obtained estimates of mean times and variances for individual jobs, the mean times and variances of strictly ordered sequences of jobs can

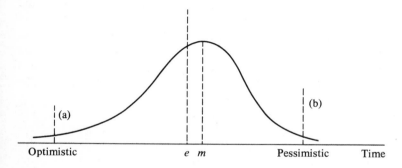

Figure 5-5

be found. For instance, if a series of n jobs are in strict sequence and the distributions of individual job times are *independent* of each other, then the mean time for completion of the sequence $E(T)$, is the sum of the individual mean job times: $E(T) = \sum_{i=1}^{n} E(t_i)$. In these circumstances the variance of time for completion of the n jobs, σ_T^2, is the sum of the individual job time variances: $\sigma_T^2 = \sum_{i=1}^{n} \sigma_i^2$. Having found the expected completion time for a section of a system and the variance for that section, a *confidence interval* could be found for completion time for the section. However, there are serious difficulties involved in extending this useful-sounding idea to the whole network. Because of the joining together of branches, and the presence of jobs common to several paths, mathematical analysis soon becomes impossible. However, a confidence interval for the whole project could still be found using *simulation* methods.

Multiple time estimates in network analysis are not quite as fashionable nowadays as they were in the early and mid-sixties. This may be because the approach is over-sophisticated in respect of many applications and because eventually a single figure is employed. Unless the complications of PERT produce a significantly better mean figure they will not be worth the cost and time involved. The choice of method should be determined by the particular problem at hand.

In fact, CPM itself can be used when job times are subject to variation. First is what might be called the 'levels of criticalness' approach. In this, critical jobs now become 'first level critical', and near-critical jobs become 'second level critical'. For instance, in a building operation, jobs with three days TF may be first level critical and jobs with four to six days TF second level critical. If all goes well the second-level critical jobs would not determine the minimum completion time for the project. But if some of these job times depend on extraneous factors (e.g., the performance of a sub-contractor) they may be 'unreliable' and become critical. If likely cases can be identified in advance it would be useful to have some contingency plans worked out for speeding up of some of the subsequent newly critical jobs.

Secondly, it should be recalled that acquisition of information costs both time and money. An economical approach to information gathering and critical path determination is as follows. For each job a rough-and-ready (and presumably therefore quick and cheap) time study is done. With these approximate times critical and near critical jobs are identified. A detailed (and presumably more expensive and time-consuming) time study is then done only for these jobs. Time and money is thus saved by having only the rough study done for the 'far-from-critical' jobs.

Finally, if one wished to err on the side of caution, a fixed percentage could be added on to the initial time estimate for each job so that although single figure estimates are then used there is a built-in 'safety margin' for delays. This approach, along with the previous two, is one of approximation. The degrees of approximation are not specified but the methods should not be dismissed. It is modifications such as these that make theoretical models more useful in practice.

5-9 COSTS

To employ CPM methods in problems where cost as well as time is a relevant consideration, it is necessary to relate cost to time in a systematic manner. The complexity of the problem hinges a good deal upon how cost varies with time. If for a particular job cost rises as time taken increases, then minimization of job time will result in minimization of cost. For a project as a whole, in these circumstances, all time saved implies reduction of cost and the minimization of completion time overall is a necessary condition for the minimization of cost; but things are rarely so convenient. Time and cost on some jobs may have an inverse relationship—speedings up may imply increases in cost.

The problem that is most frequently faced is not overall minimization of costs but the problem of making costs as low as possible subject to getting the entire project finished within a given deadline. Consider an example.

A construction project consists of nine jobs. The list of jobs, the ordering and normal durations are given in the first three columns of Table 5-4. Column (4) gives the cost for each job *if it is completed in the normal time*. Some of the jobs may be speeded up. The minimum time in which each of the jobs can be done is given in column (5), and column (6) gives the job costs associated with the minimum times. It is assumed that for those jobs which can be speeded up any time between the extreme values may be taken and that time and cost are linearly related between these extreme values.

Table 5-4

(1)	(2)	(3) Normal time (days)	(4) Cost (£)	(5) Minimal time (days)	(6) Cost (£)
Job	Predecessors				
A		10	5000	10	5 000
B	A	8	4000	8	4 000
C	A	8	4500	8	4 500
D	C	4	6000	4	6 000
E	B	7	5500	5	6 500
F	B	9	3750	4	13 750
G	D	8	2000	1	4 800
H	E, F, G	15	6500	12	14 900
I	H	10	5000	10	5 000

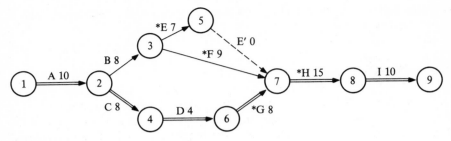

Figure 5-6

The deadline time for the project is $T = 48$ days. What time should be taken on each job such that the project is completed in this time at least cost? Figure 5-6 shows the network and critical path for which normal time for each job is assumed. Starred jobs indicate the possibility of time savings but with the normal times assumed early finish, F, $= 55$. Table 5-5 shows the particular paths, completion time with normal job times and in the third column the requisite time reductions are shown. If the whole project is to be completed in 48 days then *all* paths must be done in this time. Column (4) shows the jobs within each path on which time may be saved.

Now consider the cost per day saved in each of the jobs where time reductions are possible. The cost per day saved is given by

$$\frac{\text{Cost (normal time)} - \text{cost (minimal time)}}{\text{normal time} - \text{minimal time}}$$

The results are tabulated in Table 5-6 in which column (2) shows the cost per day saved (CPDS) and column (3) shows the maximum possible time saving in each job.

Now consider how the requisite savings are to be effected. Suppose that we begin by making savings only in jobs E, F, and G and consider variations from this starting point. The only manner in which variation can be effected is via reductions in job H. Since H is common to all the paths then, to begin with at least, each day saved in H means one day less to be saved in E, F, and

Table 5-5

(1)	(2)	(3)	(4)
Path	Duration	Reduction	*Jobs
A B E E' H I	50	2	E H
A B F H I	52	4	F H
A C D G H I	55	7	G H

Table 5-6

(1)	(2)	(3)
Job	CPDS	MS
E	500	2
F	2000	5
G	400	7
H	2800	3

G. One day saved in H would cost £2800; one day less to be saved in E, F, and G would reduce costs in these jobs by $500 + 2000 + 400 = 2900$ so the first day saved in H is worth while. The same applies to the second day saved in H, but not to a third day. When two days have been saved in H the requisite time reduction has been made for the upper path. The third day saved in H would add 2800 to cost and only bring cost reductions of $2000 + 400 = 2400$ from lower time savings in F and G. The ideal arrangement is then to save 2 days in H, 2 days in F, and 5 days in G. The whole project can then be completed in 48 days at a total cost of £53 850 as against a total cost of £42 250 if 55 days had been allowed. What has been outlined here is an essentially commonsense way of tackling the problem but in large and complicated networks this may not always be practicable. Similar ideas can sometimes be used to obtain the ideal duration of projects. Although time savings often mean higher direct costs, overheads will usually be reduced. A procedure for finding the overall least cost duration is shown in Wilkes (1977, pages 273–5).

Costs come into the picture in other ways too. We have been investigating cases in which we actively sought to minimize costs. Once the network has been laid out we can use it to estimate the *cash flows* associated with a project and the capital that will be tied up at various stages. This is explained in Wilkes (1977, pages 275–80). Such a procedure represents the *passive* use of the project network. Cost can also be used as a convenient although only approximate measure of the non-financial resources that are tied up in a job or a section of the network, but in this use, as in the other uses, there may be big practical difficulties in allocating costs to particular jobs or collections of jobs.

The level of total expenditure on a project up to a particular time can give a rough guide to the progress that is being made on the project. The expenditure figures (perhaps plotted as an S-shaped graph) may be either committed funds or funds actually spent. There are problems with the use of expenditure as a guide to progress. In particular, unanticipated inflation may give a misleading picture of advancement or show the project on schedule when it is in fact lagging. The inflation problem is lessened if *percentages* of total expenditure are used instead of money units.

5-10 RESOURCES

Although the logic of a project network may allow varying numbers of jobs to be proceeding simultaneously, the implied patterns of resources usage may not be practicable. For instance it would be obvious nonsense to have a programme that called for 500 men in week 1, 20 men in weeks 2 and 3, 600 men in week 4, 10 men in week 5, etc. The project controller in this instance may have, say, 200 men available and although this number may be increased or decreased any substantial changes could be very costly if they were even possible in the short term. How can sensible patterns of resource use be guaranteed?

First we must distinguish two categories of resource and two types of situation. Resources are frequently divided into 'pool' resources and 'non-pool' resources. A pool resource is one which if not used today can be used tomorrow. Supplies of materials provide an obvious example. An example of a non-pool resource would be labour or machine time—today's labour time is not available tomorrow. Non-pool resources in general present more difficulties than do pool resources and it is in the context of non-pool resources that we shall set the discussion. Then there are those problems in which additional resources from outside of the project can be brought in, and

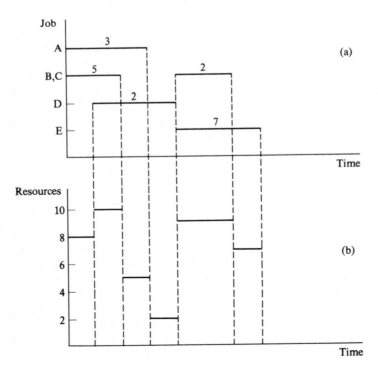

Figure 5-7

those problems in which any further resources applied to a job must be taken from other jobs (unless currently idle). In the latter case the interrelationships are more involved.

In terms of exact solutions the problem is so complex that even the most modern equipment and techniques of computation cannot cope except for rather special cases. Consequently, we shall be concerned with obtaining 'reasonable' solutions only. Let us make a start by seeing how Gantt charts can be useful in some simple cases.

Suppose that the initial arrangement of jobs on a project, based solely upon logical considerations, was as shown in Fig. 5-7(a). The numbers on the bars represent the numbers of units of a resource (say labour of a particular category) required throughout each job. Figure 5-7(b) is drawn to the same horizontal scale and shows the numbers of men required at various times. While jobs A and B are proceeding 8 men are needed. This requirement rises to 10 when A, B, and D are being worked upon simultaneously. Then only 5 are needed when only A and D are proceeding, dropping to 2 then rising to 9, and finally falling to 7. This may be too erratic a pattern.

Suppose now that it is possible to reschedule jobs B and D as shown in Fig. 5-8(a), albeit at the expense of pushing back the starts of C and E. The resulting pattern of resource requirements is shown in Fig. 5-8(b). This is altogether more desirable, showing a build-up and then decline.

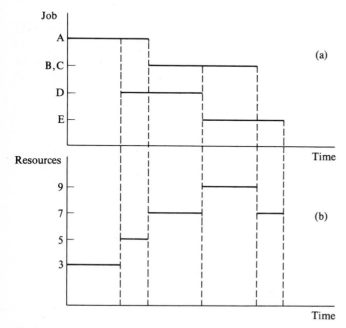

Figure 5-8

The use of Gantt charts in this manner is an informal, 'heuristic' method of resource management that, in experienced hands, can work quite well for small projects. On a larger scale the use of machines is necessitated although the objectives are similar.

The ideal approach is known as resources *smoothing* and involves the manipulation of jobs so that resource requirements over the duration of the project form smooth curves, something like flattened semi-circles. Computational problems restrict the use of this procedure to the smaller practical problems.

Next best to smoothing is the approach known as resources *levelling*. This involves the rearrangement of jobs so that pre-ordained limits on resources are not exceeded. So-called *priority rules* are employed when jobs that could logically be done simultaneously compete for limited resources. When two or more jobs conflict, examples of a priority rule would be:

1. Start that job first which has least duration.
2. Start that job first which has the earliest 'late finish'.
3. Start that job first which has least total float.

It cannot be determined in advance which of the above, or other, priority rules will work best and none is best all of the time. Computer packages for resources problems that use this approach generally allow considerable choice in priority rules. There are various ways in which the information about a network can be presented. Sections of the network can be printed out for people in control of parts of the overall project or the jobs can be printed out in order of total float so that critical jobs appear first on the list. This is a useful feature for updating networks. Notwithstanding these advantages, problems of 'practical' size can still be tackled efficiently by hand. One manager said that in his organization, projects with less than 500 jobs would normally be dealt with by hand.

5-11 PLANNING AND REVIEW

In using a CP approach, it can be convenient to divide the exercise into two stages; the *planning* stage and the *review* stage. Each of these stages can be sub-divided thus:

Planning stage	Review stage
1. Construct network	1. Modify network and/or times
2. Estimate times and analyse	2. Re-analyse times
3. Modify	3. Re-modify
4. Schedule	4. Schedule

In this context 'schedule' means determine the actual starting dates of jobs (somewhere within their floats). This can be a tricky process which can be approached in the following manner:

1. Assign specific dates to each job.
2. Use a bar chart on a calendar time-scale along with a separate network diagram.
3. Relate events to calendar time in the usual network diagram.
4. Use a modified network diagram in which all of the job lines are drawn horizontally to a time-scale as in a bar chart. In this manner the various floats and interactions between jobs are clearly indicated.

An illustration of the latter method is given in Figs. 5-9(a) and (b). The alternative representation of the project of Table 5-1 is shown in Fig. 5-9(a). Horizontal dashed lines show free float in jobs. The diagram is drawn against a time-scale of working days. Figure 5-9(b) shows the jobs in a possible 'scheduling' that may be dictated by resources considerations. The diagram is drawn against a calendar time-scale for which five working days per week

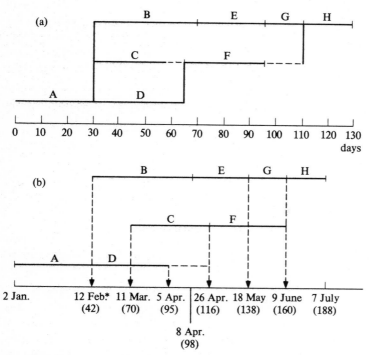

Note: *End of job A. Jobs B and D commence 13 Feb

Figure 5-9

are assumed. Holidays during the project are assumed to cover three working days at Easter and one at the Spring Bank holiday. The dates shown represent scheduled completion or start dates of jobs and the bracketed numbers beneath these dates show the numbers of days since the start of the project. Thus although only 130 working days are required, the project takes 188 days to complete.

5-12 FURTHER APPLICATIONS

The earliest applications of CPM were in respect of manufacturing and assembly operations. In subsequent years the area of application widened considerably to include more general administrative problems. Instances are:

1. The establishment of a new branch or department of a firm.
2. Introduction of a large-scale new procedure.
3. Planning and occupation of a new building.
4. The installation of major new equipment (e.g., a computer).
5. Large-scale movement of staff.
6. Planning provisioning procedures.
7. Contract preparation.
8. Control of research and development projects.
9. Planning and control of maintenance procedures.
10. Planning exhibitions, conferences, and training schemes.

An increasing number of administrative applications is also being found within the Government Service. Instances of actual or possible applications are:

1. Passage of a Bill through Parliament.
2. Putting into effect changes in legislation.
3. Planning a census.
4. Planning and control of publicity campaigns.
5. Planning and control of protocol procedures.
6. Planning and controlling the process of metrication.

5-13 CONCLUSIONS

Although, as we have seen, CPM in its various guises is an immensely valuable technique, the widespread use of CPM-type methods within any organisation can create some difficulties. The project-orientated nature of CPM may conflict with the functional structure of the organization, so that increased flexibility or change may be called for. By and large, CPM tends to facilitate 'management by exception'.

Although conceived of separately from linear programming, since there is frequently a programming aspect of the problems to which CPM is addressed (e.g., minimization of cost subject to a constraint on completion time), it is not surprising that linear programming methods are being increasingly used in CPM problems (see Wilkes, 1977, pages 280–4). There is also a tie in with capital budgeting methods as we have seen. The pattern and timing of cash flows associated with a project can be deduced from diagrams such as Fig. 5-9(b) and discounting can then be conducted.

EXERCISES

5-1 Discuss the benefits and limitations of bar charts as project monitoring and control tools.

5-2 A construction project is divided into seven activities:

Activity	Linking events	Duration (days)
A	1–2	2
B	2–3	7
C	2–4	9
D	3–4	4
E	3–5	10
F	4–5	5
G	5–6	4

(i) Construct the network.
(ii) Calculate the event times.
(iii) Identify the critical path.
(iv) Calculate total float and free float on each activity.
(v) How much time would be saved if the duration of activity E was reduced by three days?

5-3 An assembly operation involves the completion of 11 jobs. The job labels, the time required to complete each one, and the necessary immediate predecessors of each job are shown in the table:

Job	Job time (days)	Immediate predecessors
a	13	—
b	8	a
c	10	b
d	9	c
e	11	b
f	10	e
g	8	d, f
h	6	e
i	7	h
j	14	g, i
k	18	j

(i) Draw the network. Which jobs are on the critical path?

(ii) Prepare a table of floats (free and total) on the non-critical jobs.

(iii) Outline ways in which reductions can be made in network completion time. Illustrate with an example from the network of (i).

5-4 (i) Describe the PERT system of job time estimation.

(ii) By what means can confidence intervals be established for completion of all of, or part of, a network?

5-5 The normal cost/duration and other relevant information for a project is given below:

Activity	Normal duration (days)	Normal total cost £	Minimum duration if accelerated	Cost per day accelerated £
1–2	3	140	1	110
2–3	2	200	1	175
2–4	3	160	1	125
2–5	2	300	1	200
3–6	2	250	1	175
4–6	6	400	1	70
5–6	5	230	1	70
6–7	5	230	1	90

There is a bonus of £100 per day for every day saved below the contract period of 15 days, and a penalty of £200 for each day after the 15 days.

(a) Calculate the normal duration and the normal cost of the project.

(b) Calculate the minimum cost of completing the project in 15 days.

(c) State the optimum plan for the company to attempt.

(d) Revert to the normal programme and normal costs and state what action you would recommend to ensure completion by the original date, if after the tenth day the actual situation was as follows:

(i) activities completed at normal cost: 1–2; 2–3; 3–6; 2–4; 2–5,

(ii) activities not yet started: 4–6; 5–6; 6–7.

What is the revised cost of the project in these circumstances?

5-6 Stereopes Ltd undertakes special contracts. The table gives estimates of the time and cost for activities involved in completing one contract that has just been offered to the firm.

Activity	Previous activities	Normal time (days)	Normal cost (£)	Minimum time (days)	Cost for minimum time (£)
A		12	10 000	8	14 000
B		10	5 000	10	5 000
C	A	0	0	0	0
D	A	6	4 000	4	5 000
E	B, C	16	9 000	14	12 000
F	D	16	3 200	8	8 000
		60	31 200	44	44 000

'Previous activities' must be completed before the activity in question can be started. The minimum time represents the shortest time in which the activity can be completed given the use of especially costly methods of operation. Assume that it is possible to reduce the normal time to the minimum time in small steps and that the extra cost incurred will be proportional to the time saved.

You are required to:

(a) draw a network diagram for the contract and identify the critical path assuming that normal procedures are adopted,

(b) recommend what programme should be followed if the job must be completed in 30 days, and calculate the total cost for that programme, and

(c) explain how you would modify your analysis if the estimates were subject to uncertainty. Illustrate your answer by assuming that estimates of the time required for E are uncertain. Normal time is expected to be in the range 12 to 20 days, but 2 days could still be saved by spending an extra £3000. You remain confident about the estimates for other activities. Target time for the contract is 30 days and there would be a penalty of £5000 for late completion.

(Institute of Chartered Accountants in England and Wales, Professional Examination: II Elements of Financial Decisions, July 1975.)

5-7 Consider the activities required to complete the processing of a customer's order:

Activity	Preceding activities	Average time in days	Normal variable cost per day £
1. Receipt of order, checking credit rating, etc.	—	2	5
2. Preparation of material specification, availability of material, etc.	1	4	10
3. Inspection, packing, etc.	2	1	7
4. Arrangement of transport facilities, etc.	1	5	5
5. Delivery	3, 4	3	2

The time for activities 1, 3, and 5 are fixed; for activity 2 there is a 0.5 probability that it will require 2 days and a 0.5 probability that it will require 6 days; for activity 4 a 0.7 probability of taking 4 days, 0.2 of taking 6 days, and 0.1 of taking 10 days.

You are required to:

(a) draw the network (it is very simple) twice, first using an arrow diagram and secondly an activity-on-node presentation, clearly indicating the meaning of any symbols that you use;

(b) indicate the critical path, calculate average duration and variable cost under normal conditions;

(c) calculate the minimum and maximum times and the probabilities associated with them.

(Institute of Cost and Management Accountants, Professional Stage: Part I, Quantitative Techniques, November 1976.)

5-8 Consider the project which requires the following activities:

Activity		Activity time in days		Total cost (normal) £	Resources, normal number of men per day
Initial node	Terminal node	Normal	Crash		
0	9	6	3	480	4
0	10	10	5	900	5
10	7	7	4	490	5
7	8	9	2	540	4
9	2	8	4	560	6
3	4	5	2	300	4
7	3	6	3	500	4
6	11	6	3	520	6
1	6	7	4	510	5
8	4	10	5	920	6
4	5	8	4	580	6
2	8	10	5	940	5
0	1	9	6	560	4
11	4	8	4	480	4

The activities that can be 'crashed' must either take the normal time or the crash time. There is no opportunity to reduce the time of an activity by one or two days. The cost of crashing any activity is £100 per day.

You are required to:

(a) calculate the normal duration of the project, its normal cost, and the critical path;

(b) state the number of different paths from start to finish;

(c) calculate the minimum time in which the project can be completed and state the critical activities;

(d) state the maximum number of men required to complete the project if all activities commence at the earliest start date.

(Institute of Cost and Management Accountants, Professional Stage: Part 1, Quantitative Techniques, May 1978.)

5-9 Each autumn the Quantitative Accountants' Association prepares and distributes an annual programme. The programme gives dates of meetings and a list of speakers with summaries of their talks. Also included is an up-to-date list of paid-up members. The activities to be carried out to complete the preparation of the programme are as follows:

	Activity	Immediate predecessor	Estimated time (days)
A	Select dates for programme	—	4
B	Secure agreement from speakers and prepare summaries of their talks	A	12
C	Obtain advertising material for programme	A	11
D	Mail membership renewal notices	—	20
E	Prepare list of paid-up members	D	6
F	Send membership list to printer and read proofs	B, C, E	7
G	Print and assemble programme	F	10
H	Obtain computer-printed address labels of members	E	5
I	Send out programmes	G, H	4

Required:

(a) Draw a network for the scheme of activities set out above. Include full information on earliest and latest event times and indicate the critical path.

(10 marks)

(b) Draw a bar chart for the scheme and state the total float for each activity.

(8 marks)

(c) If each activity requires one member of the office staff of the Association, so that the activities may be completed in the estimated times, what is the minimum number of staff that should be allocated to the scheme?

(3 marks)

(d) What would be the effect on the total time if one of the allocated staff was taken ill for the duration of the scheme and not replaced?

(4 marks)

(Association of Certified Accountants, Professional Examination: Section 2, paper 12, Management Mathematics, December 1976.)

CHAPTER
SIX

STOCK CONTROL

6-1 INTRODUCTION

An efficient inventory policy is always an important requirement for the successful management of manufacturing and distributing enterprises. Usually about one-fifth to one-quarter of the total assets of manufacturing industry are in the form of stock, so that improvements in stock control policy can bring major benefits for companies.

Any temporarily idle resource may be thought of as an inventory. Rather more vividly, stocks have been described as 'money in disguise'. Indeed the stock may be of money itself, as in the case of holdings of cash and, as we shall see, it is possible to apply inventory models to cash management problems.

In terms of physical goods it is conventional to distinguish three types of inventory:

1. Pre-production inventory.
2. In-process inventory.
3. Finished goods inventory.

Pre-production inventory is raw materials or other inputs secured from outside the firm. In-process inventory is work-in-progress (possibly at several stages in the production process). Finished goods are the products of the enterprise awaiting sale.

The purpose of inventory is to allow each stage of the production and

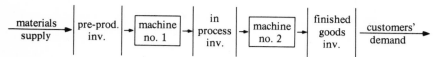

Figure 6-1

distribution system to operate economically by insulating it from different or varying rates of activity at other stages. The most obvious illustration of this is the role that finished goods inventory plays as a cushion between production and sales. Even if the rate of sales is predictable and steady it may be uneconomical to produce continually at just that rate, while if demand is erratic it would be nonsense to keep changing the rate of production.

The same considerations apply within the production process itself. If a product must be processed on several machines which operate at different rates or at different times then in-process inventory is desirable. Even if the different stages of production operate at the same rates and the same times, mechanical failures will not be simultaneous so that in-process inventory still has a useful function to perform.

The entire production process usually needs insulating from irregularities in the arrival of supplies. This is the main function of pre-production or raw materials inventory. In times of inflation there may be a speculative role too. The role of inventories as buffers is shown schematically in Fig. 6-1 in which manufacturing takes place on two machines (in sequence).

The stock control problem is to find the ideal balance between the costs and benefits of inventory. We shall be looking for the best obtainable stock control *policies* in a variety of situations. A stock control policy is a rule or collection of rules which determine: (a) the size, timing, and nature of stock replenishment, and (b) what to do when calls on stock cannot be fulfilled.

In the description of the models we shall be thinking in terms of finished goods inventory usually for a single product. The same principles would apply to in-process or pre-production inventory.

6-2 THE BASIC MODEL

The basic model dates back over 60 years and is sometimes referred to as the classical static model. The assumptions employed are:

1. Single item of stock.
2. All parameters known and constant.
3. Instantaneous replenishment of stock.
4. No variable 're-order' costs.

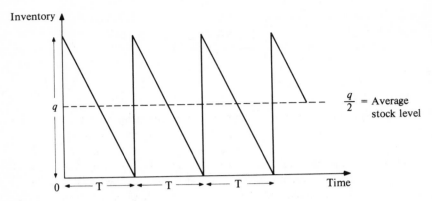

Figure 6-2

The parameters referred to in assumption (2) are data for costs and for the rate of demand (or in general, rate of depletion) of stock. Figure 6-2 shows the graph of inventory level against time and has the characteristic 'saw-tooth' shape. The problem is to determine the best value of q, the replenishment size. The diagram starts with inventory at its maximum level, q, which declines at the uniform rate. When stocks have fallen to zero level, it is assumed that they are immediately replenished in full.

The length of time required for stocks to go from peak-to-peak (or equivalently from trough-to-trough) is one inventory *cycle*. We do not aim to minimize costs per cycle however. This would be achieved by setting $q = 0$ and keeping no inventory at all. Rather it is the objective to minimize costs *per annum* (or some other suitable length of time). Now consider costs in more detail. The costs fall into two categories: (a) holding costs and (b) replenishment costs.

Under the heading of holding costs are included storage, insurance, deterioration, and interest charges. The second category relates to replacement of stock. There will normally be a fixed and a variable component here. The fixed component will include administrative costs of placing an order if supplies are brought in from outside or the set-up costs of machinery if the goods are produced by the firm itself. Variable costs depend on the amount re-ordered. The following notation will be employed:

$$C_m = \text{the cost of procuring one unit of the item}$$
$$i \cdot C_m = \text{the cost of holding one item in stock for one year}$$
$$C_O = \text{the fixed cost of a replenishment order of } \textit{any} \text{ size}$$
$$A = \text{the annual rate of demand}$$

The use of the term $i \cdot C_m$ for the holding cost reflects the view that it is frequently the case that annual holding costs are proportional to the 'value' (cost) of an item stocked. This can prove to be a clumsy arrangement but as the scheme seems to be catching on, particularly with examining bodies, it is presented here.

First consider the annual holding costs. From the holding cost point of view it is as if half the maximum level of inventory was being constantly held throughout the year. This being so we can write:

$$\text{Total holding costs per annum} = \frac{q}{2} \cdot i \cdot C_m \qquad (6\text{-}1)$$

Assumption (4) of the basic model means that, for the moment, procurement costs will be ignored. They will be specifically brought into the model in Sec. 6-4.

Costs arising from replenishment will be C_O times the number of stock refills needed. If annual demand is for A units of stock and replenishment size is q units then there will be A/q replenishments needed. Thus we can write:

$$\text{Total replenishment costs per annum} = \frac{C_O A}{q} \qquad (6\text{-}2)$$

So that, overall, total costs per annum, C, are given by:

$$C = \frac{q}{2} \cdot i \cdot C_m + \frac{C_O A}{q} \qquad (6\text{-}3)$$

The only unknown on the right-hand side of Eq. (6-3) is q, and we wish to determine the value of q which minimizes C. Figure 6-3 graphs the situation. Total costs and each component of costs are graphed against replenishment size q. The ideal value of q is that corresponding to the lowest point of the total cost curve; this is marked as $\bar{q}$. Although it so happens with this model that the minimum of the total cost curve is above the intersection point of the holding and replenishment cost curves, it is *rates of change* that are

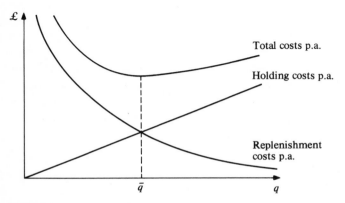

Figure 6-3

important. What is being sought is an optimal balance or 'trade-off' between those costs which rise with q (holding costs) and those which fall with q (replenishment costs). The optimal balance is struck where the rate at which holding costs are going up is equal to the rate at which replenishment costs are coming down.

The slope of the holding costs line is $i \cdot C_m/2$ and the slope of the replenishment costs curve is $-C_O A/q^2$. That is, replenishment costs are *coming down* at the rate of $C_O A/q^2$. So that to find the best value of q we set:

$$\frac{i \cdot C_m}{2} = \frac{C_O A}{q^2}$$

$$\therefore \quad q^2 = \frac{2AC_O}{i \cdot C_m}$$

$$\therefore \quad q = \sqrt{\frac{2AC_O}{i \cdot C_m}} = \bar{q} \tag{6-4}$$

Equation (6-4) is most important. It is known as the *square root rule*. The best value of q, $\bar{q}$ is called the *economic lot size* (ELS), or *economic order quantity* (EOQ), or economic batch size (EBS). Generally we shall use the term EOQ here.

6-3 TWO EXAMPLES

A company faces demand of 2000 items per annum. Stock replenishment costs are fixed at £100 irrespective of the scale of replenishment. It costs £2.50 to hold one item in stock for one year. Calculate the EOQ.

Clearly $C_O = 100$, $A = 2000$, and $i \cdot C_m = 2.5$. Thus substituting in the EOQ formula gives

$$\bar{q} = \sqrt{\frac{2(100)(2000)}{2.5}} = \sqrt{160\,000} = 400$$

So the EOQ is 400 units and 5 replenishments will be needed each year.

Now consider a slightly better-disguised example. A company's stock is depleted at the constant rate of 10 units per day. Storage costs per unit per calendar month are 40p. Cost per re-order is £150. At what intervals should replenishments be made?

On an annual basis $A = 3650$, $i \cdot C_m = 4.8$, and $C_O = 150$. First find the EOQ. This will be:

$$\bar{q} = \sqrt{\frac{2(150)(3650)}{4.8}} = 477.62$$

Ignoring the problem of fractions for the moment, a replenishment size of 477.62 with an annual demand of 3650 means that there will be $3650 \div 477.62 = 7.64$ replenishments needed per annum which produces an interval between replenishments (as we should expect from the daily demand figure) of 47.76 days.

There would be no dramatic rise in costs if these figures were rounded off to $\bar{q} = 480$ ordered every 48 days. Let us see what the annual costs would be. Substitution in Eq. (6-3) gives:

$$C = \tfrac{1}{2}(477.62)(4.8) + \frac{150(3650)}{477.62} = 2292.60$$

If the re-order size was rounded to 480 costs would be

$$C = \tfrac{1}{2}(480)(4.8) + \frac{150(3650)}{480} = 2292.63$$

an increase in costs of 3p per annum on a total bill of almost £2300!

Two interesting facts emerge. First, annual costs, C, are not particularly sensitive to small variations in q. Secondly, at the optimum total annual holding costs equal total annual re-order costs! Both are equal to 1146.29 in the 'exact' case above. This is not a freak result for the particular numbers that we have used here; it is true in general.

The very restrictive nature of the basic model can be relaxed in various ways. This will be the objective of the following sections.

6-4 UNIT COSTS

Here we bring back the C_m figure into the picture. In addition to the costs so far considered the firm has to pay C_m per unit to acquire the item for stock. If the firm is manufacturing the good itself then C_m will usually be the unit variable costs of production. If the firm is a wholesaler or retailer then it will be charged C_m per unit ordered. Of course, it is assumed that C_m is a known constant. In this case, re-order costs for a re-order of size q will now be $C_O + C_m \cdot q$ and there will still be A/q re-orders necessary per annum. Total costs per annum are now given by:

$$C = \frac{q}{2} \cdot i \cdot C_m + (C_O + C_m \cdot q)\frac{A}{q} = \frac{q}{2} \cdot i \cdot C_m + \frac{C_O A}{q} + C_m \cdot A \qquad (6\text{-}5)$$

From Eq. (6-5) it is evident that the EOQ remains unchanged since $C_m \cdot A$ is a constant term. Annual costs themselves are increased but it still pays to replenish stock in the same quantities as before. All this assumes, of course, that the firm intends to satisfy fully the total annual demand. Thus the EOQ formula still applies. All this does not mean that the unit cost figure can always be ignored, as we shall see in the following question.

Plug Wholesalers Ltd hold stocks of a certain type of tap and demand for the taps is at the rate of 250 units per quarter. It costs £2 to hold one tap for a year and Plug Ltd's own administrative costs of placing a re-order with the manufacturer are £10. The manufacturer at present charges Plug Ltd £3 per tap supplied plus a charge of £30 per re-order irrespective of re-order size.

The product manufacturer has, however, recently offered Plug management an alternative scheme of charges. The price per tap would come down to £2.50 but the charge per re-order would be increased by £120. Is this new arrangement beneficial to Plug Ltd?

In order to answer the question the EOQ and consequent annual cost figures must be worked out under each arrangement; that which produces the lowest cost being preferred.

In the first instance $i \cdot C_m = £2$, $C_O = £40$ (the manufacturer's charge must be added to Plug's own cost), $C_m = £3$ and A = 1000 units per annum. Thus the resulting EOQ is:

$$\bar{q} = \sqrt{\frac{2 \times 40 \times 1000}{2}} = 200$$

and the resulting annual costs are:

$$C = \tfrac{1}{2} \times 200 \times 2 + \frac{40 \times 1000}{200} + 3 \times 1000 = 3400$$

Under the alternative scheme the EOQ would be:

$$\bar{q} = \sqrt{\frac{2 \times 160 \times 1000}{2}} = 400$$

and annual costs would be:

$$C = \tfrac{1}{2} \times 400 \times 2 + \frac{160 \times 1000}{400} + 2.5 \times 1000 = 3300$$

so that the new arrangement would produce a saving of £100 per annum for Plug and would be preferred. While both holding costs and re-order costs have increased this has been more than compensated for by the reduced value of C_m.

The importance of the unit cost figure is similarly illustrated in the next example, which is set in a very different context.

Ace Enterprises receives, at a steady rate, inflows of cash amounting to £350 000 per annum. The cash can be invested in securities to earn 12 per cent p.a. Each time that an investment is made there is a brokerage charge of £50 + 1 per cent of the sum invested. How many investments of cash should be made annually? An alternative scheme of brokerage charges is £100 + 0.8 per cent of the sum invested. Which scheme would Ace Enterprises prefer?

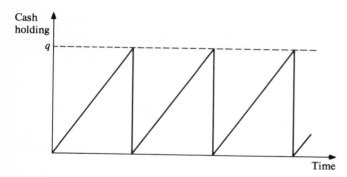

Figure 6-4

In this question we are concerned with a known rate of *inflow* rather than demand. Nevertheless the problem is an inventory problem in structure. The reason that the cash is not immediately placed in securities is because of the fixed element in the brokerage charges. The company needs to ascertain the ideal size of investment and hence with the given annual inflow the number of investments to make each year. The situation is graphed in Fig. 6-4 with q representing the size of investment.

The average holding of cash is $q/2$ and the cost of holding £1 in cash for one year is £0.12, the forgone interest. In the original scheme $C_m = £0.01$ and with A at 350 000 and C_o at £50 the square root formula produces

$$\bar{q} = \sqrt{\frac{2 \times 50 \times 350\,000}{0.12}} = 17\,078$$

so that the optimum number of investments per annum will be

$$\frac{350\,000}{17\,078} = 20.5$$

or 41 in two years. Total cost works out at

$$C = \frac{17\,078}{2} \times 0.12 + \frac{50 \times 350\,000}{17\,078} + 0.01 \times 350\,000 \simeq £5549$$

For the alternative scheme of charges we have

$$\bar{q} = \sqrt{\frac{2 \times 100 \times 350\,000}{0.12}} \simeq 24\,152$$

and annual costs would be

$$C = \frac{24\,152}{2} \times 0.12 + \frac{100 \times 350\,000}{24\,152} + 0.008 \times 350\,000 \simeq £5698$$

Thus Ace Enterprises should stay with the original scheme.

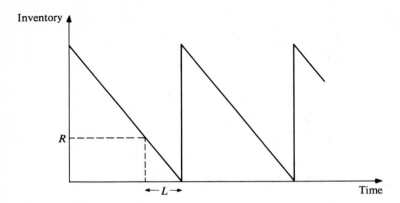

Figure 6-5

6-5 LEAD TIME

Lead time is the delay between the time of placement of an order for replenishment of stock and the time of arrival of the goods in inventory. So far we have been assuming zero lead time (instantaneous replenishment). Let us now suppose that lead time is a known and fixed number of weeks, say L weeks. The effects of this change of assumption are minimal; the order for replenishment must simply be placed when the amount of inventory falls to the level of lead time demand. This gives us the *re-order level*, R. This is shown in Fig. 6-5.

Suppose for the data of the Plug Wholesalers example there is a lead time of 3 weeks ($L = 3$). Assuming a 50-week working year, weekly demand is for 20 units so that the re-order level would be 60 units, the EOQ remaining at 400. Of course, in order to operate this re-order level policy the amount of stock on hand at any time must be known. More of this later.

6-6 BUFFER STOCKS

Buffer or safety stocks are additional stocks held in case of unforeseen contingencies. In the clockwork world of the basic model, buffer stocks are never needed since by assumption nothing is unforeseen or stochastic. However, if buffer stocks *were* added in they would represent a level below which inventory would never fall. Both the average level of stock and the re-order level are shifted up by the amount of buffer stock, B. The situation is illustrated in Fig. 6-6.

Once again the EOQ is unaffected. Lead time demand is $R - B$, the minimum level of stock is B and the maximum level is $B + \bar{q}$. Both holding

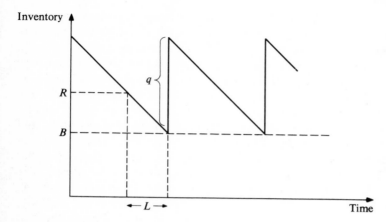

Figure 6-6

costs per annum and total costs rise by $£B\,i \cdot C_m$. The reason that buffer stocks are in fact held is that there *are* uncertainties particularly in respect of demand during any time interval and also in respect of the length of lead time itself.

The amount demanded in any period is usually a random variable although the *average* rate of demand may be known. Thus instead of the 'sharp' sides of the saw-tooth diagrams we should have the rather ragged edges of Fig. 6-7. If the re-order is now set at *average* lead time demand and there is no buffer stock, then clearly if demand during lead time happens to

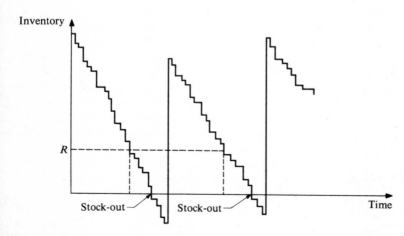

Figure 6-7

be brisk all orders during this period cannot be filled at once—a 'stock-out' situation occurs. Figure 6-7 has been drawn on the assumption that orders during the stock-out period may be filled as soon as supplies arrive. This is sometimes called the *backlogged demand* situation. This will not always be the case; some orders may be lost. In any event there will almost always be costs associated with stock-outs. These costs relate to lost custom in the future, possible failure to meet contractual liabilities, recompense for delay, etc. Any estimate of stock-out costs will be subject to uncertainty and account must be taken of this fact (see below). However, it would be foolish to ignore these costs and thus implicitly assume that they are zero. If buffer stocks are kept, then the chance of a stock-out occurring is reduced. The larger the buffer stock the lower the probability of a stock-out each cycle. As buffer stock is increased, expected stock-out costs are reduced but, of course, holding costs increase. Once again the problem is one of finding the best balance—specifically the level of buffer stock which minimizes:

Buffer stock-holding cost (BSHC)+expected stock-out costs (SOC)   (6-6)

in which both BSHC and SOC are expressed on an annual basis. Expression (6-6) represents costs which are *additional* to the holding and re-order costs already determined and can be thought of as 'the price of uncertainty'. We shall examine two kinds of approach to the problem. The first is rather ambitious and seeks to find an overall optimum while the second contents itself with a lesser objective.

6-7 STOCHASTIC DEMAND (i)

In the case of the first approach consider an especially simplified problem to begin with. In the context of the Plug Wholesalers example, now suppose that there are 'occasional irregularities' of demand which, in the absence of any buffer stock, would cause stock-out costs of £70 per annum. Let the normal level of buffer stocks be two weeks' demand, and to simplify matters even more suppose that the alternative to this policy is to keep no buffer stock at all. In this case it is readily apparent that the buffer stock is not worth while since the alternatives are, at one extreme, to keep the buffer stock and incur holding costs of £80 per annum (40 units at £2 per unit per annum) with no stock-out costs and, at the other, to have no buffer stock-holding costs but to incur the £70 stock-out costs per annum.

A rather more challenging problem is the following (in which the objective is to determine the optimal size of buffer stock and hence the re-order level).

Phil T. Luker Enterprises operate a 50-week working year. Demand for their product, the Argent, during any week in the year, is described by the probability distribution:

Demand (X)	Probability (P)
0	0.07
1	0.10
2	0.11
3	0.13
4	0.15
5	0.17
6	0.13
7	0.08
8	0.04
9	0.02

Demand can only be satisfied (if at all) from stocks. The stock-holding costs are £2 per item per year. Fixed costs per re-order are £8 and the variable re-order costs are £15 per unit. Lead time is one week. The costs of being out of stock are £6 per unit short.

The first step is to determine average weekly demand and hence average annual demand. Multiplying each level of demand by its probability of occurrence and summing the results gives the arithmetic mean weekly demand. Thus a $P \cdot X$ column is formed, the elements of which are:

$$P \cdot X$$

$$
\begin{array}{c}
0 \\
0.10 \\
0.22 \\
0.39 \\
0.60 \\
0.85 \\
0.78 \\
0.56 \\
0.32 \\
0.18 \\
\hline
\end{array}
$$

$$\Sigma P \cdot X = 4.00$$

Thus the mean weekly demand is for four units and the mean annual demand $A = 200$. Employing this figure in the familiar square root formula produces

$$\bar{q} = \sqrt{\frac{2 \times 8 \times 200}{2}} = 40$$

So the EOQ is 40 units which would produce an average of *five* cycles per annum. Now to determine the best re-order level we need to determine the level of buffer stock which minimizes BSHC + SOC. The re-order level will then be $B + 4$. Since there is only a small number of possible levels of demand during any week, a process of *complete enumeration* is possible: that is, we shall determine BSHC + SOC for each possible level of buffer stock.

Suppose to begin with that buffer stock was zero. Re-order level would then be set at mean lead time demand of four units and shortage would occur if demand during lead time was for five or more units. We must first determine the *expected shortage per cycle* at buffer stock zero. The requisite workings are:

		$B = 0$	
Demand (X)	Shortage (S)	Probability (P)	$P \times S$
5	1	0.17	0.17
6	2	0.13	0.26
7	3	0.08	0.24
8	4	0.04	0.16
9	5	0.02	0.10
			$\Sigma PS = 0.93$

It emerges that the expected shortage per cycle, $\Sigma PS = 0.93$. This figure will be used to determine costs later on. The expected shortage per cycle must now be computed for the other possible levels of buffer stock for which workings are shown below. In each case shortage arises when lead time demand exceeds the mean value of four plus the buffer stock. With buffer stock set at five units there can be no shortage since maximum demand is for nine units. Obviously there would be no point in having buffer stock in excess of five.

		$B = 1$				$B = 2$	
X	S	P	PS	X	S	P	PS
6	1	0.13	0.13	7	1	0.08	0.08
7	2	0.08	0.16	8	2	0.04	0.08
8	3	0.04	0.12	9	3	0.02	0.06
9	4	0.02	0.08				$\Sigma PS = 0.22$
			$\Sigma PS = 0.49$				

		$B = 3$				$B = 4$	
X	S	P	PS	X	S	P	PS
8	1	0.04	0.04	9	1	0.02	0.02
9	2	0.02	0.04				$\Sigma PS = 0.02$
			$\Sigma PS = 0.08$				

Conceivably however buffer stock might be *negative*. If re-order level was set at three units this would correspond to $B = -1$. This situation would be 'desirable' if shortage costs were very low and storage costs high. As will be evident shortly, negative buffer stock is clearly non-optimal in the present case nor should we expect it to be so in practice. We are also taking a short cut in not working with expected surpluses when demand is low. The method can be made more precise in this respect but the improvement is very small.

The next step is to compile a table in which costs associated with each level of buffer stock are deduced. Suppose that buffer stock is zero. The expected shortage per cycle is 0.93 but since there are on average five cycles per annum expected annual shortage is $5 \times 0.93 = 4.65$ units and, with a shortage cost of £6 per unit short, expected shortage cost per annum will be $6 \times 4.65 = £27.9$. Since there are no buffer stocks BSHC $= 0$ and BSHC $+$ SOC $= £27.9$ for $B = 0$ and $R = 4$. Similar calculations are performed for each value of B and the results are detailed in Table 6-1.

Entries in column (6) show that the optimal value of B is three units so that the re-order level should be $R = 7$. Clearly, however, there is little to choose between buffer stocks of three or four units and this suggests the question as to how sensitive are the results to variations in the original parameters of the problem. This is the field of sensitivity analysis. In particular there may be considerable uncertainty surrounding the shortage cost figure. We shall now determine the range of values of the shortage cost figure for which the original solution remains optimal.

If the shortage cost figure is S, then the entries in column (6) can be expressed as linear functions of S. The results are:

B	BSHC + SOC
0	$4.65S$
1	$2.45S + 2$
2	$1.1S + 4$
3	$0.4S + 6$
4	$0.1S + 8$
5	10

Table 6-1

(1) B	(2) ESPC	(3) = 5 × (2) ESPA	(4) = 6 × (3) SOC	(5) BSHC	(6) = (4) + (5) BSHC + SOC
0	0.93	4.65	27.9	0	27.9
1	0.49	2.45	14.7	2	16.7
2	0.22	1.10	6.6	4	10.6
3	0.08	0.40	2.4	6	8.4*
4	0.02	0.10	0.6	8	8.6
5	0	0	0	10	10.0

* ESPC = expected shortage per cycle, ESPA = expected shortage per annum.

For the original solution to remain optimal, S must be such that the $B = 3$ cost figure of $0.4S + 6$ must not exceed any of the other values. As the value of S rises, the higher levels of buffer stock may become attractive and so the $B = 4$ and $B = 5$ cost figures will set *upper* bounds on S. Whichever sets the *least upper bound* (LUB) will determine the maximum value to which S can rise. Conversely, the lower values of buffer stock may become attractive as S falls. Each entry in the cost column for $B = 0$ to $B = 2$ will set a *lower* bound for S and the *greatest lower bound* (GLB) is the relevant one. The workings are

$$0.4S + 6 \leqslant 0.1S + 8$$
$$\therefore \quad S \leqslant 6.67 \qquad \text{*LUB}$$

$$0.4S + 6 \leqslant 10$$
$$\therefore \quad S \leqslant 10$$

$$0.4S + 6 \leqslant 1.1S + 4$$
$$\therefore \quad S \geqslant 2.86 \qquad \text{*GLB}$$

$$0.4S + 6 \leqslant 2.45S + 2$$
$$\therefore \quad S \geqslant 1.95$$

$$0.4S + 6 \leqslant 4.65S$$
$$\therefore \quad S \geqslant 1.41$$

Thus provided that the true value of S lies in the range

$$\boxed{2.86 \leqslant S \leqslant 6.67}$$

none of the alternative values of B produces a lesser cost figure than $B = 3$.

Sensitivity analysis on the other parameters—for instance C_O—can also be carried out. The workings in these cases are somewhat less straightforward as the EOQ value and hence the number of cycles per annum are affected. The reader will find procedures given in Samuels and Wilkes (1980a, Chapter 17).

6-8 STOCHASTIC DEMAND (ii)

The second, less ambitious approach to the problem of stochastic demand is the *service level* approach. In this method the idea is to set the re-order level so as to achieve a given (small) probability of a stock-out occurring each inventory cycle. The chosen level of probability may be that which prevails throughout the trade or it may be that which is 'thought to be best' as a result of previous experience. In either event the level is predetermined rather than being calculated. The method will be explained in the context of an example.

Suppose that a firm experiences a mean weekly demand for its item of stock of 150 units. Let demand in each week of the year be closely approximated by a normal distribution and be *independent* of demand in any other week. Let standard deviation of demand in any week be 25 units. Then within any one week there is a 95 per cent chance that the level of demand will be in the range

$$150 \pm 1.96 \times 25$$

In other words the 95 per cent *confidence interval* for demand in any week is

$$101 \text{ to } 199$$

In general terms if W is the mean weekly demand and σ represents standard deviation, then in 19 weeks out of 20 weekly demand will be in the range:

$$W \pm 1.96\sigma$$

Wider or narrower confidence intervals can be obtained by varying the coefficient of σ. The number 1.96 is appropriate to 95 per cent confidence; 2.58 would give 99 per cent confidence and 1.65 would give 90 per cent confidence. However, it is only demand in the *upper part* of the interval (i.e., above average) that will concern us so far as stock-outs go.

Periods greater than one week can be considered similarly. With the assumption of independently distributed demand in each week, over an L-week period demand will be distributed about a mean value of LW and with a variance of $L\sigma^2$; in other words the *variances* can be added. Hence the standard deviation of demand in the 4-week period is $\sqrt{L\sigma^2} = \sigma\sqrt{L}$. Thus the 95 per cent confidence interval for demand in a 4-week period (suppose that four weeks is the lead time) with the above data, is

$$LW \pm 1.96\sigma\sqrt{L} = 600 \pm 98 = 502 \text{ to } 698$$

where LW is the mean lead time demand and $1.96\sigma\sqrt{L}$ is the level of buffer stock. There is only a $2\frac{1}{2}$ per cent chance that demand during the four weeks of lead time will exceed 698.

In the deterministic case re-order level was set at lead time demand and there was no chance of a stock-out occurring. If in the present case the re-order level was set at 600 (the mean lead time demand) there would be a 50 per cent chance of a stock-out but if re-order level was set at 698 there would only be a $2\frac{1}{2}$ per cent chance. The chance that a stock-out does *not* occur in any cycle is said to be the *service level* provided. Thus in the present case if re-order level is set at 698 the level of service provided is $97\frac{1}{2}$ per cent.

Zeta Limited experiences average annual demand for an item of stock of 7500 units. The cost of holding one unit of stock for a year is £3. Fixed costs per re-order are £200. Lead time is 4 weeks. There is a 50-week working year. Standard deviation of demand in any week is 25 units. It can be assumed that demand in each week is normally distributed about the weekly average and is independent of demand in other weeks.

1. What is the re-order level that would provide a $97\frac{1}{2}$ per cent level of service?
2. What would be the average number of stock-outs per annum at a $97\frac{1}{2}$ per cent level of service?
3. Zeta estimates that each stock-out costs £400. From the company's point of view is the $97\frac{1}{2}$ per cent level of service superior to an alternative 90 per cent level of service?

Annual demand of 7500 corresponds to weekly demand of 150 thus our workings above have answered part (1). The re-order level needed to provide $97\frac{1}{2}$ per cent service level is 698. In order to answer part (2) the average number of cycles per annum must be determined. In the usual fashion the EOQ is determined as

$$\bar{q} = \sqrt{\frac{2 \times 200 \times 7500}{3}} = 1000$$

which implies an average of 7.5 re-orders (i.e., 7.5 inventory cycles) per annum. Thus with a 0.025 probability of stock-out on each of these cycles the expected number of stock-outs per annum is $7.5 \times 0.025 = 0.1875$.

Now consider a 90 per cent service level. The re-order level here would be 1.28 standard deviations above the mean lead time demand, the entry under $z = 1.28$ in Table A being the nearest to 0.9000. So, re-order level is $600 + 1.28 \times 25 \times 2 = 664$ and the expected number of stock-outs per annum is $7.5 \times 0.1 = 0.75$. Now compare costs in the two cases. At the $97\frac{1}{2}$ per cent service level the buffer stock is 98 giving an annual BSHC of £294. Thus BSHC + SOC = $3 \times 98 + 400 \times 0.1875 = £369$. At the 90 per cent service level BSHC + SOC = $3 \times 64 + 400 \times 0.75 = £492$ so that Zeta would prefer the $97\frac{1}{2}$ per cent level of service. If the specific size and nature of stock-out costs was unknown it would follow that in order for the $97\frac{1}{2}$ per cent service level to be preferred to the 90 per cent level the difference in the SOC's must be at least as great as the difference in the BSHC's. The difference in the BSHC's is $294 - 192 = 102$. The difference in stock-out costs is constrained to be not less than this sum, viz.

$$S \times 0.75 - S \times 0.1875 \geqslant 102$$

which solves for $S \geqslant 181.\overline{33}$. The point of this is that while the stock controller or financial manager would be unable to give a precise figure for stock-out costs, he may be aware that it is grossly different from $181.\overline{33}$ thus enabling a choice of policy to be made.

6-9 QUANTITY DISCOUNTS

It is common business practice to offer discounts for volume of purchases—
the greater the order size the less the unit cost. Alternatively, if an inventory
holder manufactures the product itself the unit cost of production may
decrease as volume increases. In either case instead of a constant, C_m, for the
unit cost of the items it may be either a continuous variable or may take on a
number of discrete values depending on the re-order size. Suppose this latter
case is the situation facing a firm which keeps an item in stock, how can the
best level of replenishment order size now be determined? Consider the
following problem.

A company holds one item of stock, demand for which is at the rate of
200 units per annum. The cost of holding one item of stock for one year is
£16 (regardless of the price per unit). There is a fixed charge of £64 per re-
order. The company's supplier will charge a price per unit supplied that
depends upon the number ordered each replenishment. Details are:

Number ordered (q)	Price per unit
$0 \leqslant q < 25$	£27
$25 \leqslant q < 50$	£25
$50 \leqslant q < 75$	£24
$75 \leqslant q$	£23.50

What size of replenishment order should be placed? (Note that the holding
cost is constant at £16. This shows the $i \cdot C_m$ notation at its clumsiest since

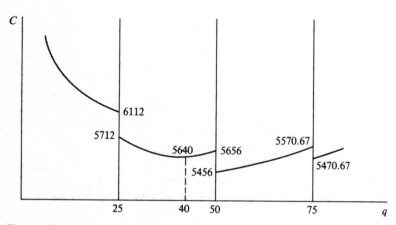

Figure 6-8

here $i \cdot C_m = 16$ regardless of C_m.) This kind of problem is also known under the heading 'price breaks'. The aptness of this description can be seen from a graph of the problem. This is shown in Fig. 6-8 in which the value of costs at each crucial level of q is indicated. At the EOQ of 40 units $C = £5640$ since $C_m = 25$ here. As q rises towards 50, C rises towards £5656 at which point the value of C_m suddenly drops by £1 bringing costs at $q = 50$ down to £5456. As q rises towards 75 C rises towards £5570.67 but drops abruptly to £5470.67 at $q = 75$.

It is evident from Fig. 6-8 that the candidates for optimal value of q in these circumstances are the EOQ or one of the price break points above the EOQ. Price break points below the EOQ cannot be optimal. Total annual costs, C, must be determined at the EOQ and at the higher break points in each case using the appropriate value of C_m.

6-10 THE BUILD-UP MODEL

Many firms that produce a range of several similar products (e.g., different sizes and types of wheel) do not keep all items in continuous production. Rather they have production runs on each item lasting days, weeks, or months. Sometimes the entire anticipated annual demand is produced; on other occasions there may be a number of shorter 'runs' each year.

Consider the problem relating to one such item produced by a firm (it will be assumed that there are no tight constraints on storage). The decision required is how much to produce at each run. Alternatively, given a steady rate of production, the problem could be re-expressed in terms of the *length of time* that each run should last.

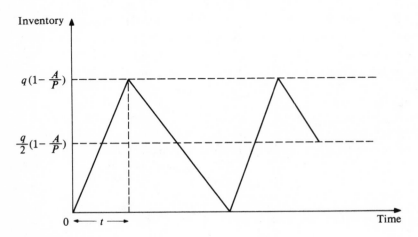

Figure 6-9

The graph of inventory level over time in this case is shown in Fig. 6-9. Starting from zero level (buffer stock can be grafted on to this model) inventory steadily rises while the production run lasts (for time t). The rate of build-up of stock is the excess of the production rate over the demand rate. When the run is completed inventory declines at the demand rate.

Let the amount produced in time t be q. With the production rate at P units per annum then $t = q/P$. Demand during the production run is $tA = qA/P$. Maximum inventory will then be given by the total amount produced less demand during the production run. Thus maximum and average inventory are as shown in Fig. 6-9. Annual holding costs will be

$$\frac{q}{2} i \cdot C_m \left(1 - \frac{A}{P} \right)$$

Replenishment costs per cycle (i.e., per production run) will, as before, be given by $C_O + qC_m$, where C_m is the unit variable production cost and C_O is the cost of setting up the equipment for the run. Total replenishment costs per annum will then be

$$(C_O + qC_m) \frac{A}{q}$$

so that total costs to be minimized are

$$\frac{q}{2} i \cdot C_m \left(1 - \frac{A}{P} \right) + (C_O + qC_m) \frac{A}{q}$$

and minimization produces the formula

$$\bar{q} = \sqrt{\frac{2AC_OP}{i \cdot C_m(P - A)}}$$

Note that the value of $\bar{q}$ in this case is the old EOQ formula multiplied by the factor $\sqrt{P/(P - A)}$ so that $\bar{q}$ will be larger than in the instantaneous production rate case. The faster the production rate the nearer is the result to the instantaneous case, since $\sqrt{P/(P - A)}$ approaches unity as P approaches infinity.

Consider an example. Each time that a firm starts a production run of a certain product there are set-up costs of £400. Production is at the rate of 12 000 units p.a. and demand is at the rate of 8000 units p.a. It costs £7.50 to hold one item for one year. How many production runs should there be each year?

Substitution into the formula for $\bar{q}$ gives:

$$\bar{q} = \sqrt{\frac{2 \times 12\,000 \times 400 \times 8000}{7.5(12\,000 - 8000)}} = 1600$$

Thus five runs would be needed each year.

6-11 TYPES OF INVENTORY POLICY

In the *re-order level* model, as we have seen, the policy was that an order for replenishment be placed when inventory fell to or below the re-order level. The size of replenishment (the EOQ) was fixed. This policy calls for the continuous monitoring of stock and this can be expensive. The *periodic review* policy retains the concept of a re-order level but stock on hand is not constantly known; instead there are periodic stock takings. If at the time of stock-taking inventory is at or below the re-order level a replenishment order, of fixed size, is placed. Otherwise there is no re-ordering. The interval between reviews is fixed in this model and has to be determined as do both q and the re-order level R. In comparison with the re-order level policy information costs are reduced, but this is at the expense of holding more stock on average or/and increased stock-out costs.

The *re-order cycle* policy dispenses with the re-order level and replenishment orders are placed at every review, but the size of replenishment order is now variable. The amount of stock ordered is the difference between a maximum inventory level, S, and the level of stock at review. In comparison with the periodic review policy there is less chance of a stock-out occurring. If the interval between reviews is similar in the two models (it may tend to be longer in the re-order cycle case) the average level of stocks and hence stock-holding costs would tend to be higher, although strictly this would depend on the value chosen for S. If the interval between reviews is similar, then re-order costs will be higher.

The rather ominously entitled *s, S policy* combines features of the periodic review and re-order cycle policies. In this case inventory is again reviewed at regular intervals but an order for replenishment is only placed if the stock level at review is at or below the level s. The amount re-ordered, if there is a re-order, is calculated as in the re-order cycle policy—an amount sufficient to bring the stock on hand at review up to the level S. So with I = inventory, the amount re-ordered is given by the decision rule:

$$\text{Amount re-ordered } q = S - I \quad \text{if } I \leqslant s$$
$$= 0 \quad \text{if } I > s$$

In any application the choice between the models described (and other models) depends upon the features of the particular system in question. Although no one model is *always* superior, an (s, S) approach can be shown to be optimal in several cases. The original basic EOQ model can be expressed in (s, S) terms. In this model negative inventory was prohibited—fixing $s = 0$ and $S = \bar{q}$.

6-12 OTHER MODELS AND APPROACHES

Many books on inventory control are very substantial volumes. There is space here for mention of just two further methods of stock control.

We have said little about the multi-item case. Usually more than one item is kept in stock. If these items do not compete for common scarce resources (e.g., storage space or management time) they can be optimized separately. If some goods *do* compete for (say) scarce storage space, if only a few products are involved, then methods of constrained optimization may be usable. The reader is referred to Samuels and Wilkes (1980a) for discussion of such methods.

Where very many products are stored a quite different approach is called for. Some chemicals companies may have over 20 000 items in stock and in such cases detailed analysis of all products is quite impossible. One method that has been gaining popularity in recent years is the *ABC classification* method originally developed by the General Electric Corporation. The items of stock are ranked by turnover as follows:

Category A: Those items that account for most of the turnover (in value terms). It is often the case that just 10 per cent of the product range accounts for 70 per cent of total turnover.

Category C: A large part of the product range, perhaps 60 per cent, may account for only a small proportion of turnover, say, 10 per cent. These are category C items.

Category B: This is the intermediate section of the product range with, say, 30 per cent of the total number of items stocked accounting for 20 per cent of total turnover.

Clearly, the category A items should receive the greatest amount of control effort with sophisticated forecasting and recording systems and detailed analysis of order quantities and buffer stocks. Category B items would receive less detailed treatment with simpler forecasting methods and rougher estimates of EOQ's. For the category C items only very simple treatment would be warranted. A possibility here is the *'two bin' system* (keep two 'bins' of stock; re-order when one is empty, i.e., re-order level $= \bar{q}/2$) or some other rule-of-thumb method to determine re-order levels.

The ABC method is not precise—the break points are arbitrary—and it does not say what is to be done in each category. The blanks are filled in as circumstances warrant. Sometimes too another measure of 'value' may be employed instead of turnover—for instance, profit contribution. ABC is rather a style of approach than a method. It sometimes goes by the pseudonym of *Pareto analysis* or *grouping methods*.

At the other extreme from the ABC situation is the 'production-to-order' case. If orders for an item come in batches of a given size (say when a single customer is being supplied), it may be better simply to produce to order rather than stock the item at all. Suppose that a firm supplies its sole customer with x units an average n times per year. If production is to order the lot size will be x and the cost per order will be $C_0 + C_m x$ where C_m is the unit variable cost of production. So with n orders per annum the total annual cost will be $n(C_O + C_m x) = nC_O + nC_m x$. On the other hand if the item was stocked the EOQ quantity would be

$$\bar{q} = \sqrt{\frac{2C_O nx}{i \cdot C_m}}$$

which, by substitution in the cost equation $(A = nx)$, gives cost $= \sqrt{2C_O nx \, i \cdot C_m} + nC_m x$ and algebraic manipulation reveals that the production-to-order cost is lower if

$$n < \frac{2x \, i \cdot C_m}{C_O} \tag{6-7}$$

In which case the item would not be kept in stock.

This decision rule (6-7) is a good guide to the stock/do not stock decision if there is a fairly substantial difference between n and $2x \, i \cdot C_m / C_O$. It is only a 'good guide' since a slight injustice is done to the EOQ approach (which in fact should use a whole number multiple of x as the size of replenishment).

6-13 CONCLUSIONS

The EOQ concept has proved widely useful in practical inventory control but the models presented here, for the most part, would require a great deal of elaboration to address complex practical problems. In practice inventories are often kept at several levels and perhaps at different locations. Some companies use a *centralized store* at some location thus enabling lower stocks to be kept at retail outlets. Some car manufacturers adopt this approach to spare parts inventory. There are also cases where *simulation* rather than analysis would be indicated. Finally, decisions on inventory should ideally be taken interdependently with decisions on prices, output levels, sales promotion, etc. This can rarely be done in a formal manner in practice but the implications (for, say, the marketing department) of changes in inventory policy should be borne in mind.

EXERCISES

6-1 Outline the principal reasons for holding inventory and explain why good inventory management is likely to be one of the most important aspects of overall company management. What other areas of company management is the inventory problem likely to impinge upon?

6-2 Describe the basic static model for the management of inventory of a single product and explain the principal results.

6-3 A company experiences annual demand for 2500 units of the single product that it stocks. The replenishment cost for inventory is fixed at £400 regardless of the size of the replenishment. Annual holding costs are £8 per unit. What is the optimum number of replenishments per annum?

6-4 The annual demand for a company's single item of stock is 1000 units. It costs the company £6 to hold one unit of stock for one year. Each time that a replenishment order is made the company incurs a fixed cost of £75.

(i) Determine the economic order quantity to two decimal places.

(ii) Suppose that the company's supplier of stock introduces a condition that normally there shall be no more than five orders for replenishment per annum. How much would the company be prepared to pay in order to avoid having to meet this condition?

6-5 A company receives, at a steady rate, inflows of cash amounting to £250 000 per annum. Such cash can be invested to earn $12\frac{1}{2}$ per cent per annum. Each time the company makes an investment there is a brokerage charge of £25 plus 1 per cent of the sum invested (both sums payable at the time the investment is made).

(i) How many investments of cash should be made per annum?

(ii) If the brokerage charges were revised to $£100 + \frac{3}{4}$ per cent of the sum invested, in what amounts should investments now be made? Which scheme of brokerage charges would the company prefer?

6-6 Xerxes Holding Co. have a 50-week working year. The demand for a particular product stocked by Xerxes is subject to random variability. Demand for this product during any one week of the working year is described by the probability distribution:

Units demanded	Probability
0	0.03
1	0.06
2	0.07
3	0.09
4	0.11
5	0.21
6	0.17
7	0.12
8	0.08
9	0.06

Demand can only be satisfied (if at all) from stocks. The stock-holding costs are £40 per unit per annum. Each time that a re-order is made a cost of £50 is incurred irrespective of re-order size and the cost of the item is £180 per unit. There is a lead time of one week. The cost of being out of stock is estimated as £20 per unit short. Xerxes desires to minimize annual inventory costs.

(i) Determine the economic order quantity.

(ii) Find the optimal re-order level and size of buffer stock.

(iii) For what range of values of the shortage cost figure would the re-order level found in (ii) remain optimal? (Assume all other data at their original values.) Could a similar sensitivity analysis be conducted on the holding cost figure?

6-7 Circa Holding Co. is examining its inventory policy in relation to one type of light-weight car wheel that it stores. Demand for the wheel runs at the average rate of 1000 units per quarter. It costs Circa £8 to hold one wheel for one year. When a re-order is necessary, Circa has fixed administrative costs of £40 irrespective of order size. The manufacturer charges Circa £12 per wheel supplied plus a charge of £120 no matter how large the order.

(a) (i) Determine the economic order quantity.

(ii) An alternative scheme of charges would produce total costs per annum (including the £12 per wheel) of £52 000. Should Circa adopt the alternative scheme?

(b) Assume a 50-week working year. Lead time is four weeks. Variance of demand in any week is 156.25 units. It can be assumed that demand in each week is normally distributed about the weekly average and is independent of demand in other weeks.

(i) Determine the re-order level that would produce a $97\frac{1}{2}$ per cent 'service level'.

(ii) Circa management, in an attempt to economize, is considering a reduction of the service level to 80 per cent. Each stock-out is estimated to cost Circa £120. Is the planned reduction in service level advisable?

6-8 A firm has production set-up costs of £500 per run. The firm can achieve economies of scale in production and estimates of unit variable costs of production for various run sizes are as follows:

Production per run	Unit cost
< 800	2.3
800–1999	1.9
2000–2999	1.7
3000 +	1.2

Inventory is depleted at the steady rate of 100 units per week over a 50-week year and inventory holding costs are £5 per unit per annum. Determine the optimum size of production run.

6-9 A firm has set-up costs of £600 per production run and variable production costs are proportional to the quantity produced. The company operates a 50-week working year. When production is in progress 500 units per week are made. Demand is at the steady rate of 200 units per week during the working year. Inventory holding costs are £5 per unit held per annum. How many production runs should be made each year?

6-10 The directors of Arges Ltd are concerned at a recent increase in the company's working capital requirements. They have initiated a special study of the levels of stocks of each product in an attempt to effect economies. One of the main products is the Cyclops. It is manufactured in batches and sold at £25 per unit. At this price, sales are expected to be 5000 units per annum, spread evenly through the year. The Cyclops requires the following resources:

Materials: Cost £7 per unit.

Labour hours: One grade is employed for machining and assembly. Preparation and machine set-up time require 16 hours at the start of production of each batch. Subsequently each unit of output requires 2 labour hours. The wage rate is £0.99 per hour. Labour is currently subject to a substantial amount of idle time because of a recession in the industry. The directors have decided not to dismiss any employees nor to reduce the number of hours for which employees are paid.

Machine hours: One standard type of machine is used. Set up time for a batch is 9 hours and each unit of output requires 1 machine hour. Machine costs amount to £4 per hour.

Stocks are kept in a warehouse which was rented on a long lease 10 years ago for £2 per square foot per annum. Warehouse space available exceeds current requirements and spare capacity is sublet on annual contracts at £3 per square foot per annum. Each unit of Cyclops requires 3 square feet of space. Other costs of holding Cyclops in stock are estimated at £7 per unit per annum.

You are required to:

(a) Calculate the optimal batch size and the associated maximum and average stock levels. [Square root formula was supplied with examination question.]

(b) explain shortly the rationale of the square root formula; and

(c) explain for the benefit of the managing director (who is not familiar with accounting) the reasons for your treatment of the cost of labour and warehouse space.
(Institute of Chartered Accountants in England and Wales, Professional Examination: II Elements of Financial Decisions, July 1975.)

6-11 Vaal Ltd manufactures several products including a chemical called Zand. Stocks of the chemical have to be stored in special warehouses and the firm is now undertaking calculations of the optimal level of their stocks of Zand with a view to determining whether an additional warehouse should be purchased.

Products are manufactured in batches using common processing plant which has an output rate of 100 tons per hour. Zand is sold for £72 per ton and demand is 40 000 tons per annum, spread evenly over the year. Each time Vaal commences the processing of a 'batch' of Zand, special costs of £12 for materials are incurred; 20 hours of grade E labour are also required in setting up the plant for the processing and grade E labour is paid £2 per hour; if they were not working on the setting-up of the process, however, the employees would be undertaking semi-skilled work saving the employment of lower grade employees at £1 per hour.

The variable cost of production of a ton of Zand is £40. Warehouses suitable for Zand may be erected only in a standard size with a capacity of 500 tons. Vaal owns one such warehouse at the present time. Warehouses cost £5000 and have indefinitely long lives; they involve annual maintenance costs of £120. Vaal's cost of capital is 10 per cent per annum.

There is to be no minimum level below which stocks are not allowed to fall.
You are required to:

(a) Calculate (i) the optimal level of maximum stocks of Zand assuming that a second warehouse is purchased; (ii) the optimal level of maximum stocks assuming that a second warehouse is not purchased; (iii) the total annual costs of the policies under (i) and (ii) and hence (iv) estimate whether purchase of the second warehouse is worth while.

(b) Explain, for the benefit of a director who has no familiarity with quantitative techniques, the rationale of your calculations. Ignore taxation and inflation.
(Institute of Chartered Accountants in England and Wales, Professional Examination: II Elements of Financial Decisions, July 1976.)

6-12 Electropoint Ltd has expanded the production of its domestic robots and now requires each year, and at a constant rate, 200 000 positronic circuits which it obtains from an outside supplier. The cost of placing each order for the positronic circuits is £32. For any circuit in stock it is estimated that the annual holding cost is equal to 10 per cent of its cost. The circuits cost £8 each. No stock-outs are permitted.
Required:

(a) What is the optimal order size, and how many orders should be placed in a year?

(b) What are the ordering and holding costs and hence what is the total relevant inventory cost per annum?

(c) If the demand has been underestimated and the true demand is 242 000 circuits per annum, what would be the effect of keeping to the order quantity calculated in (a) above and still meeting demand, rather than using a new optimal order level?

(d) What does your answer to (c) tell you about the sensitivity of your model to changes in demand?
(Association of Certified Accountants; Management Mathematics, Professional Examination: Section 2, June 1977.)

6-13 In an assembly process your company consumes annually 125 000 small screws at an even rate of 2500 per week. The cost of the screws is £4 per 1000. The cost of placing an order irrespective of the quantity ordered is £5. The risk of obsolescence is negligible and the cost of storage has been estimated at £1 per 1000 screws per year. The company's minimum required rate of return on capital is 20 per cent.
You are required to:

(a) calculate the order quantity and state the optimum ordering policy from a supplier who can guarantee immediate delivery;

(b) state the change required in the re-ordering policy if there were a lead time of two weeks;

(c) calculate the optimum production policy if the company decided that it could make the screw for £2 per 1000, plus an order cost of £5 and a set-up cost of £10, at a rate of 25 000 per week;

(d) state the considerations that should be taken into account if requirements fluctuated owing to changes in demand for the assembly;

(e) state the re-ordering considerations that should be taken into account if demand varies within the range of 1000 to 4000 screws required per week. A general stocking policy has now been agreed to ensure there is no problem if demand is 50 per cent higher than average. A stock-out owing to demand being 100 per cent higher than average will be tolerated.

(Institute of Cost and Management Accountants, Professional Stage: Part 1, Quantitative Techniques, May 1978.)

SEVEN

QUEUEING THEORY

7-1 BACKGROUND

Queues are commonplace experiences, e.g.,

1. People waiting in shops and at service counters.
2. Cars waiting at traffic lights.
3. Aircraft waiting to land.
4. Ships waiting to enter port.

And, as less obvious examples of queues:

1. Machines waiting for repair.
2. Goods waiting in inventory.
3. Telephone subscribers waiting for a clear line.
4. Papers in an in-tray.

In principle, at least, these problems can be addressed by queueing theory methods. A theory of queues is possible because of certain regularities about the patterns of arrival and service of customers. These regularities can be described statistically and analytical results (formulae) sometimes follow. Queueing theory is about *delay* whether or not an actual queue is observed. Why does delay occur at all? The reason is that it is not possible or not worth while to tailor the supply of a service exactly to the demand for it. A *trade-off* situation arises; delay can be costly but it is also costly to make provision to avoid or to reduce delay. However, the costs do not always fall on the same parties.

Sometimes a system of serving customers can be developed by *experimentation*, for example, changing the provision of cashiers at supermarket checkouts at different times of the day. In other cases such intervention in the real situation would be either impossible or prohibitively expensive. This is so where large or irreversible investments are involved — for instance, the number of lanes on a motorway cannot readily be changed. Very complex systems have to be *simulated* (an example is provided in the chapter on simulation). This was done in determining traffic flow arrangements in central London.

7-2 THE TYPES OF QUEUEING MODEL

Queueing systems are completely characterized by the differing nature of:

1. The arrival pattern of customers.
2. The queue 'discipline'.
3. The service mechanism.
4. Capacitation.
5. Population.

Arrivals

The pattern of arrivals may be *deterministic* (e.g., items on a production flow line) or more usually random. 'Customers' may arrive one at a time or *en masse*. 'Customer' or 'item' are general words for the queueing elements: they do not have to be people. Arrivals may or may not depend on the state of the system (e.g., a customer may *balk* if he sees a large queue). The arrival rate may be constant or may vary over time. Customers may be identical or different (e.g., civil, military, private and distressed aircraft at airports).

Queue 'discipline'

The simplest arrangement is FIFO (first in, first out). There is also LIFO (last in, first out, as in items drawn from stock or redundancies in a workforce) or *random*. As an example of the latter case it does not matter how long you have been trying to call the Isle of Wight ferry office, someone dialling for the first time will stand just as much chance of a connection. Then there may be several queues; here customers may change from one to another (*jockey*). Some customers may join a queue and then leave before service (*renege*).

Service Mechanism

There may be one or many servers, who may differ in speed of service. The speed of service at any service point may be constant or random and may vary with the time of day. Servers may be in *parallel* (as in a supermarket) or in *series* (as in a self-service cafeteria).

Capacitation

Some systems have a maximum number of customers that can be contained in the system.

Population

The 'population' from which customers arrive may be infinite (effectively) or finite.

7-3 SIMPLE QUEUES

There is a surprisingly large number of conditions that need to be satisfied for a so-called *simple queue* situation to obtain. Precisely how many depends on how they are grouped together. One list is:

1. Random arrivals and service.
2. Large population of indivisible customers.
3. Single queue, unlimited capacity.
4. FIFO queue discipline, no reneging or balking.
5. Single service point.
6. One at a time service.
7. Average rate of service greater than average rate of arrivals.

There is a standard notation in queueing theory:

$$\lambda = \text{mean rate of arrivals}$$

$$\mu = \text{mean rate of service}$$

When arrivals are purely random the expected number of arrivals ('expected' in a statistical sense) in a 'short' time period is given by the *Poisson* distribution

$$P(n \text{ arrivals in time interval } T) = \frac{(\lambda T)^n e^{-\lambda T}}{n!}$$

For instance, if $\lambda = 0.4$ per second, the probability of three arrivals ($n = 3$) in a two-second interval ($T = 2$) would be

$$P(3 \text{ in } 2) = \frac{(0.8)^3 e^{-0.8}}{6} = 0.03834$$

Tables of Poisson probabilities facilitate this kind of calculation (see Table B, page 271). If arrivals are Poisson the distribution of *time between* arrivals is *negative exponential.* It is written as

$$f(T) = \lambda e^{-\lambda T}$$

$f(T)$ is a density function. The probability of up to T seconds elapsing between arrivals is the proportion of the total area under the curve $f(T)$ that lies between O and T. This calculation requires integration and will not be stressed here.

Much more important are the *system parameters* that can be obtained if a simple queue situation obtains. The most commonly used of these measures are:

Traffic intensity:

$$\rho = \frac{\lambda}{\mu} \tag{7-1}$$

Probability of system containing n customers:

$$P_n = \rho^n(1-\rho) \tag{7-2}$$

Probability that there are *at least* N customers in the system:

$$\rho^N \tag{7-3}$$

Average number of customers in the system:

$$\frac{\lambda}{\mu-\lambda} \tag{7-4}$$

Average length of queue (number of items in queue):

$$\frac{\lambda^2}{\mu(\mu-\lambda)} \tag{7-5}$$

Average length of queue (excluding zero queues):

$$\frac{\mu}{\mu-\lambda} \tag{7-6}$$

Average system process time (ASPT):

$$\frac{1}{\mu-\lambda} \tag{7-7}$$

Average queueing time:

$$\frac{\lambda}{\mu(\mu-\lambda)} \tag{7-8}$$

Average number of customers being served:

$$\frac{\lambda}{\mu} \tag{7-9}$$

The traffic intensity is a measure of use of the system and in a simple queue situation must be less than one. ρ is also the probability of an arrival having to wait. In other words it is the probability that there are one or more customers already in the system. Thus, since the system must be in some *state* (must contain *some* number of customers) $1 - \rho$ is P_0, the probability that there are no customers in the system at any time. All the other states of the system (containing $1, 2, \ldots, n \ldots$ members) are related to P_0 by Eq. (7-2). Equation (7-3) results from the summation from N to ∞ of the P_n in Eq. (7-2).

The most important system parameters are Eqs (7-4)–(7-9) and we shall illustrate the use of these by example.

Example 7-1 On average, cars arrive at a petrol station every 3 minutes. The single attendant is capable of serving on average 30 cars per hour. Service times and inter-arrival times follow a negative exponential distribution.

(i) What is the probability of a car arriving and having to wait for service?

(ii) What is the probability of a car arriving and (the arriver!) finding at least one car already at the petrol station?

(iii) What is the average number of customers at the garage at any moment?

(iv) What is the length of time that a customer (acquainted with all relevant data, armed with a formidable knowledge of queueing theory, fired by insatiable curiosity, and possessed of awesome powers of intellect!) would expect to spend at the garage?

(v) What is the average number of customers in the garage who are not being served?

(vi) The garage proprietor considers that unless customers can expect to be served immediately on arrival 40 per cent of the time, trade will eventually drop off. With the original demand pattern what percentage reduction in service time would be necessary to achieve this result?

ANSWER If, on average, a car arrives every 3 minutes this means an average of 20 per hour; so, choosing an hour as the basic time unit, $\lambda = 20$. Clearly $\mu = 30$. The sentence 'service times and inter-arrival times follow a negative exponential distribution' is a roundabout way of suggesting that simple queue conditions prevail, i.e., we can use the formulae. So:

(i) This is $\rho = \dfrac{\lambda}{\mu} = \dfrac{20}{30} = \dfrac{2}{3}$.

(ii) This is also $\rho = \dfrac{2}{3}$.

(iii) This is $\dfrac{\lambda}{\mu-\lambda} = 2$. Note that 'in the system' means in the queue or being served.

(iv) This is the average system process time perhaps the most important of all parameters,

$$\frac{1}{\mu-\lambda} = \frac{1}{10} \text{ hour or } \underline{6 \text{ minutes}}$$

(v) Assuming that there are no general hangers-on this means that the average number in the queue... $\dfrac{\lambda^2}{\mu(\mu-\lambda)} = 4/3$. Note, if we had considered only those times when a queue actually existed, the average length would be $\dfrac{\lambda}{\mu-\lambda} = 3$.

(vi) The reduction in service time must be such as to produce $P_0 = 0.4$. A person will be served immediately only if there is no one already there. Thus $P_0 = 1-\rho = 0.4$ so that $\rho = 0.6$. With a given arrival rate of $\lambda = 20$ we therefore require that $\dfrac{20}{\mu} = 0.6$ so that $\mu = 33\tfrac{1}{3}$.

This value of μ implies a service time of $\dfrac{1}{33\tfrac{1}{3}} \times 60$ minutes $= 1.8$ minutes which is a 10 per cent reduction on the original time.

Example 7-2 Customers arrive in a shop at the average rate of 42 per hour. The shopkeeper takes on average one minute to serve each customer. Simple queue conditions prevail.

(i) What proportion of his time does the shopkeeper spend serving customers?
(ii) What is the average queueing time for customers?
(iii) What is the probability that:
    (a) There are three customers in the shop?
    (b) There is one customer queueing?
    (c) There are four or more customers in the shop?
    (d) There are three or fewer customers in the shop?

ANSWER We note that $\lambda = 42$ and $\mu = 60$ (both per hour).
(i) This is the proportion of the time when there are one or more customers in the system. It is $P_1 + P_2 + P_3 + \cdots + P_\infty$. More conveniently this is $1 - P_0$, in fact it is ρ itself, the traffic intensity or the average number of customers being served. Thus the answer is

$$\rho = \frac{42}{60} = 0.7.$$

(ii) This is $\dfrac{\lambda}{\mu(\mu-\lambda)} = \dfrac{42}{60(60-42)}$ hours $= \dfrac{7}{180}$ hours $= 2\frac{1}{3}$ minutes.

(iii) (a) We shall assume here that 'being in the shop' means being in the system. The two concepts are not in fact identical. The 'system' is the queue plus the service point. Browsing in the shop is not strictly being 'in the system' but, putting this possibility aside:

$$P_3 = (1-0.7)(0.7)^3 = 0.1029$$

(b) If one customer is queueing this must mean that one is being served so that there are two in the system. Thus

$$P_2 = (1-0.7)(0.7)^2 = 0.147$$

(c) Here we have simply:

$$P(4 \text{ or more}) = \rho^4 = (0.7)^4 = 0.2401$$

(d) To simplify workings we note that 'three or less' and 'four or more' cover all possibilities so that:

$$P(3 \text{ or less}) = 1 - P(4 \text{ or more})$$
$$= 1 - 0.2401 = 0.7599$$

Example 7-3 A coin operated telephone is installed in a staff canteen. At present, on average eight people per hour use the telephone and the average call length is three minutes. The staff association want another instrument installed but the GPO will only do this if staff on average must expect to wait three minutes or more to use the phone. Determine the percentage increase in demand necessary to produce this result.

ANSWER We note that $\lambda = 8$. Clearly the 'service time' is the length of call so that with an average call length of three minutes, $\mu = 20$ per hour. Expected queueing time is given by $\lambda/\mu(\mu-\lambda)$ and with $\mu = 20$, queueing time is $\lambda/20(20-\lambda)$ and we require this to equal $1/20$ hour. Thus solving for λ

$$\frac{\lambda}{20(20-\lambda)} = \frac{1}{20} \qquad \therefore \quad 20\lambda = 400 - 20\lambda$$

$$40\lambda = 400$$

$$\lambda = 10$$

So that a 25 per cent increase in demand (measured by rate of arrivals) would be needed.

Example 7-4 A toll road is approached by a single line of traffic arriving Poisson fashion. There is one toll booth which on average takes six

Table 7-1

λ	5	6	7	8	9	9.5	9.7	9.9	9.99
$\rho = \dfrac{\lambda}{\mu}$	0.5	0.6	0.7	0.8	0.9	0.95	0.97	0.99	0.999
Q_t	0.1	0.15	$0.2\overline{33}$	0.4	0.9	1.9	$3.2\overline{33}$	9.9	99.9
Q_1	0.5	0.9	$1.6\overline{33}$	3.2	8.1	18.05	$31.36\overline{33}$	98.01	998

seconds to deal with each car. By taking various values of the mean arrival rate show how the queue length increases disproportionately as the traffic intensity rises.

ANSWER Clearly, $\mu = 10$ per minute. Using this value Table 7-1 shows the results for values of λ ranging from 5 to 9.99. The second row gives λ/μ, the traffic intensity, Q_t is the expected queueing time and Q_1 stands for the expected length of queue, all times considered.

It is evident from Table 7-1 that as traffic intensity rises there is always a larger proportionate increase in both Q_t and Q_1. Even for $\rho = 0.5$ a 20 per cent increase in traffic intensity to $\rho = 0.6$ produces a 50 per cent rise in Q_t and an 80 per cent rise in Q_1. If we take a 20 per cent increase of ρ from 8 to 9.6 the resulting Q time goes up from 0.4 minutes to 2.4 minutes, an increase of no less than 500 per cent while Q length rises by 620 per cent. Now while queue length depends only on the traffic intensity (why?) the queueing *time* depends also on the absolute value of λ. In Table 7-2 both λ and μ have been doubled. This leaves queue lengths unaffected but halves the queueing time (why?). However, it must be pointed out that as traffic intensity approaches one there is an increasing *variance* in both queue length and time.

The graph of queue length against traffic intensity gives a vivid impression of the results. In Fig. 7-1 the vertical scale has been compressed (try drawing the figure yourself) for convenience. As $\rho \to 1$ queue length 'takes off'. Above, say, $\rho = 0.7$ the effect is most marked; small increases in traffic intensity producing huge increases in queue length. You may have noticed this effect yourself on winter mornings. Only a slight deterioration in

Table 7-2

λ	10	12	14	16	18	19	19.4	19.8	19.98	
ρ	0.5	0.6	0.7	0.8	0.9	0.95	0.97	0.99	0.999	$\mu = 20$
Q_t	0.05	0.075	$0.11\overline{66}$	0.2	0.45	0.95	$1.61\overline{66}$	4.95	49.95	
Q_1	0.5	0.9	$1.6\overline{33}$	3.2	8.1	18.05	$31.36\overline{33}$	98.01	998	

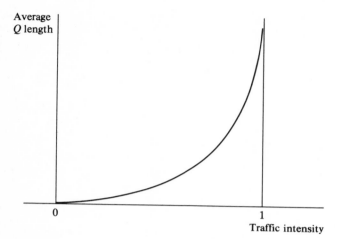

Figure 7-1

road conditions seems to cause huge traffic jams. This is because (although it is not of course a simple queue problem) the 'traffic intensity' is high. It only takes a slight slowing down (reduction in μ) to give a slight increase in intensity which causes huge increases in queues.

7-4 MULTIPLE SERVICE CHANNELS

There are many ways in which the rigid conditions of a simple queue can be relaxed. One of these concerns the number of service points that are operated. We shall now consider the consequences of having several service points instead of one. It will be assumed that these service points are approached by *one queue only*—the customer at the head of the queue going to the next service point or server that becomes free. This kind of arrangement is often seen at parts counters and discount stores and in some banks, but not apparently in post offices, most banks, or vehicle licensing departments! We shall see later on that a single queue gives the best theoretical performance (this is why we consider it first of all) and we shall endeavour to explain why multiple queues are nevertheless also commonly observed.

First, the single queue, multi-server case. We shall assume there are no other changes from the simple queue situation and the distribution of service time at each point is (the same) negative exponential distribution. Some new formulae will be required here. Actually, the ones used so far are special cases of the more general results. It is somewhat more convenient to write these formulae in terms of ρ. The main results, with c identical service points, are:

probability of a customer having to wait for service

$$= \frac{(\rho c)^c}{c!(1-\rho)} P_0 \tag{7-10}$$

average number of customers in the system

$$= \frac{\rho(\rho c)^c}{c!(1-\rho)^2} P_0 + \rho c \tag{7-11}$$

average number of customers in the queue

$$= \frac{\rho(\rho c)^c}{c!(1-\rho)^2} P_0 \tag{7-12}$$

average time a customer is in the system

$$= \frac{(\rho c)^c}{c!(1-\rho)^2 c\mu} P_0 + \frac{1}{\mu} \tag{7-13}$$

average time a customer is in the queue

$$= \frac{(\rho c)^c}{c!(1-\rho)^2 c\mu} P_0 \tag{7-14}$$

in which

$$P_0 = \frac{c!(1-\rho)}{(\rho c)^c + c!(1-\rho)\left\{ \sum_{n=0}^{c-1} \frac{1}{n!} (\rho c)^n \right\}} \tag{7-15}$$

and where, most importantly, it should be noted that

$$\rho = \frac{\lambda}{c\mu} \tag{7-16}$$

This all looks very forbidding, but it is not really so. Nothing worse than division and multiplication is needed to use these expressions. Note that ρ is defined as λ over $c\mu$. We see that our original ρ was a special case where $c = 1$. All of the formulae involve P_0 which is the probability that there are no customers in the system. Equation (7-10) is the probability that there are c *or more* customers in the system (i.e., all the service points are occupied). This is the only circumstance in which waiting is necessary. It is usually best to begin any workings by calculating P_0 and to minimize rounding error it is best to leave things in fractional form until the very end. This will be done in the examples to follow.

Example 7-5 A bank has arranged its services so that customers requiring cash only are served from any one of 3 service points, there being one queue only. The average rate of arrivals is 72 per hour. Each cashier takes on average 2 minutes to serve a customer. The bank is considering the installation of an automatic cash machine which, although it would mean only one service point would take on average only 40 seconds to serve each customer. Which system produces the lesser average system process time?

ANSWER We observe that $\lambda = 72$ and $\mu = 30$ at each service point. Thus

$$\rho = \frac{\lambda}{c\mu} = \frac{72}{3(30)} = 0.8$$

Now find P_0. Spelt out in full it is

$$P_0 = \frac{3 \times 2 \times 1(1 - 0.8)}{(0.8 \times 3)^3 + 3 \times 2 \times 1(1 - 0.8)\left[\frac{1}{1}(2.4)^0 + \frac{1}{1}(2.4)^1 + \frac{1}{2}(2.4)^2\right]}$$

Thus

$$P_0 = \frac{1.2}{21.36}$$

Notice that in the summation in the denominator $0! = 1$. This 'result' is by no means obvious but it is the standard convention and gives correct results. Now on to the system process time itself:

$$\text{ASPT} = \frac{13.824}{6(0.2)^2 90} \times \frac{1.2}{21.36} + \frac{1}{30} \text{ hours}$$

$$= \frac{16.5888}{461.376} + \frac{1}{30}$$

$$= 0.069288 \text{ hours or } 4 \text{ minutes } 9 \text{ seconds}$$

Before pressing on let us ascertain the probability of a customer having to wait for service—this will make for an interesting comparison later on. Thus using Eq. (7-10)

$$P(n \geqslant c) = \frac{13.824}{1.2} \times \frac{1.2}{21.36} = 0.6472$$

Now consider the proposed new arrangement. This is a simple queue situation with $\lambda = 72$ as before but with $\mu = 90$. We could use the new formulae with $c = 1$ but it is much simpler to remember that

$$\text{ASPT} = \frac{1}{\mu - \lambda} = \frac{1}{90 - 72} \text{ hours} = 3 \text{ minutes } 20 \text{ seconds}$$

So that the new arrangement is preferable. But in the new circumstances the probability of having to wait $= \rho = 0.8$ which is *greater*. Under the old arrangements there was more chance of a customer

Table 7-3

	Cashiers	Machine
Probability of having to wait	0.6472	0.8
Average number in the system	4.99	4
Average number in the queue	2.59	3.2
Average system process time	4′ 9″	3′ 20″
Average queueing time	2′ 9″	2′ 40″

getting served right away. Table 7-3 gives a more extensive comparison between the two arrangements.

Perhaps the comparison is not so clear-cut as it first appeared, especially so as we are not considering the 'personal factor' and the fact that queueing time may be psychologically more significant than overall process time. These factors should be borne in mind in the practical situation.

In this problem we contrasted the performance of three service points and one queue with one queue and one service point working three times as fast. Another possibility would be to have three service points each with its own separate queue. To evaluate this last arrangement start by assuming no jockeying, no reneging, and no balking with random arrivals at the rate of $\lambda/3$ into each queue. We specifically assume that the rate of arrivals into each queue is *not state dependent*, viz., that a new arrival is equally likely to join any of the queues regardless of their relative lengths. This being the case we have the arrangement:

$$\lambda = 24 \quad \boxed{\mu = 30}$$
$$\lambda = 24 \quad \boxed{\mu = 30}$$
$$\lambda = 24 \quad \boxed{\mu = 30}$$

Clearly, for each of these three simple queue situations

$$\text{ASPT} = \frac{1}{30-24} = \frac{1}{6} \text{hour} = 10 \text{ minutes}$$

which is by far the worst performance of the three arrangements. The following ordering (by ASPT) is generally true:

1. Single queue single server operating at rate $n\mu$.
2. Single queue n servers operating at rate μ.
3. n queues n servers operating at rate μ.

Why then is the third system, apparently the worst, commonly observed in such places as post offices and banks? Of course there may be plain inefficiency or carelessness or the servers may, in fact, perform different functions (or some other of our simple queue assumptions may be violated). But an important factor is that our arrival and queue discipline assumptions are too severe. In practice people join the shortest queue and jockeying is allowed. This brings the performance of the multi-queue arrangement much closer to the single-queue result with the added bonus of not having a huge queue snaking round the service area!

7-5 OPTIMIZATION OF QUEUEING SYSTEMS

In Example 7-5 we compared two systems on the basis of physical and temporal characteristics. We saw that altering the arrangements altered the system parameters. There are many ways (other than a change in the number of servers) of affecting system performance. On the service side it may (at a price) be possible to speed up service, for example, by providing change-making machines for cashiers or by motion study of the operations involved. On the arrivals side a frequently encountered problem is one of 'peak-loading'—uneven demand during the day (or week or year). The post office, for example, attempts to smooth out demand for telephone services by differential charges ('phone your friends when they're out—it's cheaper') and British Rail operates a system of 'off-peak' fares. An alternative possibility is to regulate demand by an appointments system. However, care must be exercised here for although *visible* queues may be reduced, there may be hidden queues (e.g., sick people waiting at home for appointments with a general practitioner). Monopolistic providers of services find it easier directly to regulate demand than do those in competitive industry where regulation by price is more common.

Even the simplest queueing system is so complex that it is rarely possible to optimize—to obtain ideal performance. Usually we have to be satisfied with good performance from a limited range of alternatives rather than the unobtainable optimum. The next two examples bring money into the picture to help to accomplish this.

Example 7-6 The average rate of arrivals at a self-service store is 30 per hour. At present there is one cashier who on average can attend to 45 customers per hour. The store proprietor estimates that each extra minute of system process time per customer means the loss of £0.05 profit. An assistant can be provided for the cashier (to weigh and wrap goods, etc.) and in these circumstances the service point can deal with 75 people per hour on average. The wage rate of the assistant would be £1.50 per hour. Is it worth taking on the assistant?

ANSWER $\lambda = 30$, $\mu = 45$ thus the average system process time originally is: $1/(\mu - \lambda) = 1/15$ hour per customer so that *per customer* there is an opportunity loss of £1/15 × 60 × 0.05 = £0.20; but there are thirty customers per hour to consider so that the store's lost profit per hour is £0.20 × 30 = £6 per hour with the original arrangement. With the assistant provided, ASPT = $1/(75 - 30) = 1/45$ hour per customer so that the opportunity loss per hour is $1/45 × 60 × 0.05 × 30 = £2$, a reduction of £4 on the original figure. If we now deduct the assistant's wages there is a net saving of £2.50 per hour so that it is definitely worth while having the assistant.

The question arises as to where the £0.05 per minute cost comes from. Such figures (rather like the shortage loss in stock control) are notoriously difficult to assess. In such cases it is advisable to conduct a sensitivity analysis on the result. What is the least value of the lost profit per minute for which the assistant would be worth while? This is L such that:

$$\frac{1}{45} \times 60 \times L \times 30 + 1.5 \leqslant \frac{1}{15} \times 60 \times L \times 30$$

i.e.,

$$40L + 1.5 \leqslant 120L$$
$$\therefore \quad 80L \geqslant 150\text{p}$$
$$L \geqslant 1.875\text{p}$$

It may be that while the manager was by no means sure that 5p per minute was the correct figure he may be well satisfied that it is in excess of the required minimum of 1.875p.

Example 7-7 The manager of a discount store is concerned about the delays that customers experience in the simple queue situation at the service counter. At present the average system process time is 6 minutes and the average queueing time is $4\frac{1}{2}$ minutes. The manager estimates that each minute of system process time saved per customer would increase profit by 10p (not counting the cost of effecting the reduction). There are four possible ways of speeding things up. These are:

1. Increase the mean rate of service of the one attendant to 60 customers per hour on average. It would cost an extra £1.50 per hour to do this.
2. Have two attendants, working in parallel, each providing a mean rate of service of 50 customers per hour. There would still be one queue only and the extra cost of this arrangement would be £3 per hour.
3. Have two queues, each to its own server, with each server operating at the original service rate. The additional cost of this arrangement would be £2 per hour.

4. Split the payments procedure into two stages and have one queue with two servers in series, each server being able to process an average of 80 customers per hour. It would cost an extra £4 per hour to do this.

(i) Which of the arrangements is to be preferred?
(ii) Suppose that capital expenditure was required, in a differing amount in each case, to effect the arrangements above. Briefly explain how a selection between the alternatives could be made in the circumstances.

ANSWER We are not given λ and μ explicitly but they are implied by the original system parameters:

$$\text{ASPT} = \frac{1}{\mu - \lambda} = \frac{1}{10}; \qquad \frac{\lambda}{\mu(\mu - \lambda)} = \frac{3}{40}$$

From ASPT $\mu = \lambda + 10$ and substituting into the queueing time gives:

$$\frac{\lambda}{(\lambda + 10)10} = \frac{3}{10} \qquad \therefore \quad 40\lambda = 300 + 30$$

$$\therefore \quad 10\lambda = 300$$

$$\therefore \quad \lambda = 30, \mu = 40$$

The lost profit due to system process time is £6 per hour per customer. Thus originally this lost profit amounted to

$$\frac{1}{10} \times 6 \times 30 = \text{£18 per hour}$$

1. Here μ becomes 60 so the lost profit is:

$$\frac{1}{60 - 30} \times 6 \times 30 = \text{£6}$$

giving a gross saving of £12 and a net saving of

$$\text{£12} - \text{£1.50} = \boxed{\text{£10.50}}$$

2. In this case $\lambda = 30, \mu = 50, c = 2$,

$$\therefore \quad \rho = \frac{\lambda}{c\mu} = 0.3$$

So that

$$P_0 = \frac{2(0.7)}{(0.6)^2 + 2(0.7)(1 + 0.6)} = \frac{1.4}{2.6}$$

So

$$\text{ASPT} = \frac{(0.6)^2}{2(0.7)^2 100} \times \frac{1.4}{2.6} + \frac{1}{50} = 0.021978 \text{ hours}$$

Lost profit therefore equals £0.021978(6)(30) = £3.96; so that there is a gross saving of £18 − £3.96 = £14.04 and a net saving of

$$£14.04 - £3 = \boxed{£11.04}.$$

3. Here we must assume something about the arrival pattern. The simplest thing is to assume that the arrival rate into each queue averages $\lambda/2 = 15$. So

$$\text{ASPT} = \frac{1}{40-15} = \frac{1}{25} \text{ hour}$$

giving a gross saving of £10.80 and a net saving of $\boxed{£8.80}$.

4. Here the arrangement is:

$$\lambda = 30 \quad \boxed{\mu = 80} \quad \lambda = 30 \quad \boxed{\mu = 80}$$

in which we assume no interference between the queues and note that the rate of output from the first stage is equal to the rate of arrivals (none leaves the system at this point). In this sort of arrangement

$$\text{ASPT} = 2\left(\frac{1}{\mu - \lambda}\right) = 2\left(\frac{1}{80-30}\right) = 0.04 \text{ hours}$$

giving a gross saving of £10.80 and a net saving of $\boxed{£6.80}$.

  (i) So the preferred arrangement will be (2) with two service points in parallel producing a net saving of £11.04 per hour.

  (ii) The problem now becomes a capital budgeting problem. The returns on the capital expenditures are the annual savings achieved. Thus assuming a 54-hour week (the norm for shops) and a 51-week year the *annual* saving under system (2) is £54 × 51 × 11.08 = £30 514. If there is a capital cost of K_2 needed to implement the system and a cost of capital of $100r$ per cent with a lifetime of n years the net present value of the type (2) arrangement (NPV_2) would be given by:

$$\text{NPV}_2 = \sum_{t=1}^{n} \frac{30\,514}{(1+r)^t} - K_2$$

This would be worked out for the given values of K_2 and r, with a similar calculation being performed for the other arrangements. Whichever gave the greatest NPV would be preferred.

7-6 MORE ADVANCED MODELS

There is a vast number of different queueing models, each with its own formulae and results. They are generally beyond the scope of this syllabus. A useful (but incomplete) review is found in Murdoch (1978). Some of the main variations are:

1. Capacitated systems—with limits on the numbers allowed in the queue.
2. Different service time distribution, for example, the Erlang (Gamma) distribution or indeed an arbitrary distribution.
3. Queues in networks (of which the split procedures case of Example (7-7) was the simplest possible case).
4. Transient situations (what happens if a system never has time to settle down).
5. Priority systems (different classes of customers, as in computer usage).

We will take one point only from all these possibilities. If service time is given by the Erlang distribution (a generalization of the negative exponential distribution) a limiting case of this is where service time is *fixed*. In the case of random (Poisson) arrivals and a *fixed* service time of $1/\mu$ then queueing time is halved to $\lambda/2\mu(\mu - \lambda)$ and the average length of queue is similarly halved. The average number in the system is then the average number in the queue plus λ/μ and ASPT is the average queueing time plus the fixed service time of $1/\mu$. The doubling of queue time and length in the random service time case gives a good illustration of the 'price' of variability: it is high.

7-7 CONCLUSIONS

Queueing problems in practice can be enormously complex. Analytical solutions may be impossible and if experimentation in the real situation is ruled out then the only scientific alternative is simulation. A simulation exercise in queueing theory is given in Chapter 10. In those cases where the analytical methods can be used they are extremely valuable. In any case a study of the analytical methods helps to develop 'feel' for the problem. As Murdoch points out, manufacturing industry has paid far too little attention to the 'service units' while time has been lavished on production problems. Some of the production manager's rules of thumb concerning equipment utilization are quite inappropriate in a service context. Finally, to quote Murdoch:

> The basic concepts and an understanding of modern queueing theory are requirements not only in the training of operational research staff, management scientists, etc., but also as fundamental concepts in the training of managers or in management development

programmes. The efficient design and operation of service functions is one of the main problems facing management today and the understanding obtained from a study of queueing theory is essential in the solution of these problems.

EXERCISES

7-1 Discuss the view that queueing theory is concerned with the study of *delay* whether or not an actual queue is observed. Illustrate your answer with examples.

7-2 Give some examples of the differing character of arrival patterns, queue disciplines, and service mechanisms. What other factors distinguish types of queueing system?

7-3 State the conditions that are necessary for a simple queue system. What are the most important system parameters in this case?

7-4 The number of people arriving into a particular queueing system in a 'short' time interval is described by a Poisson distribution with mean 0.4 per minute. Use Table B to obtain the following information:

    (i) The probabilities of no, one, and two customers arriving in any one-minute interval.
    (ii) The probability that more than one customer arrives in any one-minute interval.
    (iii) The probability that less than two customers arrive in any one-minute interval.
    (iv) The probability that two or three customers arrive in any one-minute interval.
    (v) The probability that two customers arrive in any *three*-minute interval.

7-5 Telephone calls arrive at a switchboard once every three minutes. The average call lasts two minutes.

    (i) Find the average system process time.
    (ii) Find the average queueing time.
    (iii) Suppose there is a 10 per cent increase in 'demand'. What per cent increase in expected queueing time does this produce?

7-6 The manager of a parts counter is comparing four possible queueing arrangements as shown below:

(i) $\lambda = 70$, $\boxed{\mu = 100}$

(ii) $\lambda = 70$ → $\boxed{\mu = 50}$, $\boxed{\mu = 50}$

(iii) $\lambda = 35$, $\boxed{\mu = 50}$
$\lambda = 35$, $\boxed{\mu = 50}$

(iv) $\lambda = 70$, $\boxed{\mu = 200}$ $\lambda = 70$, $\boxed{\mu = 200}$

In each case $\boxed{}$ indicates a service point and λ = mean rate of arrivals per hour (Poisson distribution) and μ = mean service rate per hour (service time negative exponential distribution). Except for the structural differences shown in (i), (iii), and (iv) assume that simple queue characteristics obtain. For each case calculate the expected system process time in minutes and, making clear any necessary assumptions, the probability of having to wait.

7-7 A discount house at present has two service points. Customers form one queue and apart from the number of servers simple queue conditions obtain. The manager reckons that the hourly sales revenue (R) is

$$R = \bar{R} - 10p$$

where $\bar{R}$ is a constant and p is the probability of customers having to wait for service. The mean rate of arrivals is fixed at $\lambda = 180$ and all servers operate at the rate of $\mu = 100$. The manager is thinking of increasing the number of servers to three or four. To use three servers would increase hourly variable costs by £3.80. To use four servers would raise hourly variable costs by £6.00. In addition the capital cost of providing one more server than at present would be £3000 and two more servers would require capital expenditure of £6000. The cost of capital is 10 per cent and the new arrangements can be assumed to last indefinitely. The working week is 55 hours and there is a 50-week working year. What decision should be taken?

7-8 Cronus Ltd operates an engineering factory with a very large number of employees. Each employee has to make frequent visits to the firm's stores to obtain issues of materials for his next job. The issue of one type of material is made in Section D at a counter attended by an employee of the stores section. Employees who require issues have to join a single queue and wait until the attendant is available. The average rate of arrival in the stores is 16 per hour and the average rate of service is 20 per hour.

Issues of materials are costed at the cost of materials plus 5 per cent to cover the overhead costs of storage. The overhead costs of storage in Section D include £3000 per annum for wages of the attendant at the issues counter and £600 per annum attributed to the attendant for fixed establishment costs—rent, rates, light and heat, and so on—of the service area. Average wages of directly productive employees who visit Section D are £1.60 per hour. The length of the firm's normal working year is 2000 hours.

The directors of Cronus are considering the desirability of employing an extra man as an attendant at the stores issue counter. His wages and efficiency would be the same as for the existing attendant. It would be necessary to spend £2000 on capital equipment having a life of 10 years. Any savings of the waiting time of directly productive employees would make it possible to reduce the amount of labour time for which the firm pays. The cost of capital of Cronus is 15 per cent per annum.

You may assume that arrivals in and departures from the issues section are described by Poisson distributions and that the number of employees is indefinitely large. A table of standard formulae is available.

You are required to:

(a) prepare calculations to show whether the additional attendant should be employed, and

(b) explain a technique of analysis which could be used to study the problem when Poisson distributions and simple queue discipline may not be assumed.

(Institute of Chartered Accountants in England and Wales, Professional Examination: II, Elements of Financial Decisions, December 1976.)

7-9 'There are two distinct approaches to problems arising from queueing situations. The more popular is simulation, but the formulae of queueing theory are equally useful. In fact the choice of method is largely a matter of personal taste'.

Required:

Discuss and criticize this quotation. Your answer should include the following:

(a) an example of a problem to which queueing theory might be applied;

(b) an example of a problem for which simulation is the more appropriate method;

(c) an assessment of the relative strengths and weaknesses of each method.

(Association of Certified Accountants, Professional Examination: Section 2, paper 12, Management Mathematics, June 1976.)

7-10 At the present time a servicing department provides answers through one channel, which on average can deal with 24 enquiries per hour at a cost of £3 per enquiry. Increasingly the customers are complaining that they have to wait for a long time and the department is considering alternative arrangements. These are either a two-service channel system costing £100 per hour and service rate of 15 per hour in each, or a three-service channel system costing £125 per hour and a service rate of 10 per hour in each. Customers arrive at the rate of 20 per hour.

Average time a customer is in this system $= \dfrac{(\rho c)^c}{c!(1-\rho)^2 c\mu} P_0 + \dfrac{1}{\mu}$

$$P_0 = \dfrac{c!(1-\rho)}{(\rho c)^c + c!(1-\rho)\left\{\sum_{n=0}^{c-1} \dfrac{1}{n!}(\rho c)^n\right\}}$$

You are required to calculate:

(a) the average time a customer is in the system under the present arrangement;

(b) the extra charges per enquiry that would need to be made to recover the extra cost of each of the two arrangements proposed;

(c) the implied value of customers' time per hour if they agreed to pay the extra costs of the two channel system.

(Institute of Cost and Management Accountants, Professional Stage: Part I, Quantitative Techniques, November 1977.)

7-11 Your company is considering changing the present system of serving customers who arrive in person and wait for service. The existing single service channel can service ten people an hour at a variable cost of £8 per person. The service facilities have a fixed cost of £50 per hour. The demand for these services has increased from 4 persons per hour when first offered, to the current 8 per hour and is expected to increase to 15 per hour next year.

Alternative service patterns have been considered. Either a larger single service channel that would be able to service 20 people an hour at a variable cost of £7 per person and fixed costs of £120 per hour, or the addition of another single service channel which would still have a variable cost of £8 per person but additional fixed costs of £60 per hour. Customer time has been estimated to have a value of £25 per hour. [Formula provided with examination question.]

You are required to:

(a) calculate the cost to the company of the optimum service system, ignoring customers' time, currently and next year;

(b) calculate the cost in each system to the customer next year;

(c) state which system the company should choose next year if it takes into account half the value of customers' time.

(Institute of Cost and Management Accountants, Professional Stage: Part I, Quantitative Techniques, May 1978.)

EIGHT
STATISTICAL REPLACEMENT METHODS

8-1 INTRODUCTION

Machinery and industrial equipment do not last forever, nor are they likely to be 100 per cent reliable. There are cases where there is a pattern of deterioration that is well understood and predictable—for instance, tyre wear on cars or the ribbons on typewriters—so that the approximate time of failure, or reaching a minimal level of serviceability can be forecast. These situations give us one class of replacement problems.

There is another class of problems in which failure is sudden (i.e., not gradual) and is not predictable at the level of the individual item. It is these problems that will form the substance of the discussion here. A household item such as an electric light bulb is an example of this. Items which either work properly or not at all with no intermediate level of operation generally fall into this category. Thus they tend not to signal impending failure by a change in the character of their performance.

We shall examine those problems in which there is a large number of items of a certain type and where failures cannot be allowed to stand in a failed state for very long. This may be because the efficient functioning of the whole system can tolerate only a few 'down machines' or because a prior decision has been taken to provide a high 'level of service'. Speedy replacement may be virtually forced by competitive considerations—for instance, the replacement of faulty customer television sets by a rental company. As we shall see, the method described applies not only to mechanical items but it is also useful in consideration of staffing and personnel problems.

8-2 FAILURE AND SURVIVAL PROBABILITIES

The level of service specified here will be 'pseudo' 100 per cent (the reason for the qualification will become apparent). This given, the problem is then to select a *least cost replacement policy*. Policies are distinguished according to how frequently (if ever) wholesale replacements of all items are made. For instance, how frequently should light bulbs in a building be replaced *in toto*, failed or not. The more often such *preventative* replacements are made the less frequently will relatively costly individual replacements be necessary.

We shall need to know failure and survival probabilities for the items. Although the time of failure is unpredictable for an individual item, failure statistics for large groups are likely to be stable. Failure data may be obtained from past experience, from suppliers, or by the testing of a random sample.

Consider an example. A firm's building contains 150 electric light bulbs. Failure data are as follows:

Table 8-1

Average nos failing (n_t)	Months from installation (t)
0	0
15	1
45	2
60	3
30	4
$\Sigma n_t = n = 150$	

In Table 8-1 the simplifying assumption is made that the bulbs fail at the *end* of the monthly intervals. Equivalently we can assume that any failures during a month are allowed to stand until the month's end, when replacement is made. This is the reason for the 'pseudo' 100 per cent service level. It is a 100 per cent service in so far as *all* failures are attended to at the month's end.

From Table 8-1, the probabilities of failure of an individual light bulb at different times, f_t, are ascertained empirically as:

$$f_t = \frac{n_t}{\Sigma n_t}$$

From Table 8-2 probabilities of *survival* can be obtained. S_t = probability that an individual bulb is still working at the end of month t.

Table 8-2

Time	Probability of failure
0	$0.0 = f_0$
1	$0.1 = f_1$
2	$0.3 = f_2$
3	$0.4 = f_3$
4	$0.2 = f_4$
	$\Sigma f_t = 1.0$

Table 8-3

Time	Survival probability
0	$1.0 = S_0$
1	$0.9 = S_1$
2	$0.6 = S_2$
3	$0.2 = S_3$
4	$0.0 = S_4$

If an individual bulb is still working at the end of month t then it must be the case that failure occurs later on. Thus

$$S_t = \sum_{h=t+1}^{4} f_h$$

For instance: $S_1 = f_2 + f_3 + f_4 = 0.3 + 0.4 + 0.2 = 0.9$. Alternatively, we can calculate survival probability at time t as one minus the chance that failure occurs *at or before* time t. Namely,

$$S_t = 1 - \sum_{h=0}^{t} f_h$$

So that for example $S_1 = 1 - (f_0 + f_1) = 1 - (0 + 0.1) = 0.9$.

8-3 FAILURE TREES

The *expected number of failures* at given times can be obtained from the data above. One way to do this is by the use of a *failure tree*. A failure tree is not a diseased elm but an example of a type of network that arises frequently in the analysis of problems that have many stages. In general terms a tree is a network without any loops in it. For instance, Fig. 8-1(a) represents a tree while Fig. 8-1(b) does not.

The failure tree for the light bulb data can be begun as shown in Fig. 8-2. Starting with a completely fresh installation of 150 bulbs at $t = 0$ the number

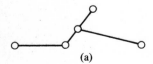

(a)

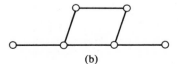

(b)

Figure 8-1

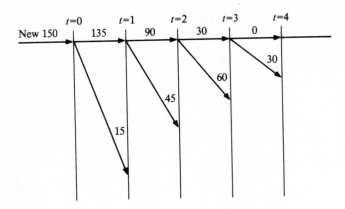

Figure 8-2

surviving at $t = 1$ is 150(0.9) = 135. This number is shown on the *horizontal* line from $t = 0$. The number failing at $t = 1$ is expected to be 150(0.1) = 15. This figure is entered on a *diagonal* line from $t = 0$. In each case the numbers are 'expected'—what would happen on average—and are the original numbers installed at $t = 0$ multiplied by the survival and failure probabilities (for one month) respectively. Continuing with the history of the original 150 produces 90 surviving at $t = 2$ (= 150(0.6)) and 45 failing at $t = 2$ (= 150(0.3)). Obviously the total number both failing and surviving at $t = 2$ must equal the number that were surviving at $t = 1$. Thus $90 + 45 = 135$. The picture is continued in a similar fashion until $t = 4$ at which time all 150 have failed.

Now consider the replacements that will have been necessary up to

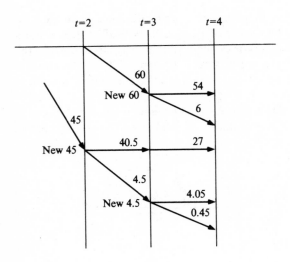

Figure 8-3

$t = 4$. Consider the 60 that failed at $t = 3$. With the pseudo 100 per cent service level assumed, these must be replaced at $t = 3$. Of these 60 the number still working after one month (i.e., at $t = 4$) is expected to be $60(0.9) = 54$ and the number that fail is, on average, $60(0.1) = 6$. Now what of the 45 that failed at $t = 2$. Of these 45, there will be $45(0.9) = 40.5$ surviving at $t = 3$ and $45(0.6) = 27$ surviving two months later at time $t = 5$. But of this 45 there is an expected number $45(0.1) = 4.5$ failures after one month at $t = 3$. These 4.5 need replacing. Of these 4.5 replacements made at $t = 3$ $4.05 = 4.5(0.9)$ will be working at $t = 4$ and $0.45 = 4.5(0.1)$ will be failed at $t = 4$. These decimal values are perfectly sensible as we are dealing with *averages* throughout. This history of the replacements needed at $t = 2$ and $t = 3$ is shown in Fig. 8-3. Of course the 15 failures at $t = 1$ of the

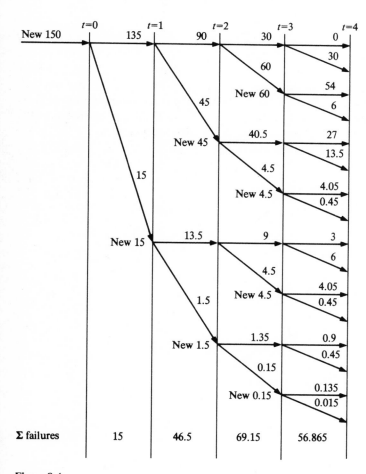

Figure 8-4

original 150 must be replaced and further branches will emanate from this point. The treatment is identical to that already described and the full picture is shown in Fig. 8-4.

From the complete tree of Fig. 8-4 can be obtained the expected number of failures, F_t (and therefore replacements necessary) at each point in time. Using the tree, F_t will be the sum of numbers on diagonal lines in month t. These values are shown at the bottom of each column in the figure. Of course the number surviving at time t, S_t, $= 150 - F_t$. If the tree was continued for long enough the expected number of failures in any month will approach the *mean number of failures* ($\bar{F}$), viz., $F_t \rightarrow \bar{F}$ as $t \rightarrow \infty$. This convergence is of an oscillatory nature and settles down quite quickly as will be illustrated later on. From $t = 9$ variations in F_t from period to period are within 1 per cent of $\bar{F}$. However, $\bar{F}$ may be calculated directly. If $\bar{x}$ is the *mean life* of a bulb then the mean number of failures is given by

$$\bar{F} = \frac{n}{\bar{x}}$$

For example, if the bulbs had a mean life of two months ($\bar{x} = 2$) then $\bar{F} = 150/2 = 75$. The mean rate of failures would be 75 per month. Sometimes it is clearer to see a relationship if the terms are rearranged. Thus $\bar{x} = n/\bar{F}$. So that if, on average, there were $\bar{F} = 50$ failures per month, this would correspond to a mean life of three months. In such a case

$$\bar{x} = \frac{150}{50} = 3$$

The mean life itself is found by the usual procedure for calculating the arithmetic mean of a discrete probability distribution, viz.

Life in months (x)	Probability (f_t)	xf_t
0	0	0
1	0.1	0.1
2	0.3	0.6
3	0.4	1.2
4	0.2	0.8
	$\bar{x} = \Sigma xf_t = 2.7$	

Thus the mean number of failures per month is obtained as

$$\bar{F} = \frac{150}{2.7} = 55.\overline{55}$$

We are now in a position to evaluate the alternative policies once the cost data are obtained. Consider a problem.

8-4 AN ILLUSTRATION

Suppose that it costs a firm £90 to replace all 150 light bulbs at the same time. To do an individual replacement costs £2. Failure data are as presented above. What replacement policy should be adopted to maintain the near 100 per cent operation of bulbs at minimum cost?

There are two kinds of policy open to the firm: (i) merely replace failures as they occur, or (ii) replace all bulbs at set intervals (failed or not) and in the meantime replace individual failures as they arise. Obviously type (i) is a special case of type (ii) in which the interval between 'group replacements' is infinite. However, it is useful to evaluate this special case separately.

If policy type (i) is implemented then the monthly cost will in due course settle down to £111.$\overline{11}$ as an average 55.$\overline{55}$ will need to be replaced each month at a cost of £2 per replacement. In Table 8-4, I represents the interval between group replacements and the objective is to minimize cost per month. The optimal policy is group replacement every *two* months (it being assumed that no individual replacements are necessary in the month of group replacement). The answer has been obtained by *enumeration* which means considering all the possible alternatives. Values of $I > 5$ may be said to have been *implicitly enumerated* although this process is heuristic here (i.e., we *judge* the average weekly cost function not to dip down again below 20. More of this later).

The data requirements of the approach are:

(a) The failure probabilities.
(b) The cost data, specifically:
    (i) the cost of each item;
    (i) other 'direct' costs of making the individual and group replacements;
    (iii) disruption costs.

The cost data are listed in order of increasing difficulty of estimation. Item (i) should, by and large, be a reliable figure that is fairly easy to obtain. Item (ii)

Table 8-4

I	Group cost	Individual costs in month 1	2	3	4	Total	Monthly average
1	90	—	—	—	—	90	90
2	90	30	—	—	—	120	60 ⇐
3	90	30	93	—	—	213	71
4	90	30	93	138.3	—	351.3	87.825
5	90	30	93	138.3	113.73	465.03	93.006

can be subject to considerable uncertainty. It will therefore be worth while to conduct a sensitivity analysis on results obtained.

8-5 SENSITIVITY ANALYSIS

Consider the cost of an individual replacement. This was £2 in the original light bulb example. Let this be £R in general. The costs per month of the alternative policies will now be as presented in Table 8-5.

With all other data at their original values, for what range of values of R will the two-month group replacement policy remain optimal? This is the range of values of R for which $45 + 7.5R$ is not greater than any of the other entries in Table 5.

First, vis-à-vis the one-month policy we must have

$$45 + 7.5R \leqslant 90$$

$$\therefore \quad R \leqslant \frac{45}{7.5}$$

$$\therefore \quad R \leqslant 6$$

Thus the one-month policy gives an *upper bound* on R. The other policies all have higher coefficients of R so these will seem relatively more attractive (the constant terms are lower) the lower R is. Each of these policies will set a *lower bound* on R. The *greatest* of these lower bounds (the GLB) determines the minimum level below which R must not fall for the two-month policy to be superior to three-, four-, or five-month and individual policies.

Vis-à-vis the three-month policy

$$45 + 7.5R \leqslant 30 + 20.5R$$

$$\therefore \quad 13R \geqslant 15$$

$$R \geqslant 1.1538$$

Table 8-5

Policy	Cost per month (£)
1-month	90
2-month	$45 + 7.5R$
3-month	$30 + 20.5R$
4-month	$22.5 + 32.6625R$
5-month	$18 + 37.503R$
Individual	$55.\overline{55}R$

in comparison to the four-month policy

$$45 + 7.5R \leqslant 22.5 + 36.6625R$$

$$\therefore \quad 29.1625R \geqslant 22.5$$

$$R \geqslant 0.7715$$

in comparison to the five-month policy

$$45 + 7.5R \leqslant 18 + 37.503R$$

$$\therefore \quad 30.003R \geqslant 27$$

$$R \geqslant 0.8999$$

and, finally, in comparison with the individual policy

$$45 + 7.5R \leqslant 55.\overline{55}R$$

$$\therefore \quad 48.0\overline{55}R \geqslant 45$$

$$R \geqslant 0.9364$$

So that the range of values for which the two-month policy is optimal is

$$1.1538 \leqslant R \leqslant 6$$

since the greatest of the lower bounds was 1.1538. Clearly with an original estimate of £2 there would have to be a considerable error in percentage terms to be outside of the permitted range. Of course, the *actual cost* of the two-month policy will change as R varies but it will remain the cheapest (*ceteris paribus*) so long as R remains within the above range.

A similar sensitivity analysis could be carried out against the group replacement cost. Call this G. In this case, with $R = 2$, the costs of the policies become:

Policy	Cost per month
1-month	G
2-month	$0.5G + 15$
3-month	$0.\overline{33}G + 41$
4-month	$0.25G + 65.325$
5-month	$0.2G + 75.006$
Individual	$111.\overline{11}$

The reader may verify that the resultant range of values for G for which the two-month policy is optimal is

$$30 \leqslant G \leqslant 156$$

so that here again the parameter is centrally located in the permitted range.

But what about *joint* variation of both R and G? The original range for R applied only to the value of 90 for G, but what if G is *not* 90, and what becomes of the range for G if R is not 2? We can determine a permitted region or *area* for both G and R in the following way. First set out the policy costs in terms of both G and R. Thus we have:

Policy	Cost per month
1-month	G
2-month	$0.5G + 7.5R$
3-month	$0.\overline{33}G + 20.5R$
4-month	$0.25G + 32.6625R$
5-month	$0.2G + 37.503R$
Individual	$55.\overline{55}R$

Now for the two-month policy to be superior to the one-month policy

$$0.5G + 7.5R \leqslant G$$
$$\therefore \quad G \geqslant 15R$$

From the three-month case we obtain

$$0.5G + 7.5R \leqslant 0.\overline{33}G + 20.5R$$
$$0.1\overline{66}G \leqslant 13R$$
$$G \leqslant 78R$$

From comparison with the four-month case

$$0.5G + 7.5R \leqslant 0.25G + 32.6625R$$
$$\therefore \quad 0.25G \leqslant 25.1625R$$
$$G \leqslant 100.65R$$

From the five-month case

$$0.5G + 7.5R \leqslant 0.2G + 37.503R$$
$$0.3G \leqslant 30.003R$$
$$G \leqslant 100.01R$$

Finally from the individual case

$$0.5G + 7.5R \leqslant 55.\overline{55}R$$
$$\therefore \quad G \leqslant 96.\overline{11}R$$

So that the original policy is optimal provided

$$15R \leqslant G \leqslant 78R$$

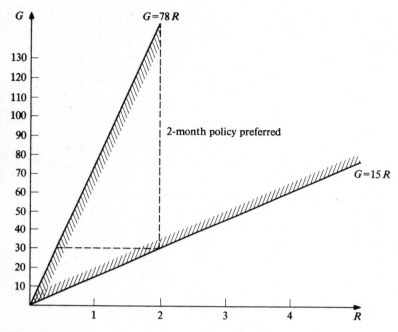

Figure 8-5

Notice that setting $R = 2$ gives the range for G alone and putting $G = 90$ gives the range for R alone.

As a diagram with, for clarity, the G scale compressed we have the situation shown in Fig. 8-5 in which the original intervals for G and R are shown as broken lines. Clearly these intervals only show a 'fraction' of the total permitted variation. Finally, we could have expressed the relation between G and R as

$$\frac{G}{78} \leqslant R \leqslant \frac{G}{15}$$

i.e., the bounds to the range of variability for one parameter are functions of the other parameter.

8-6 AN EXCEPTIONAL CASE

It was implied earlier on that cost could reach a 'local' minimum, increase, and then reach a *lower* local minimum value. If there are no further minima, this second value is the *global* minimum in this case. With $G = 90$ and $R = 2$

Table 8-6

Time	f_t
$t = 0$	0
$t = 1$	0.29
$t = 2$	0.23
$t = 3$	0.08
$t = 4$	0.40

Table 8-7

Interval between group replacements	C_m
1	90.0
2	88.50
3	90.41
4	85.64
5	102.38
Individual	115.83

as before, this situation occurs with the failure probabilities of Table 8-6. These data give a mean life of 2.59 months and a mean number of failures of 57.915 per month. The familiar calculations produce the values of monthly cost, C_m shown in Table 8-7.

This is an uncommon situation but can occur if the failure probability distribution is 'peculiar' as in the 'hollowed out' case in this instance. Another possible circumstance is if replacement costs per item or for the group vary from month to month. These kinds of factors are borne in mind when we 'judge' that a function does not have a second minimum.

8-7 THE ALGEBRAIC METHOD

It is not in fact necessary to draw a failure tree to solve problems of this type. Indeed, in problems where the number of periods over which group replacement is to be considered is high, the use of trees will be impractical. In such cases a tabular approach can be used. It is easy enough to demonstrate that where L is the maximum number of periods of life that any item can have ($L = 4$ in the current example) the number of failures in any month m can be written as

$$F_m = \begin{cases} nf_m + \sum_{t=1}^{m-1} f_t F_{m-t} & \text{for } m \leqslant L \\ \sum_{t=1}^{L} f_t F_{m-t} & \text{for } m > L \end{cases}$$

where it will be recalled that the f_t are the failure probabilities, the F_t are the actual numbers failing and n is the total number of items. The formula is simpler to use than might appear at first glance. The results for the original light bulb example are presented in Table 8-8. As an exercise in the use of Table 8-8 the reader may wish to verify that (to two decimal places) $F_8 = 53.75$, $F_9 = 55.44$, $F_{10} = 56.07$.

Table 8-8

$F_1 = nf_1$	$= 15$
$F_2 = nf_2 + f_1F_1$	$= 46.5$
$F_3 = nf_3 + f_1F_2 + f_2F_1$	$= 69.15$
$F_4 = nf_4 + f_1F_3 + f_2F_2 + f_3F_1$	$= 56.415$
$F_5 = \quad f_1F_4 + f_2F_3 + f_3F_2 + f_4F_1$	$= 47.9865$
$F_6 = \quad f_1F_5 + f_2F_4 + f_3F_3 + f_4F_2$	$= 58.68315$
$F_7 = \quad f_1F_6 + f_2F_5 + f_3F_4 + f_4F_3$	$= 56.660265$

8-8 A FURTHER EXAMPLE

Kudos Corporation needs 200 components to fulfil a particular function. Its research department have produced two alternative designs for the components, the Gremlin and the Spanna. For the Gremlin the numbers failing at the end of 1, 2, and 3 weeks from a fresh installation of 200 are estimated to be:

Week	Nos failing
1	40
2	60
3	100

The cost of an individual Gremlin replacement would be £2. Replacement of all 200 at one go would cost £175.

For the Spanna the failure data are:

Week	Nos failing
1	20
2	120
3	60

The cost of an individual Spanna replacement would be £2.50 and group replacement would cost £190. The board of directors have chosen the Gremlin on the grounds that: (a) individual replacement is cheaper; (b) group replacement is cheaper; and (c) mean life is longer. The question to be decided is whether or not these arguments are sound. Consider each

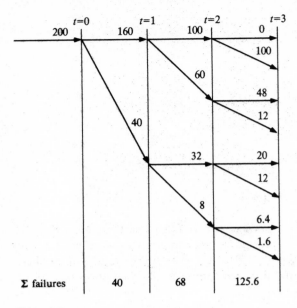

Figure 8-6

component individually—the Gremlin to begin with. The Gremlin failure and survival probabilities are:

t	f_t	s_t
0	0	1
1	0.2	0.8
2	0.3	0.5
3	0.5	0

and the Gremlin failure tree is shown in Fig. 8-6. The Gremlin mean life and mean number of failures are found as follows:

f_t	Life (t)	$t \cdot f_t$
0	0	0
0.2	1	0.2
0.3	2	0.6
0.5	3	1.5
		2.3 = mean life

$$\text{mean number of failures} = \frac{200}{2.3} = 86.96$$

So that with an individual failure costing £2 and group replacement costing £175 the policies can now be costed:

I	Group cost	Costs in week 1	2	3	Total	Weekly average
1	175				175	175
2	175	80			255	127.5
3	175	80	136		391	130.$\overline{33}$
4	175	80	136	251.2	642.2	160.55
∞						173.92

Thus a two-weekly policy would be best for the Gremlin design producing an average weekly cost figure of £127.5. Note that the individual replacements only policy corresponds to an infinite interval between group replacements. Incidentally, a five-week interval would produce a weekly average cost of £154.65.

Now consider the Spanna design in a similar fashion. Summarizing, the mean life is 2.2 weeks and the mean number of failures per week is 90.$\overline{90}$. By use of the failure tree or Table 8-8 we find that:

$$F_1 = 20, \ F_2 = 122, \ F_3 = 84.2$$

so that with group cost at £190 and individual replacements at £2.5 the table of costs is:

I	Group cost	Costs in week 1	2	3	Total	Weekly average
1	190				190	190
2	190	50			240	120
3	190	50	305		545	181.$\overline{66}$
4	190	50	305	210.5	755.5	188.875
∞						227.$\overline{27}$

So that again a two-month policy would prove to be optimal, but the cost is only £120! The reason is that the bulk of the Spanna failures occur in the second month and are thus 'caught' by the group replacement at month two.

Thus the directors were in error and the Spanna design should be selected despite some contrary but superficial indications.

8-9 DISCOUNTING IN STATISTICAL REPLACEMENT

Where there are lengthy periods of time involved—years rather than weeks or months—it is important to take interest into account. This can easily be done. If we return to Table 8-4 and for the purposes of illustration suppose that the time periods are *years* rather than months then the *annual equivalent annuity* method may be used. Table 8-9 shows the revised calculations for an interest rate of 15 per cent.

Table 8-9

I	Group cost ($t = 0$)	Individual costs at year				Present value	AE factor (15%)	Annual equivalent annuity
		1	2	3	4			
1	90	—	—	—	—	90	1.15	103.50
2	90	30	—	—	—	116.0880	0.6151	71.41
3	90	30	93	—	—	186.4053	0.4380	81.65
4	90	30	93	138.3	—	277.3376	0.3503	97.15
5	90	30	93	138.3	113.73	342.3684	0.2983	102.13
Individual								111.1̄1

As regards the AE factors of Table 8-9 it should be noted that in this method the first of the notional annuity payments occurs *after one year*. So that, for example, in the case of the one-month policy, an *annuity due* of £90 has the same present value as an *immediate annuity* of £103.5 when the interest rate is 15 per cent.

8-10 CONCLUSIONS

We have considered problems in which the nature of the failures is sudden and unpredictable and in which, although failure is costly, it is not absolutely disastrous. In this latter case the problem is one of devising fail-safe procedures or of minimizing failure probabilities. Gradual failures are best dealt with in a 'repair–replace' context so that they have not been discussed here. We have presented a basic framework upon which elaboration is possible to take account of the special features of any particular problem. As with all other OR techniques sensitivity analysis has an important role to play and discounting can be added to the procedure if the time intervals warrant it.

EXERCISES

8-1 Describe the two main classes of replacement problem. Give examples of both types.

8-2 The failure statistics for a certain type of light bulb are:

End of month	1	2	3	4	5	6
Probability of failure	0.05	0.10	0.25	0.25	0.2	0.15

There are 200 bulbs in use, the cost of replacing an individual failed bulb is £1.00 and the cost of a group replacement of all bulbs averages £0.4 per bulb. It has been decided to replace failed bulbs at the end of the month of failure and to replace all bulbs periodically.

(i) Find the expected number of failures one, two, three, four, and five months after a fresh installation. (*Hint:* the algebraic method is preferable here.)

(ii) At what intervals should group replacement occur? (Individual failures need not be attended to separately in the month of group replacement.)

8-3 Repco Ltd has a large number of machines which incorporate a particular component which is liable to sudden failure. Repco's present policy is to replace each component individually upon failure. Records have been kept of the working lives before failure of 800 of the components and the following data were obtained:

Number of components	Length of life (months)
120	1
360	2
240	3
80	4
800	

Repco is now considering the possibility of periodic replacement of all components, failed or not. Each individual failure costs £10 to replace, but in a replacement of all components the cost per unit replaced is £6.25.

Individual failures in months prior to the group replacement would still have to be attended to, with the exception of those which occur in the month of the group replacement itself.

(i) What is the best interval between group replacements?

(ii) Conduct a sensitivity analysis on the cost of an individual replacement.

(iii) Conduct a joint sensitivity analysis on the individual and group replacement costs.

(iv) Suppose that capital expenditure of £20 000 was necessary to change over to the group replacement policy. With an interest rate of 20 per cent, and a practically infinite horizon, what figure may be placed on the benefit of the changeover to the optimal policy?

8-4 A new department store plans to employ 250 sales staff. Experience suggests that 60 per cent of the staff will leave after one year and only 10 per cent will still be employed after two years, but these 10 per cent are expected to stay for a further two years before leaving. At the end of each year all vacancies that have arisen are filled by employing new staff, the 'leaving rates' for whom may be assumed to be the same as for the original 250.

(i) How many sales staff will be expected to leave at the end of three and four years?

(ii) What is the average number of resignations per year?

(iii) It is thought that the poor state of canteen facilities causes some employees to leave earlier than they would otherwise have done. If £400 per year was spent on improving canteen facilities the percentage of employees leaving at the end of the first year would be reduced to 40. However, the extra 20 per cent who do stay will leave at the end of the second year. The cost of recruiting a new sales employee is £20. Is it worth improving the canteen facilities?

8-5 Coltel Ltd have just begun to hire out a total of 200 coloured television sets. Market research has shown that out of a hundred hirings the pattern of the length of hire is as follows:

Length of hire (years)	1	2	3	4
Number of hirings	20	40	30	10

Required:

(a) Determine the number of new rentals required each year for the next four years to maintain Coltel's total rentals at 200 (round to nearest whole number in your calculations).

(10 marks)

(b) What is the average length of hire period?

(4 marks)

(c) What is the average number of new rentals required each year?

(4 marks)

(d) Coltel Ltd, in an attempt to reduce their administrative overheads, are launching an advertising campaign aimed at their existing customers to encourage them to rent for longer periods. They would regard their campaign as successful if the following pattern of hiring was achieved in the long-run:

Length of hire (years)	1	2	3	4	5
Number of hirings	10	30	35	15	10

If the administrative cost of arranging a hire is £20, what is the maximum amount Coltel Ltd should spend on their advertising campaign each year?

(7 marks)

(Association of Certified Accountants, Professional Examination: Section 2, paper 12, Management Mathematics, December 1978.)

NINE

FORECASTING METHODS

9-1 INTRODUCTION

James Morrell (1972) gives the objective of forecasting as: 'To minimize uncertainty and to identify and evaluate risk'. This succinct statement of the role of forecasting is in sharp contrast with the bewildering array of techniques at the disposal of the decision maker. As in medicine, a multitude of remedies often measures the degree of ignorance of the underlying condition. The medical analogy can be pushed a little further. Many ailments receiving a single label—such as 'cold' or 'hayfever'—in fact cover a multitude of conditions that have broad similarities but many differences of detail. We are labouring the point that requirements for information about the future can differ tremendously and there is no one forecasting technique that is best for all cases. Wheelwright and Makridakis (1977) go on to amplify this point by detailing the different areas of management activity in which forecasts are needed. One classification is as follows:

1. Production planning.
2. Inventory management.
3. Equipment replacement.
4. Marketing.
5. Finance and accounting.
6. Personnel management.
7. Policy making.

Under (1) the production manager wants to know about future demand for all of the items produced, materials requirements, availability, and prices. Under the closely related area (2) the main problem is comparatively short-term forecasting of demand for stocked items. We have already seen that (3) requires estimates of costs and revenues from capital equipment. Under (4) product demand estimates are needed in both absolute and relative terms (market share) along with more general trends in prices and design. Only with this kind of information can sales promotional efforts be designed. Under (5) the main requirement is for cash flow forecasts. In obtaining these it will usually be necessary to predict separately the various ingredients in the cost and revenue pies. Forecasts of relevant capital costs are also vital. In financial management more generally it is useful to have advance information about requirements for working capital and the actual receipt of accounts receivable. Under (6) future staff requirements in various categories are needed to design recruitment (or redundancy) and training programmes. Under (7) is the vital but much more nebulous area of strategic planning about the scale and timing of major future activities, with information about the general market, economy-wide, and political trends.

It should be obvious that these many and varied requirements will not be met by a single technique or even by a single general class of techniques. The three main classes of method are:

(a) *Quantitative techniques* (e.g., moving averages, exponential smoothing, regression).
(b) *Qualitative techniques* (e.g., technological forecasting).
(c) *Subjective methods* (e.g., analysts' expectations in portfolio analysis).

In this section we shall be concentrating on a few of the quantitative methods which tend to work better for the *short* and *medium* terms. It is often convenient to partition the future into four slices:

(i) The *very short term*: sometimes the syntactical monstrosity 'immediate term' is employed. Here is meant a period of days or a few weeks. The appropriate length depends on the context varying from *hours* (stock market) through *days* at the retail level or *weeks* at the wholesale level.
(ii) The *short term*: perhaps 1 to 6 months again depending generally on the distance of remove from final demand.
(iii) The *medium term*: a 'few' months to a 'few' years depending on context. Perhaps from as little as three months in retailing to five years (investment in government securities).
(iv) The *long term*: more than a 'few' years.

Here it will be the moving averages and exponential smoothing that apply mainly to (i) and (ii) and regression that applies mainly to (iii) although cavalier extrapolations can be made someway into (iv).

9-2 REQUIREMENTS PLANNING

Where a product is composed of fixed numbers of numerous component parts—for instance, a particular make of car—*given* the level of demand for the finished product there will be absolutely precise consequent requirements for the components. The given levels of sales of the complete product are 'exploded' to determine component requirements. The method of *materials requirement planning*, or MRP, goes on to aggregate and project these requirements over time. MRP is especially useful in production-to-order companies, Ordnance factories and specialized machine tools providing examples. As C. D. Lewis points out (Littlechild, 1977), when finished product demand is subject to fluctuations the MRP approach will *magnify* the errors in absolute terms. The amplification may be damped by inventories of components and semi-finished work but the consequences can still be serious.

9-3 COMPOSITION OF SERIES

We shall make a start on the quantitative methods with some simple examples of series to illustrate how a time series of observations may be composed. The treatment here follows that in Makower and Williamson (1967).

The simplest series of all is just the repetition of a given number, viz.

$$5, 5, 5, 5, 5, 5, 5, 5, 5, 5, 5, \ldots$$

Given this data there are few who would quarrel with a forecast of 5 for the next term in the series! Now consider the series

$$5, 7, 9, 11, 13, 15, 17, 19, 21, 23, 25, 27, \ldots$$

Again the pattern is obvious. It is an arithmetic series with first term 5 and difference 2. It seems clear that it will continue $\ldots, 29, 31, 33$, etc. This is a case of *linear trend* (the plotted points lie on a straight line on ordinary graph paper).

The series

$$5, 10, 20, 40, 80, 160, 320, \ldots$$

is a geometric series with first term 5 and factor of difference 2. The next terms would be $\ldots, 640, 1280, \ldots$. This series exhibits *exponential growth*.

One word of warning before we go any further. We have quite casually ventured predictions and stated that such and such a series 'is' a geometric series. In practice we rarely *know*. For instance, suppose that the device used to generate the first series above (the string of 5's) was the characteristic (the whole number part) of the natural logarithm of the integers starting at 149, viz.

$$149, 150, 151, 152, \ldots$$

Thus the first 255 terms of the relevant series are 5's but the 256th is a 6. We cannot be sure of the prediction unless the underlying 'mechanism' that generates the numbers is fully known. It follows that sound background knowledge or a theoretical framework (if it is not part of the forecasting device itself) in which to view the results is valuable.

Now consider the series

$$5, 9, 6, 3, 5, 9, 6, 3, 5, 9, 6, 3, \ldots$$

This series has a *cyclical* or *oscillatory* pattern (as with ice-cream sales in spring, summer, autumn, and winter). If the pattern continued unchanged the next two entries would be 5 and 9. Now consider the series

$$10, 16, 15, 14, 18, 24, 23, 22, 26, 32, 31, 30, \ldots$$

Before reading any further try to predict the next four terms. The series is in fact the sum of the linear trend and cyclical series shown earlier on. The reader might find it instructive to plot this series on graph paper.

Next consider the series

$$10.0, 16.3, 14.8, 13.9, 18.0, 24.2, 23.0, 22.1, 25.9, 31.7, 31.3, 29.8, \ldots$$

which is the linear trend plus cyclical series with the incorporation of *errors*. The reader may verify that the error terms are

$$0, +0.3, -0.2, -0.1, 0, +0.2, 0, +0.1, -0.1, -0.3, +0.3, -0.2$$

Note that the sum of the errors is zero and also that there is no obvious pattern to the magnitude or sign of the errors. This would be the case (on average) if the errors were random about a mean or expected value of zero. This last series is getting closer in character to a (well-behaved) time series. Economic time series will always contain 'errors', there will almost always be a trend (but not necessarily linear), there is frequently seasonal or monthly variation, and there may be longer-term cyclical factors. One of the most frequently used devices to estimate linear trend is regression analysis.

9-4 SIMPLE LINEAR REGRESSION

The name 'regression' relates to an early use of the method in a study of the psychological process of the same name. 'Simple' means only that *one* independent variable is involved rather than many. The method of least squares has its origins in eighteenth-century studies of errors of observation and was formulated by Gauss in 1798.

In simple linear regression, given two random variables X and Y, we attempt to fit an equation of the form

$$Y = a + bX \qquad (9\text{-}1a)$$

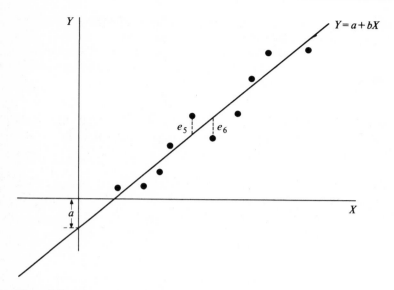

Figure 9-1

where a and b are constants that have to be determined. In the relationship as expressed by Eq. (9-1a) X is called the independent variable and Y is said to be dependent. There should generally be some grounds for supposing that changes in X *actually cause* changes in Y. For instance X may be income and Y expenditure, or X may be sales promotion expenditure and Y might be total sales revenue. If neither variable actually brings about a change in the other then we could equally well write (9-1a)

$$X = c + dY \qquad (9\text{-}1b)$$

and unless there is perfect correlation between X and Y there will be inconsistent estimates of Y from X and X from Y.

Figure 9-1 (a scatter diagram) shows a possible case in which Y tends to increase as X increases $(\therefore b > 0)$ and where a, the intercept term, is negative. The actual pairs of values of X and Y in the sample are related by

$$Y_i = a + bX_i + e_i \qquad (9\text{-}2)$$

where the e_i are errors and where a and b are chosen so that the sum of the squared errors, Σe_i^2, is as small as possible. In the figure, e_5 would be positive and e_6 would be negative and they would almost cancel—hence the squaring. We trust that the least squares coefficients a and b are unbiased estimates of the 'true' parameters that would be obtained from a study of the entire population of X and Y values. Under certain favourable conditions (which will not be detailed here) we can say that a and b are 'best, linear, unbiased estimators' of the population parameters (best meaning least variance).

Formulae for a and b, obtained by use of calculus methods, come in a variety of guises. The expressions that will be used here are:

$$a = \bar{Y} - b\bar{X} \qquad (9\text{-}3)$$

$$b = \frac{N\Sigma XY - (\Sigma X)(\Sigma Y)}{N\Sigma X^2 - (\Sigma X)^2} \qquad (9\text{-}4)$$

where in Eq. (9-3) $\bar{X}$ and $\bar{Y}$ are the arithmetic means of X and Y. Although Eq. (9-4) looks complicated at first glance nothing other than simple arithmetic is required to ascertain b. The example shown in Table 9-1 illustrates this.

The columns headed X and Y in Table 9-1 are sample data (which we are given) consisting of 15 pairs of values of X and Y. The first step is to calculate ΣX and ΣY and hence $\bar{X}$ and $\bar{Y}$. Thus:

$$\bar{X} = \frac{\Sigma X}{N} = \frac{300}{15} = 20; \quad \bar{Y} = \frac{\Sigma Y}{N} = \frac{876}{15} = 58.4$$

The next column squares every entry in the X column and the sum of the squared X values is 6616. In the XY column each X value is multiplied by its corresponding Y value. The sum if 19052. For the moment we do not require the Y^2 column, but this will be needed later on. Thus, substituting in Eq. (9-4) gives

$$b = \frac{15(19\,052) - (300)(876)}{15(6616) - (300)(300)} = \frac{22\,980}{9240} = 2.487$$

Table 9-1

X	Y	X^2	XY	Y^2
10	33	100	330	1089
12	37	144	444	1369
15	45	225	675	2025
13	41	169	533	1681
17	51	289	867	2601
18	53	324	954	2809
17	54	289	918	2916
16	50	256	800	2500
21	60	441	1260	3600
22	66	484	1452	4356
25	70	625	1750	4900
25	69	625	1725	4761
28	77	784	2156	5929
30	82	900	2460	6724
31	88	961	2728	7744
$\Sigma X = 300$	$\Sigma Y = 876$	$\Sigma X^2 = 6616$	$\Sigma XY = 19\,052$	$\Sigma Y^2 = 55\,004$

and substitution of $b = 2.487$, $\bar{X} = 20$ and $\bar{Y} = 58.4$ into Eq. (9-3) gives

$$a = 58.4 - 2.487(20) = 8.66$$

so that the regression equation of Y upon X obtained from the sample is

$$Y = 8.66 + 2.487X$$

9-5 CORRELATION

Now, before going any further we shall need to know how good a 'fit' we have. The formulae will always give values for a and b regardless of whether or not there is any real relationship between X and Y. The reader might like to plot the scatter and put in the regression line. This graphical work will suggest that the fit is very good—all the points are 'close' to the line.

A quantitative measure of the goodness of fit is the coefficient of linear correlation, r. This is given by

$$r = \frac{N\Sigma XY - (\Sigma X)(\Sigma Y)}{\sqrt{(N\Sigma X^2 - (\Sigma X)^2)(N\Sigma Y^2 - (\Sigma Y)^2)}} \tag{9-5}$$

and it can be shown that

$$-1 \leqslant r \leqslant +1$$

If $r \simeq 0$ there is no linear correlation between the variables; if r *is* significantly positive this means that there is linear correlation and the regression line slopes up. If r is significantly negative the regression line slopes down. Thus in Fig. 9-2(a) there is good positive linear correlation. Figure 9-2(b) exhibits good negative linear correlation. In Fig. 9-2(c) there is clearly no relation so $r \simeq 0$. In Fig. 9-2(a) there is strong *curvilinear* relationship but the coefficient of linear correlation would still be zero or thereabouts. Thus zero correlation should not be interpreted as *necessarily* implying no relationship of any kind.

In our example, bringing in the Y^2 column and substituting in the formula for r gives

$$r = \frac{22\,980}{\sqrt{(9240)(57\,684)}} = 0.995$$

which is a very high value, suggesting a very strong linear relation between X and Y. We would thus have good justification for use of the estimated regression equation for predictive purposes. In the testing of economic models (which usually involve multiple regression) it is not uncommon to have correlation coefficients well over 0.9. This will be so when the model has been properly formulated and all important variables included.

The *square* of the correlation coefficient is called the *coefficient of determination* and gives the proportion of the variation in Y that is explained

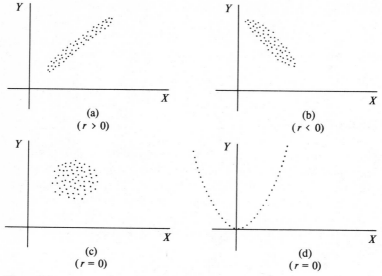

Figure 9-2

by variation in X. In our case, variation in X accounts for 99 per cent of the variation in Y. When r drops below about 0.7 then X is accounting for less than half the variation in Y and we should have cause to be dissatisfied with the performance of the model if a comprehensive explanation of variability is sought. It should be pointed out, however, that r^2 values can sometimes be 'manipulated' by changes of variable and that low values *can* be satisfactory if one factor among several is being studied.

Generally, a test of significance (using the 't' distribution) should be conducted on r. Whether a value of r is 'significant' depends not only upon the value itself but also on the number of observations in the sample. Hypotheses concerning the values of the regression coefficients can be similarly tested. Here, we shall simplify matters very much and say that if there is a reasonable number of observations (say 10 or more) and a good value of r (say 0.7 or more) then the correlation is significant.

9-6 FORECASTING WITH REGRESSION:
(i) POINT ESTIMATES

There are two kinds of forecasts that we shall be concerned with. The first use *interpolation*. This involves predicting a value for Y *when the X value is within the range of X values in the sample*. The procedure is very simple. Insert the value of X into the regression equation (call this special value X* and the resulting forecast Y^*) to determine the predicted value of Y. Thus if $X^* = 20$

$$Y^* = 8.66 + 2.487(20) = 58.4$$

(which confirms the fact that the regression line should pass through the *centroid* of the data, $\bar{X}, \bar{Y}$). Similarly if $X^* = 14$

$$Y^* = 8.66 + 2.487(14) = 43.478$$

and if $X^* = 27$

$$Y^* = 8.66 + 2.487(27) = 75.809$$

Recall that the forecast values of Y have been marked with a star to distinguish them from actual observations.

Next is *extrapolation*. Here the X^* values are outside of the sample range. Thus if $X^* = 32$

$$Y^* = 8.66 + 2.487(32) = 88.244$$

if $X^* = 8$

$$Y^* = 8.66 + 2.487(8) = 28.556$$

if $X^* = 35$

$$Y^* = 8.66 + 2.487(35) = 96.705$$

and if $X^* = 40$

$$Y^* = 8.66 + 2.487(40) = 108.14$$

The cases of interpolation and extrapolation are distinguished because there is generally more confidence in the model structure remaining valid if

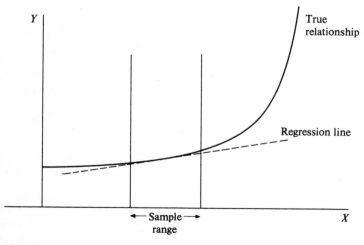

Figure 9-3

X^* stays within the range of the sample experience. The further that X^* goes outside of the range then the less sure we are that the model structure will still apply. This is shown in Fig. 9-3 where in fact although the X, Y relationship is exponential, linear predictions are satisfactory within or near to the sample range of values.

9-7 FORECASTING WITH REGRESSION:
(ii) CONFIDENCE INTERVALS

The questions naturally arise as to what confidence we may have in the predictions—and can this be quantified? Our predictions are point estimates (which should be rounded off) but we know that a reasonable margin of error should be allowed. It would be nice to be able to give a bracketed prediction with a stated degree of confidence. Unfortunately, this is no easy matter. To accomplish this we need to know the *prediction error variance*. This could then be used to give 95 per cent confidence intervals for the forecasts made. The 95 per cent confidence band-width increases with movement away from the point $(\bar{X}, \bar{Y})$ as shown in Fig. 9-4. The region of 95 per cent confidence is unshaded and for X values a 'long way' from the mean it becomes very wide. It is narrowest for interpolative forecasts near the mean, in which we may have greatest confidence. When extrapolation is involved there are the additional possible sources of error (unspecified and not included in the prediction error variance) resulting from the possible inappropriateness of the model structure. Given that the model structure is valid we can give the following formula for the 95 per cent confidence

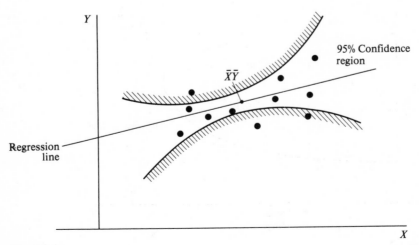

Figure 9-4

Table 9-2

$d = 10$	11	12	13	14	15	16	17	
$t = 2.228$	2.201	2.179	2.160	2.145	2.131	2.120	2.110	
$d = 18$	19	20	21	22	23	24	25	
$t = 2.101$	2.093	2.086	2.080	2.074	2.069	2.064	2.060	
$d = 26$	27	28	29	30	40	60	120	∞
$t = 2.056$	2.052	2.048	2.045	2.042	2.021	2.000	1.980	1.960

interval for the prediction

$$Y^* \pm t\hat{\sigma}\left[1 + \frac{1}{n} + \frac{(X^* - \bar{X})^2}{\Sigma(X - \bar{X})^2}\right]^{1/2} \qquad (9\text{-}6)$$

in which t is the appropriate value of the 't' statistic and where $\hat{\sigma}^2$, the sample based estimate of the variance of the error term, is given by

$$\hat{\sigma}^2 = \frac{\Sigma(Y_i - Y^*)^2}{n - 2}$$

The value of t for the 95 per cent confidence interval depends on the number of 'degrees of freedom' (d). This is the number in the sample less two. Thus there were 13 degrees of freedom in the example above. Values of t (for the 95 per cent range) for selected d are shown in Table 9-2.

Now consider the use of the formula (9-6) in the numerical example previously given. First compute $\Sigma(X - \bar{X})^2$. We have the results as shown in Table 9-3.

Table 9-3

X	$X - \bar{X}$	$(X - \bar{X})^2$
10	-10	100
12	-8	64
15	-5	25
13	-7	49
17	-3	9
18	-2	4
17	-3	9
16	-4	16
21	$+1$	1
22	$+2$	4
25	$+5$	25
25	$+5$	25
28	$+8$	64
30	$+10$	100
31	$+11$	121
	$\Sigma(X - \bar{X})^2 =$	616

Now determine $\hat{\sigma}^2$. For this we need the 'forecast' values Y^* given by the regression equation for the original sample values of X. Thus when $X = 10$, $Y^* = 8.66 + 2.487(10) = 33.530$. The other Y^* entries in the workings of Table 9-4 were similarly obtained. So that

$$\hat{\sigma}^2 = \frac{(Y - Y^*)^2}{n-2} = \frac{35.496}{13} = 2.730$$

So $\hat{\sigma} = 1.652$.

Table 9-4

X	Y	Y^*	$Y - Y^*$	$(Y - Y^*)^2$
10	33	33.530	−0.530	0.281
12	37	38.504	−1.504	2.262
15	45	45.965	−0.965	0.931
13	41	40.991	0.009	0.000
17	51	50.939	0.061	0.004
18	53	53.426	−0.426	0.181
17	54	50.939	3.061	9.370
16	50	48.452	1.548	2.396
21	60	60.887	−0.887	0.787
22	66	63.374	2.626	6.896
25	70	70.835	−0.835	0.697
25	69	70.835	−1.835	3.367
28	77	78.296	−1.296	1.680
30	82	83.270	−1.270	1.613
31	88	85.757	2.243	5.031
				$35.496 = \Sigma(Y - Y^*)^2$

Now consider a 95 per cent confidence interval for Y if $X^* = 32$. In using Eq. (9-6) we note that the appropriate t value is that for $15 - 2 = 13$ degrees of freedom and is thus 2.160. Note also that the point estimate, $Y^* = 88.244$. The range will then be:

$$88.244 \pm (2.160)(1.652)\left[1 + \frac{1}{15} + \frac{(32-20)^2}{616}\right]^{1/2}$$

$$= 88.244 \pm (2.160)(1.652)(1.140)$$

$$= 84.176 \text{ to } 92.312$$

which had better be rounded off to

$$84.2 \text{ to } 92.3$$

because of rounding errors in the fifth figure and so as not to give a false impression of accuracy.

To get the 95 per cent confidence interval for $X^* = 35$ we have

$$95.705 \pm (2.160)(1.652)\left[1 + \frac{1}{15} + \frac{(35-20)^2}{616}\right]^{1/2}$$

which gives

$$91.4 \text{ to } 100$$

and, throwing caution to the winds, the reader may verify that for $X^* = 40$ the range is 103.5 to 112.8.

9-8 A FURTHER EXAMPLE

Quite often an economic variable (such as company profits) is recorded against time as the X variable. In the example below the first observation is for 1969 which is set as $X = 1$, 1970 becomes $X = 2$ and so on. Suppose it is required to forecast profits in 1982 and 1983 and to establish 95 per cent confidence intervals for these predictions. With the Y variable as profits (in £millions) the data and workings are shown in Table 9-5. So

$$b = \frac{13(2087.3)-(91)(266.5)}{13(819)-8281} = 1.219$$

whence

$$a = 20.5 - 1.219(7) = 11.967$$

So that the regression equation is

$$Y = 11.967 + 1.219X$$

Table 9-5

Year	X	Y	X^2	XY	Y^2
1969	1	13.2	1	13.2	174.24
1970	2	14.2	4	28.4	201.64
1971	3	16.0	9	48.0	256.00
1972	4	17.1	16	68.4	292.41
1973	5	17.6	25	88.0	309.76
1974	6	18.9	36	113.4	357.21
1975	7	21.0	49	147.0	441.00
1976	8	21.6	64	172.8	466.56
1977	9	23.0	81	207.0	529.00
1978	10	24.0	100	240.0	576.00
1979	11	25.5	121	280.5	650.25
1980	12	26.6	144	319.2	707.56
1981	13	27.8	169	361.4	772.84
	$\Sigma X = 91$	$\Sigma Y = 266.5$	819	2087.3	5734.47
	$\therefore \bar{X} = 7$	$\bar{Y} = 20.5$			

Checking for goodness of fit, the correlation coefficient is

$$r = \frac{13(2087.3) - (91)(266.5)}{\sqrt{(13(819) - 8281)(13(5734.47) - 71\,022.25)}} = 0.998$$

which is excellent. So the point estimates will be

For 1982 $(X = 14)$: $Y^* = 11.967 + 1.219(14) = 29.033 \simeq 29.0$

For 1983 $(X = 15)$: $Y^* = 11.967 + 1.219(15) = 30.252 \simeq 30.3$

Now for the confidence intervals further work is required as shown in Table 9-6.
So that

$$\hat{\sigma} = \sqrt{\frac{0.916502}{13 - 2}} = 0.289$$

With $n = 13$ there are 11 degrees of freedom so that the correct t value equals 2.201 and the confidence interval for the 1982 prediction $(X = 14)$ is

$$29.033 \pm (2.201)(0.289)\left[1 + \frac{1}{13} + \frac{(14 - 7)^2}{182}\right]^{1/2}$$

which results in

$$28.3 \text{ to } 29.8$$

and for 1983 the range is

$$30.252 \pm (2.201)(0.289)\left[1 + \frac{1}{13} + \frac{(15 - 7)^2}{182}\right]^{1/2}$$

Table 9-6

$X - \bar{X}$	$(X - \bar{X})^2$	Y^*	$Y - Y^*$	$(Y - Y^*)^2$
−6	36	13.186	0.014	0.000 196
−5	25	14.405	−0.205	0.042 025
−4	16	15.624	0.376	0.141 376
−3	9	16.843	0.257	0.066 049
−2	4	18.062	−0.462	0.213 444
−1	1	19.281	−0.381	0.145 161
0	0	20.500	0.500	0.250 000
1	1	21.719	−0.119	0.014 161
2	4	22.938	0.062	0.003 844
3	9	24.157	−0.157	0.024 649
4	16	25.376	0.124	0.015 376
5	25	26.595	0.005	0.000 025
6	36	27.814	−0.014	0.000 196
	182			0.916502

which results in

$$29.5 \text{ to } 31.0$$

This latter range appears no wider than the 1982 range, but this is caused by rounding.

9-9 TIME SERIES ANALYSIS

A time series may be broken down into a number of parts. There are two types of model, the *additive* and the *multiplicative*. The original data (Y) may be decomposed into trend (T), seasonal variation (S), cyclical variation (C) and *residual variation* (R). The models are:

Additive	Multiplicative
$Y = T + S + C + R$	$Y = TSCR$

We saw something of the additive approach in Sec. 9-3. Each of the ingredients of the models T, S, C, R, are themselves series. Only in very long series is it worth trying to identify the cyclical ingredient (there is debate as to whether it is ever worth doing) and we shall consider only T, S, and R in the work to follow. There are various ways in which a trend series can be produced. One of the simplest is by *moving averages*, which we shall illustrate in the context of an additive model.

An n period moving average of a series of observations, $Y_1, Y_2, Y_3, Y_4, \ldots$, is the series of arithmetic means:

$$\frac{Y_1 + Y_2 + Y_3 + \cdots + Y_n}{n}, \quad \frac{Y_2 + Y_3 + Y_4 + \cdots + Y_{n+1}}{n}, \quad \frac{Y_3 + Y_4 + Y_5 + \cdots + Y_{n+2}}{n}$$

Replacing the original series by the moving average series has the effect (it is hoped!) of eliminating irregularities and revealing the underlying trend in the data. The larger the value of n, the less significant is the role of an individual observation. This is a mixed blessing. The average with large n is less affected by extreme observations but is by the same token slower to reflect change and will 'lag behind' more. Frequently there is an obvious value of n to take. With quarterly data, $n = 4$ is used; with monthly data, $n = 12$.

Below, in Table 9-7, are shown hypothetical quarterly sales data. A four-period moving average is indicated. First, a four-period moving *total* is shown in the column headed 'Sum 4'. Thus $436 = 92 + 105 + 116 + 123$. The next term $459 = 105 + 116 + 123 + 115$ and is most easily calculated as $436 - 92 + 115$. However, it will be noted that the Sum 4 term falls *between* quarters. The next column 'Sum 2' forms a *two*-period moving total of the Sum 4 elements. This has the effect of 'centring' the total so that 895 is located alongside Q_3 for 1978. There is no need to do this second summing

Table 9-7

		Y	Sum 4	Sum 2	Trend (T)	Y − T (= S + R)	Deseasonalized
1978	Q₁	92					100.09
	Q₂	105					108.03
	Q₃	116	436	895	111.875	+4.125	110.21
	Q₄	123	459	940	117.5	+5.5	117.65
1979	Q₁	115	481	990	123.75	−8.75	123.09
	Q₂	127	509	1043	130.375	−3.375	130.03
	Q₃	144	534	1094	136.75	+7.25	138.21
	Q₄	148	560	1144	143	+5	142.65
1980	Q₁	141	584	1189	148.625	−7.625	149.09
	Q₂	151	605	1231	153.875	−2.875	154.03
	Q₃	165	626				159.21
	Q₄	169					163.65

when n is an odd number. The Sum 2 entries are now divided by 8 to give the moving average version of trend.

The model that we are employing here is $Y = T + S + R$ so that $Y - T = S + R$. Thus the $Y - T$ column contains seasonal and residual effects. If the residuals are well behaved they can be eliminated by averaging. The entries in the $Y - T$ column are grouped under quarters and averaged thus:

	Q₁	Q₂	Q₃	Q₄	
			+4.125	+5.5	
	−8.75	−3.375	+7.25	+5	
	−7.625	−2.875			
Average:	−8.19	−3.13	+5.69	+5.25	[Σ = −0.38]
Adjusted average:	−8.09	−3.03	+5.79	+5.35	

The sum of the averages should ideally be zero. In fact it comes to -0.38. Each average is adjusted by adding 0.1 ($\simeq 0.38 \div 4$) to bring the total nearer to zero. These adjusted averages represent the *seasonal fluctuations* (S). If these are subtracted from the original data a *deseasonalized* series is produced. Official statistics are often given in this form. This is shown in the last column of workings.

If there is very little trend in the data, the moving average can be used to forecast one period ahead. The forecast for period $t + 1$, $\hat{y}_{t+1}$ would then be

$$\hat{y}_{t+1} = \frac{1}{n}(y_t + y_{t-1} + y_{t-2} + \cdots + y_{t-n-1})$$

In our example—ignoring the presence of trend and seasonal factors—the moving average forecast for Q_1 of 1981 using the formula above would be $626/4 = 156.5$. The forecast can be improved by taking the seasonal fluctuations into account and/or making some 'freehand' allowance for trend. An illustration of this process is provided in the answer to question 9.8 on page 312. However, the use of moving average as a forecasting device is best limited to the most simple cases.

The moving average version of trend is not, however, the most convenient for forecasting purposes. Trend calculated by least squares regression is more useful. We shall now use this in an illustration of the multiplicative model $Y = TSR$. There would frequently be occasion to use constant *compound* growth in the multiplicative model, but here we shall stick to linear trend T given by $\bar{Y} = a + bX$ where a and b are the least squares regression coefficients calculated in the usual manner. Workings are shown in Table 9-8. For practice, an alternative version of the slope formula is employed. It is stated below. In this model the seasonal/residual mix SR is given by the original series *divided* by the trend value. For convenience $100(Y \div T)$ is shown in the table and the entries in this column are then grouped by quarter and averaged as before. The sum of the averages should be 400 and the adjustment mechanism is to multiply each unadjusted figure by 400/399.95.

Table 9-8

		X	Y	X^2	XY	Trend (T) ($\bar{Y}$)	$100\left(\dfrac{Y}{T}\right)$	Deseasonalized
1978	Q_1	1	92	1	92	97.63	94.23	97.84
	Q_2	2	105	4	210	104.06	100.90	106.46
	Q_3	3	116	9	348	110.49	104.99	111.31
	Q_4	4	123	16	492	116.92	105.20	119.28
1979	Q_1	5	115	25	575	123.35	93.23	122.30
	Q_2	6	127	36	762	129.78	97.86	128.76
	Q_3	7	144	49	1008	136.21	105.72	138.18
	Q_4	8	148	64	1184	142.64	103.76	143.52
1980	Q_1	9	141	81	1269	149.07	94.59	149.95
	Q_2	10	151	100	1510	155.50	97.11	153.10
	Q_3	11	165	121	1815	161.93	101.90	158.33
	Q_4	12	169	144	2028	168.36	100.38	163.89
		78	1596	650	11 293			

$$\bar{X} = 6.5, \quad \bar{Y} = 133$$

$$b = \frac{n\Sigma XY - \Sigma X \Sigma Y}{n\Sigma X^2 - (\Sigma X)^2}$$

$$\therefore \quad b = \frac{12(11\,293) - (78)(1596)}{12(650) - (6084)} = \frac{11\,028}{1716} = 6.43$$

$$\therefore \quad a = 133 - 6.43(6.5) = 91.2$$

$$\therefore \quad \text{Trend} = 91.2 + 6.43X$$

	Q_1	Q_2	Q_3	Q_4	
	94.23	100.90	104.99	105.20	
	93.23	97.86	105.72	103.76	
	94.59	97.11	101.90	100.38	
Unadjusted:	94.02	98.62	104.20	103.11	$\Sigma = 399.95$
Adjusted:	94.03	98.63	104.21	103.12	

The *seasonal factors* are 0.9403 for the first quarter, 0.9863 for the second, 1.0421 for the third, and 1.0312 for the fourth quarter. Deseasonalized data in this model are found by *dividing* the original data by the seasonal factors. Thus the first entry in the deseasonalized column, $97.84 = 92 \div 0.9403$. The second entry $106.46 = 105 \div 0.9863$, etc.

The reader should compare the trend and deseasonalized results produced by the two approaches. By and large the correspondence is good. In general it cannot be said that one method is *always* superior to the other. That model is better which most faithfully reflects the nature of the underlying economic mechanism generating the data, but this is sometimes unknown. However, if there is a significant trend in the data it is more likely that seasonal effects will be *proportional* to trend rather than additive—this suggests the multiplicative model (but what happens if logs are taken in the multiplicative model?) Furthermore, as can be seen from the example, the moving average method 'loses' data—only eight trend values can be obtained. Finally, estimating trend by regression (rather than moving average) is more convenient for forecasting purposes.

To use the model for forecasting, the trend component is first determined and then multiplied by the appropriate seasonal factor. To illustrate, suppose forecasts are required for the four quarters of 1981. First determine the trend values for these times. For the first quarter (which would correspond to $X = 13$) we should have

$$1981 \ Q_1 \ \text{trend} = a + b(13)$$
$$= 91.2 + 6.43(13)$$
$$= 174.79$$

and for Q_2:

$$1981 \ Q_2 \ \text{trend} = 91.2 + 6.43(14)$$
$$= 181.22$$

Table 9-9

		X	Trend	S factor	Forecast ($=TS$)
1981	Q_1	13	174.79	0.9403	164.36
	Q_2	14	181.22	0.9863	178.74
	Q_3	15	187.65	1.0421	195.55
	Q_4	16	194.08	1.0312	200.14

Obviously, all that is being done is the addition of a further 6.43 each quarter. Thus the 1981 Q_3 trend = 187.65 and for the final quarter the trend value is 194.08. Each of these values must now be multiplied by the appropriate seasonal factor. The full results are given in Table 9-9.

9-10 EXPONENTIAL SMOOTHING

This final forecasting method that we shall examine is in its most rudimentary form, the simplest of all. The technique was brought to the fore in the late nineteen-fifties. The method irons out irregularities in the data (hence 'smoothing') and can be expressed as a model in which coefficients of successive terms diminish exponentially—hence 'exponential smoothing'.

Exponential smoothing methods are widely used for short-term forecasting. Lewis (Littlechild, 1977) cites the fact that a survey by the American Production and Inventory Control Society showed that 30 per cent of the society's members were using some form of the technique in 1973, and the trend was rising.

The exponential smoothing model can be presented in a number of ways. One is to write

$$\hat{y}_{t+1} = \alpha y_t + (1-\alpha)\hat{y}_t \qquad (9\text{-}7)$$

in which t refers to the current period, $\hat{y}_{t+1}$ is the forecast for the next period, y_t is the *actual value* of the variable in the current period and $\hat{y}_t$ was the previous forecast (generated in the same way). α is the exponential smoothing constant, $0 \leqslant \alpha \leqslant 1$. The value of α has to be decided upon by some means, but is typically in the range 0.05 to 0.3. More of this shortly.

The relationship (9-7) can be spelt out to fully reveal the recursive character of the device. The forecast for period t would have been

$$\hat{y}_t = \alpha y_{t-1} + (1-\alpha)\hat{y}_{t-1} \qquad (9\text{-}8)$$

Substituting for y_t from (9-8) into (9-7) gives

$$\hat{y}_{t+1} = \alpha y_t + \alpha(1-\alpha)y_{t-1} + (1-\alpha)^2\hat{y}_{t-1} \qquad (9\text{-}9)$$

but by the same process

$$\hat{y}_{t-1} = \alpha y_{t-2} + (1-\alpha)\hat{y}_{t-2} \qquad (9\text{-}10)$$

and repeated substitution produces the result

$$\hat{y}_{t+1} = \alpha y_t + \alpha(1-\alpha)y_{t-1} + \alpha(1-\alpha)^2 y_{t-2} + \cdots + \alpha(1-\alpha)^n y_{t-n} + \cdots \qquad (9\text{-}11)$$

which reveals the 'autoregressive' scheme in which it is seen that the forecast value for the next period is a *weighted* average of current and past values of the variable. Since $(1-\alpha) < 1$ the weights decline exponentially. The meaning of this is that the older the observation *the less emphasis it receives in framing the forecast*. This should be contrasted with the moving average case in which *equal* weight is given to all observations included in the average. Note that the weights in Eq. (9-11) form a geometric progression with first term α and constant difference $(1-\alpha)$. The sum to infinity (S_∞) of the weights is therefore

$$S_\infty = \frac{\alpha}{1-(1-\alpha)} = 1$$

as must be the case with a true average.

By way of illustrating the declining influence of data of increasing age, if $\alpha = 0.2$ the first six coefficients $(\alpha, \alpha(1-\alpha), \text{etc.})$ in Eq. (9-11) would be

$$0.2, 0.16, 0.128, 0.1024, 0.08192, 0.065536$$

The bigger the value of α the less important are the older data. For instance with $\alpha = 0.4$ the first six coefficients are:

$$0.4, 0.24, 0.144, 0.0864, 0.05184, 0.031104$$

in which it is seen that (in comparison with $\alpha = 0.2$) more weight is given to the first three terms and less to all subsequent ones, with the sixth term being halved in importance. In the extremes, if $\alpha = 1$ only the current value of the variable is of any importance—the forecast for the next period being this period's value. At the other extreme as α approaches zero the past periods have almost equal weights. As $\alpha \to 0$ the forecast tends towards the arithmetic mean of a large number of periods, i.e., it approaches a very long period moving average value.

For actual usage of exponential smoothing it is convenient to rearrange the terms in Eq. (9-7) as

$$\hat{y}_{t+1} = \hat{y}_t + \alpha(y_t - \hat{y}_t) \qquad (9\text{-}12)$$

which reads: 'The new forecast is equal to the old forecast plus a proportion, α, of the difference between the current value and the old forecast of that value'. The term $y_t - \hat{y}_t$ is called the *current forecasting error*. Consider an example. A series of fifteen monthly observations of a variable are shown in the first column of Table 9-10. The first observation is 148 and the forecast of

Table 9-10

Actual observation (y)	Forecast ($\hat{y}$)	Forecasting error ($y - \hat{y}$)	$\alpha = 0.3$ correction	Next forecast
148	146	+2.00	+0.60	146.60
147	146.60	+0.40	+0.12	146.72
149	146.72	+2.28	+0.68	147.40
146	147.40	−1.40	−0.42	146.98
144	146.98	−2.98	−0.89	146.09
145	146.09	−1.09	−0.33	145.76
145	145.76	−0.76	−0.23	145.53
147	145.53	+1.47	+0.44	145.97
146	145.97	+0.03	+0.01	145.98
143	145.98	−2.98	−0.89	145.09
145	145.09	−0.09	−0.03	145.06
146	145.06	+0.94	+0.28	145.34
147	145.34	+1.66	+0.50	145.84
148	145.84	+2.16	+0.65	146.49
146	146.49	−0.49	−0.15	146.34

this figure (boxed) was 146. This is a given datum. We can now proceed to forecast the second entry in the 'actual observation' column. The forecasting error is $+2$ and so, using $\alpha = 0.3$, the correction is $+0.6$ giving a forecast of 146.6. This becomes the next entry in the Forecast column and corresponds to an actual observation of 147. And so on; the procedure is simplicity itself. The list of forecasts is the 'exponentially smoothed' series. As an exercise the reader might try $\alpha = 0.1$ and $\alpha = 0.5$ and compare the results with the data of Table 9-10.

It is important to audit or 'monitor' forecast results. There are two respects in which the situation can change. The first is that while demand remains trendless the degree of variability of the data may increase, i.e., the variable may become more volatile. This volatility can be measured by standard deviation or mean absolute deviation of the forecasting errors. In *adaptive forecasting* the sensitivity of the forecast is adjusted to reflect changes in data volatility. In the present model this would correspond to alteration of the value of α. The word 'adaptive' is here used to refer to the adaptation of forecasting technique itself—the automatic revaluing of parameters as conditions are perceived to change. The continual adjustment of parameters to reduce forecast errors is called *adaptive filtering*.

Then there may be a change in the level of demand. For instance there may be a sudden and unforeseen dip, jump or 'ramp' in demand. This situation can be detected (in a probabilistic sense) by a 'tracking signal', but discussion of these methods is beyond the scope of this text (a good discussion is found in Littlechild (1977, Chapter 10). Exponential smoothing yields unbiased forecasts of 'stationary' series but (as with all moving averages) lags behind (i.e., becomes biased) after structural changes take place. The method can be extended to cope with the presence of trend (e.g., *Holt's* method). A famous generalization was provided by Box and Jenkins in 1962; the *Box–Jenkins* approach now being widely used.

9-11 CONCLUDING REMARKS

The last 25 years have seen a burgeoning of forecasting techniques, and quantitative methods have gained wide and growing acceptance in industry and government. The reason for this is that the methods have proved to be well worth while in general: better (though by no means perfect) results are obtained *with* statistical forecasting methods than without them. This alone is sufficient justification for their usage. The increasing acceptance of the methods has been greatly facilitated by the development and spread of computers. All computer companies offer forecasting packages, ready made or modifiable.

The selection of technique to use in a particular situation can be difficult, but the firm is unlikely to be in an entirely unique situation and industrial experience can greatly narrow the range. One factor that should be borne in mind is the degree of detail that is required. Wheelwright and Makridakis (1977) cite the illustration that: 'The corporate planning department would see little value in having a forecast by individual items in the company's product line; similarly, the production foreman would find little value in having a general sales estimate of total corporate sales when he is trying to schedule his weekly production.' There is also the problem that the introduction of new methods and changes in decision-making procedures in an organization will usually meet with resistance. As a rule it is best to introduce first those forecasting methods that are most closely related to existing procedures.

A number of caveats should be mentioned. The first is that we have presented here only the simplest versions of a few procedures. Techniques in actual usage can be very much more complicated. In the case of regression, for instance, the effects of several factors can be taken into account simultaneously in *multiple linear regression* by fitting an equation of the form

$$Y = a_0 + a_1 X_1 + a_2 X_2 + \cdots + a_n X_n$$

An example of the use of this form would be with four of the X's as seasonal 'dummies'. In other words, seasonal analysis can be conducted by regression methods alone if multiple regression is employed.

Less commonly, non-linear regression may be used. Sometimes, however, non-linear relationships can be estimated by use of linear regression methods. If the true relationship is of the form

$$Y = aX^b$$

(as for instance in the case of growth at a compound rate) then by taking logarithms we can fit

$$\log Y = \log a + b \log X$$

We have also said little about data, its collection and quality. While the normal accounting processes will produce a good deal of data, and sales records will normally be kept, the collection of much new data can be time-consuming and costly. However, 'you get what you pay for' in business life as elsewhere; in material terms little of value is entirely free. In respect of expense, the importance of the decision and its likely repetition need to be borne in mind. Computer people have a famous acronym—GIGO—'garbage in, garbage out'. The quality of forecasts is dependent upon the quality of data as well as the forecasting techniques. Finally, recall that as with other OR methods, to justify themselves (taking costs into account) forecasting methods need not produce pinpoint accuracy. Nothing can do that. *They have only to improve on what would otherwise have been done.* That this is generally the case has been amply demonstrated by business experience in the past 25 years.

EXERCISES

9-1 In what areas of management activity are forecasts needed? Give examples of the kind of information that is likely to be required in each area.

9-2 (a) What are the three main classes of forecasting methods?

(b) Explain what is meant by 'very short term', 'short term', 'medium term', and 'long term'. What quantitative techniques are likely to be useful in each case?

9-3 Briefly explain what is meant by materials requirement planning (MRP).

9-4 Produce simple examples of series to illustrate (a) linear trend; (b) exponential growth; (c) oscillations; and (d) random errors.

9-5 Given the following time series data:

X	Y
106	155
90	110
92	130
100	145
112	160

(i) Find the least squares regression equation of Y upon X.

(ii) Use the equation to predict the value of Y for $X = 120$.

(iii) Find the value of the coefficient of linear correlation. What does this value measure?

(iv) Find the value of the coefficient of determination. What does this value measure?

9-6 The data below show road accident and traffic figures between November 1964 and October 1965. (Source: *Monthly Digest of Statistics*, February 1966.)

Month	Traffic index	Casualties (thousands)
Nov.	129	33
Dec.	126	33
Jan.	124	29
Feb.	121	25
Mar.	138	31
Apr.	153	32
May	160	34
June	169	35
July	179	36
Aug.	185	36
Sept.	161	34
Oct.	155	34

(i) Find the least squares regression line and the coefficients of correlation and determination.

(ii) Find 95 per cent confidence intervals for casualties for the following values of the traffic index: 150, 190, 220.

9-7 For the data of question 9-5 find the 95 per cent confidence interval for the prediction of Y when $X = 120$. (For three degrees of freedom the appropriate value of the t statistic is 3.182.)

9-8 Given the following quarterly time series data:

		Y
1977	Q_1	269
	Q_2	280
	Q_3	256
	Q_4	241
1978	Q_1	277
	Q_2	280
	Q_3	258
	Q_4	247
1979	Q_1	281
	Q_2	284
	Q_3	260
	Q_4	253

(i) Produce a deseasonalized series using the additive model with moving averages.

(ii) Produce a forecast for the first quarter of 1980 based solely upon the four-period moving average (ignoring any trend and seasonal effects).

(iii) **Devise** a means of making some allowance for trend and seasonal effects and produce another forecast value. (*Hint:* First look at the way the Trend (T) data have been changing and try to extend this series.)

9-9 For the following quarterly time series data:

		Y
1978	Q_1	82
	Q_2	79
	Q_3	90
	Q_4	96
1979	Q_1	87
	Q_2	103
	Q_3	110
	Q_4	117
1980	Q_1	116
	Q_2	120

(i) Produce a deseasonalized series using a regression estimated trend in a multiplicative model.

(ii) Produce forecasts for the third and fourth quarters of 1980 and the first two quarters of 1981.

9-10 For the following monthly production data produce an exponentially smoothed series using a value of 0.4 for the smoothing constant. Also, give a forecast for June of 1980. The forecast value for June 1979 was 300.

Year	Month	Actual production
1979	June	304
	July	302
	Aug.	306
	Sept.	300
	Oct.	296
	Nov.	298
	Dec.	298
1980	Jan.	302
	Feb.	300
	Mar.	296
	Apr.	298
	May	300

9-11 (i) Briefly explain the idea of multiple linear regression. How can seasonal effects be taken into account in such a model?

(ii) Give an example of a non-linear relationship that can be estimated by the use of linear regression methods.

9-12 The following data were collected from the Industrial Products Manufacturing Company Limited.

Month	Total overhead (y)	Direct labour hours (DLH) (x)	Plant hours (PH)
Jan.	15 000	736	184
Feb.	14 500	800	160
Mar.	15 750	1008	168
Apr.	15 250	880	176
May	16 250	1056	176
June	15 000	840	168
	$\Sigma y = 91\,750$	$\Sigma x = 5320$	
	$\bar{y} = 15\,291.7$	$\bar{x} = 886.7$	

You are required to:
  (a) compute a least squares equation based on direct labour hours;
  (b) compute the coefficient of determination (r^2) for (a);
  (c) compare and discuss the relationship of your solution in (a) to the equation of:

$$\text{Total overhead} = 5758 + 4.7\,\text{DLH} + 31\,\text{PH}$$

(where DLH = direct labour hours, PH = plant hours), obtained by a regression using DLH and PH as variables and coefficient of determination $R^2 = 0.9873$;
  (d) estimate the total overhead for a month with 1000 DLH and 168 PH, using the equation in (c).
(Institute of Cost and Management Accountants, Professional Stage: Part I, Quantitative Techniques, May 1979.)

9-13 The results of the Mercia division of Offa Ltd over the last five years are summarized as follows:

Year	1	2	3	4	5
			£'000		
Sales	70	93	119	118	152
Costs: Materials	20	28	42	37	48
Labour	27	36	39	48	54
Overheads	24	24	28	33	32
	71	88	109	118	134
Net profit	(1)	5	10	0	18
Sales units	2100	2800	3400	3100	4000

The Mercia Division manufactures a single product. Stocks have been negligible at all relevant times. Price changes have been rare in Offa's business. During the last five years, the only changes in the prices of resources used have been an increase in the price of materials of 25 per cent three years ago (at the end of year 2), and an increase in wage rates of $33\frac{1}{3}$ per cent two years ago (at the end of year 3); overhead costs have not been affected by price changes. Plans for the coming year (year 6) are now being prepared. No further increases in the prices of resources are expected. The sales manager has provided the following estimates of the sales price–volume relationship for the coming year:

Volume	Price
4500	£37
4000	£40
3400	£42

You are required to:

(a) estimate the optimal selling price from amongst the three possible prices £37, £40, or £42 using linear regression analysis to estimate the cost–volume relationship; and

(b) discuss the advantages and limitations of linear regression analysis for the estimation of cost–volume relationships.

(Institute of Chartered Accountants in England and Wales, Professional Examination: Part II, Elements of Financial Decisions, July 1977.)

TEN

SIMULATION

10-1 INTRODUCTION

Simulation, also known as simulated sampling or more fully as Monte-Carlo simulation, is as much an art as a technique. It has been described as 'what to do when all else fails'. Some problems in OR may depend on so many stochastic variables in such a way that analytical results are unobtainable. In simulation a (mathematical) model is constructed and artificial (but appropriately selected) data are fed in. The desired parameters of the system (such as expected queue length in a queueing application) are then determined from the output of the model. Imaginary 'runs-through' are conducted. These generate the output from which the performance of the system can be judged. In a capital budgeting application the exercise may produce the (empirical) probability distribution of NPV from which 'risk profiles' and mean and variance of NPV may be calculated.

Rather like sensitivity analysis, simulation is not in itself an optimizing technique. It merely provides a convenient representation of reality and in some more advanced work can be used to improve system performance by adjusting certain variables under the decision maker's control (e.g., advertising expenditure). The art of the process comes in at two levels: the construction of the model and the judgement of changes to be made to controllable variables.

Simulation is an increasingly widely used technique both inside and outside OR. It is likely to prove valuable in any complex logistical problem. Within management science, queueing theory, investment appraisal, and marketing exercises have frequently called upon simulation. Outside of business management simulation has found use in such widely diverse areas as military gaming, demographic analysis, cosmogony, and neo-Darwinian evolution theory.

We shall present the method by way of example. Starting with a capital investment exercise, then a business profitability study, followed by a more involved queueing theory exercise. Finally, there will be a brief example in the area of traffic flow management. Of course, the exercises will be much less complicated than most practical problems, but they should capture the essential features of the subject. The comparative simplicity will also allow the results of the simulation to be checked against the analytical results.

10-2 INVESTMENT APPRAISAL EXERCISE

Suppose that it is known with certainty that the outlay on a project would be £50 000, the discount rate is 10 per cent and the project would run for four years. Risk is attached only to the returns in each year. Suppose that these are given by the probability distribution below (the same for each year, independence between years):

Probability (p)	Return (R)
0.10	9 000
0.25	12 000
0.35	18 000
0.25	24 000
0.05	36 000

Now, the mean or 'expected' return in each year is $\Sigma pR = 18\,000$. *If* there was no variability and this mean return occurred each year then the net present value would be

$$-50\,000 + \frac{18\,000}{(1.1)} + \frac{18\,000}{(1.1)^2} + \frac{18\,000}{(1.1)^3} + \frac{18\,000}{(1.1)^4}$$

However, the returns are *not* assured, and feigning ignorance of elementary probability theory, we shall use simulation to estimate the mean and variance of present value.

The first step in the simulation exercise is to allocate blocks of *two-digit numbers* to each value of return. The size of each block in relation to the total *must be such as to correspond to the probabilities above.* The numbers used will be:

$$00, 01, 02, 03, \ldots, 97, 98, 99$$

For the 9000 return (which has probability 0.1) we assign 10 per cent of the one hundred, 2-digit numbers 00 to 99. In principle *any* ten of the numbers would suffice, but for convenience sake we shall select 00 to 09 inclusive. Now the 12 000 return has probability 0.25 of arising so that 25 per cent of the 2-digit numbers are assigned to this eventuality. Again these 25 could be any of the remaining 90 numbers but we shall employ 10 to 34 inclusive. The procedure is applied in a similar fashion to the remaining returns with the results shown below:

Return	Nos allocated
9 000	00–09
12 000	10–34
18 000	35–69
24 000	70–94
36 000	95–99

Next, a string of random numbers is obtained from a calculator or a pre-prepared table of such. Suppose the string of numbers is

$$0358579353819388232296790614946 7$$

We are now ready for the first 'run' of the simulation. A pair of digits is selected from the given string—for convenience let this be the first pair, 03. This number is used to give the hypothetical first year return in run one. The number 03 falls in the range 00–09 so that the first return is 9000. The second return is then given by the next pair of digits in the string. This is 58 and being in the range 35–69 signifies a return of 18 000 in year 2. In similar fashion the third and fourth year returns are 18 000 and 24 000 as pointed to by the numbers 57 and 93. This completes the 'drawings' for Run no. 1, the cash flow being:

$t = 1$	$t = 1$	$t = 2$	$t = 3$	$t = 4$
− 50 000	9000	18 000	18 000	24 000

It is important to note that this cash flow pattern *is in no sense a prediction* of what would happen if the project was accepted. It is merely a simulated sample of possible futures drawn according to the appropriate probabilities. Discounting the Run no. 1 cash flow at 10 per cent gives an NPV of + 2974. Now Run no. 2 is started. The first return here (recall that the outlay is always 50 000 in this example) is 18 000 as given by the next pair of digits in the string, 53. Working along the line of digits the reader may verify that the results of the second and subsequently third and fourth runs are as shown in Table 10-1.

Table 10-1

	Run number			
	1	2	3	4
$t = 0$	$-50\,000$	$-50\,000$	$-50\,000$	$-50\,000$
$t = 1$	$9\,000$	$18\,000$	$12\,000$	$9\,000$
$t = 2$	$18\,000$	$24\,000$	$12\,000$	$12\,000$
$t = 3$	$18\,000$	$24\,000$	$36\,000$	$24\,000$
$t = 4$	$24\,000$	$24\,000$	$24\,000$	$18\,000$
NPV	$+2974$	$+20\,622$	$+14\,266$	$-1\,575$

Now four runs would be quite insufficient in a practical case. For safety a much larger number would be required, but for convenience we shall restrict ourselves to four runs here. The important row of Table 10-1 is the last one—an array of numbers being four observations of NPV. From these numbers we obtain the simulation estimate of expected net present value (ENPV*) as the *arithmetic mean of the NPV output* thus:

NPV
$2\,974$
$+20\,622$
$+14\,266$
$-1\,575$
$+36\,287$

$$\therefore \quad \text{ENPV*} = \frac{36\,287}{4} = 9072$$

Next we can obtain an estimate of the standard deviation of NPV from the data generated using the expression for standard deviation of an array of numbers (using $N-1$ if extra-sample inferences are to be drawn) we obtain

$$\sigma^*_{\text{NPV}} = \sqrt{\frac{\Sigma(\text{NPV} - \text{ENPV*})^2}{N-1}}$$

where N is the number of observations, i.e., the number of runs of the simulation. Using rounded numbers the workings are:

NPV	NPV $-$ ENPV*	(NPV $-$ ENPV*)^2
$2\,974$	$-6\,098$	$37\,185\,604$
$20\,622$	$+11\,550$	$133\,402\,500$
$14\,266$	$+5\,194$	$26\,977\,636$
$-1\,575$	$-10\,647$	$113\,358\,609$
		$310\,924\,349$

thus

$$\sigma^*_{NPV} = \sqrt{\frac{310\,924\,349}{3}} = 10\,180$$

It then follows that the simulation estimated *coefficient of variation*, c^*, will be

$$c^* = \frac{10\,180}{9072} = 1.12$$

The coefficient of variation is often a useful statistic in investment appraisal. It can be viewed either as an index of risk, in which account has been taken of the scale of the investment; or as a criterion of acceptability in a single-project framework. In the latter role the coefficient of variation states units of standard deviation per unit of mean or, interpreted in the usual fashion, units of risk per unit of return. Thus the lower c is the better.

Now let us check these results by direct calculation. We have seen that the mean yearly return is £18 000. The variance of return in any year, σ^2_R (recall that independence of return between years is assumed) is $\Sigma p(R - \bar{R})^2$. Thus $\sigma^2_R = \Sigma p(R - 18\,000)^2$. The reader may verify that $\sigma^2_R = 42\,300\,000$. Now, it turns out that with no interdependence between years the variance of NPV is given by

$$\text{Var(outlay)} + \sum_{t=1}^{n} \frac{\text{Var}\,R_t}{(1+r)^{2t}}$$

(for further discussion of this see Samuels and Wilkes, 1980a). Thus with the outlay certain, we find that

$$\sigma^2_{NPV} = 0 + 42\,300\,000 \left[\frac{1}{(1.1)^2} + \frac{1}{(1.1)^4} + \frac{1}{(1.1)^6} + \frac{1}{(1.1)^8} \right]$$

$$\therefore \quad \sigma_{NPV} = 10\,366$$

so that the value produced by the four-run simulation was rather more accurate than might have been expected. Now for ENPV, discounting the expected return in each year gives the result (using the annuity factor for four years at 10 per cent)

$$\text{ENPV} = -50\,000 + 18\,000 \times 3.1699 = 7058$$

so that the simulation is somewhat out. The true coefficient of variation is given by

$$c = \frac{10\,366}{7058} = 1.47$$

Here again there is rather a difference between the theoretical true value and the simulation result. These differences are neither surprising nor alarming since, as we have already pointed out, many more than four runs would be required in practice. The patient reader equipped with random number tables may continue the exercise and see how the performance of the simulation improves.

The objective of this example has been to illustrate the mechanics of the approach in an investment context. Naturally, it will not be possible in practice to check the results by direct calculation—the simulation would be pointless if this could be, or was, done. The whole approach can be much more ambitious than described here but the procedure would in principle be the same. For instance, suppose that a half dozen factors had been singled out as important and subject to risk. These might be selling price(s), unit cost(s), sales volume(s), initial outlay, project life, and discount rate. For each of these factors a probability distribution has to be specified (perhaps normal, beta, or gamma) and simultaneous drawings are taken from these distributions to give sample values of the parameters. Then NPV is calculated using this data and the exercise is repeated many times over. The distribution of yield may thus be obtained as well as that of NPV, and 'risk profiles' can be produced. At the end of the exercise a decision is still to be taken in the light of the evidence produced.

10-3 PROFITABILITY STUDY

This material will be presented in the form of an exam-style question:

A tradesman receives supplies of a product from a wholesaler each working day. The quantity supplied by the wholesaler is a random variable as is the subsequent (same day) retail demand for the commodity. The probability distribution for the amount supplied to the tradesman by the wholesaler is:

Supply from wholesaler (units)	Probability
1	0.08
2	0.17
3	0.20
4	0.25
5	0.17
6	0.13

The probability distribution of retail customers' demand is:

Retail customers' demand (units)	Probability
1	0.07
2	0.14
3	0.22
4	0.30
5	0.18
6	0.09

The tradesman buys from the wholesaler at £10 per unit and sells to his retail customers at £20 per unit. Unsold units on any day can be stored in any required numbers and can be sold at the full price at any time in the future. However, if the tradesman is unable to satisfy retail customers' demand there is an estimated cost of £5 per unit of unsatisfied demand. The working year is 289 days. Using the digits:

07837188929284372828913418482163207 52618

(i) Simulate 10 days' business. Estimate average daily profit and give a point estimate of expected annual profits.
(ii) From the results of the run estimate the standard deviation of daily profit and obtain a 95 per cent confidence interval for yearly profits.

The allocation of digits on the supply side is:

Supply	Probability	Digits
1	0.08	00–07
2	0.17	08–24
3	0.20	25–44
4	0.25	45–69
5	0.17	70–86
6	0.13	87–99

and on the demand side:

Demand	Probability	Digits
1	0.07	00–06
2	0.14	07–20
3	0.22	21–42
4	0.30	43–72
5	0.18	73–90
6	0.09	91–99

Thus the blocks of two-digit numbers have been assigned to the various supply and demand values in accordance with the probabilities of occurrence. A convenient layout for the exercise is shown in Table 10-2. Using the digits in pairs, alternately for supply and demand, the first drawing is 07 in the group assigned to one unit supplied. Cost will therefore be £10. The next pair of digits is 83 corresponding to demand of 5 but sales can only be one unit (as nothing is in store initially). Thus revenue is £20, but with the notional shortage loss of £5 per unit of unsatisfied demand the total shortage loss on the day is £20. There is nothing to put in store and the net 'profit', Π, on the day is Revenue − Cost − Shortage Loss = $20 - 10 - 20 = -£10$. The next pair of digits is 71 which gives a second-day supply figure of 5 units. And so on. On day 4 we have the first items going into store—which builds up to be drawn upon on days 7, 8, and 9. The total profit on the 10 days' business is £300, giving an estimated daily profit figure of £30. With a working year of 289 days the point estimate of annual profit is therefore £289 × 30 = £8670.

Table 10-2

Day	Run no.	Supply	Cost	Run no.	Demand	Sales	Revenue	Sh. loss	Σ store	Π
1	07	1	10	83	5	1	20	20	—	− 10
2	71	5	50	88	5	5	100	—	—	50
3	92	6	60	92	6	6	120	—	—	60
4	84	5	50	37	3	3	60	—	2	10
5	28	3	30	28	3	3	60	—	2	30
6	91	6	60	34	3	3	60	—	5	—
7	18	2	20	48	4	4	80	—	3	60
8	21	2	20	63	4	4	80	—	1	60
9	20	2	20	75	5	3	60	10	—	30
10	26	3	30	18	2	2	40	—	1	10

Total Π = £300

Before turning to the next part of the question, we can estimate the value of the storage facilities to the firm. Using the same data, simply recalculate the profit (Π) column if store facilities had *not* been available. The Sales, Revenue, Shortage Loss, and Profit columns would then have been as shown in Table 10-3 page 204. Only on days 7, 8, and 9 is any impact felt, but here the effects are quite considerable. The result is that estimated daily profit drops to £17.50. The difference between this, and the earlier figure of £30 with storage—£12.50—represents the daily value of the facilities. In other words if there had been a proposal to rent storage facilities for £10 per day, this

Table 10-3

Day	Sales	Revenue	Sh. loss	Π
1	1	20	20	−10
2	5	100	—	50
3	6	120	—	60
4	3	60	—	10
5	3	60	—	30
6	3	60	—	—
7	2	40	10	10
8	2	40	10	10
9	2	40	15	5
10	2	40	—	10
			Total Π =	175

would have been acceptable since the firm would have been left a £2.50 net improvement.

Now for the standard deviation of profit. This will simply be:

$$\sqrt{\frac{\Sigma(\Pi-\bar{\Pi})^2}{n-1}} = \sqrt{\frac{\Sigma(\Pi-30)^2}{9}}$$

and the workings are shown in Table 10-4. $\bar{\Pi}$ the mean daily profit we have seen to be £30 and we have 10 'observations' ($n = 10$) on Π from the runs of the simulation. Thus daily standard deviation is

$$\text{daily s.d.} = \sqrt{\frac{6400}{9}} = \frac{80}{3} = £26.\overline{66}$$

Table 10-4

Π	Π−$\bar{\Pi}$	(Π−$\bar{\Pi}$)²
−10	−40	1600
50	20	400
60	30	900
10	−20	400
30	0	0
0	−30	900
60	30	900
60	30	900
30	0	0
10	−20	400
	6400 =	Σ(Π−$\bar{\Pi}$)²

The daily variance is, of course, 6400/9, and this figure enables us to estimate annual variance. With assumed independence of each day's events, the annual variance will be the sum of the daily variances, i.e.

$$\text{Annual variance} = 289\left(\frac{6400}{9}\right)$$

So that

$$\text{Annual standard deviation} = 17\left(\frac{80}{3}\right) = £453.\overline{33}$$

Now even though profit is not normally distributed on a daily basis, the sum of a large number of days' profit *will* be approximately normally distributed. Thus the usual confidence intervals can be determined, viz., there is a 95 per cent chance that annual profit will be within 1.96 standard deviations of the mean annual figure. That is, the range is

$$8670 \pm 1.96(453.33)$$

giving

$$7781 \text{ to } 9559$$

as the 95 per cent confidence range.

10-4 QUEUEING THEORY EXPERIMENT

In this exercise we shall simulate an uncomplicated situation. This will enable the work to be kept within reasonable bounds and will also allow the results to be checked analytically. In what is known to be a simple queueing situation, the following inter-arrival times are observed:

Arrival no.	1	2	3	4	5	6	7	8	9	10
	38	3	41	20	57	10	46	99	87	221

The time units are seconds. The numbers were, in fact, generated by a process that will be described later, and represent drawings from a negative exponential distribution with a mean of 60 seconds. Thus while the *average* time between arrivals is 60 seconds, the first 'person' arrives 38 seconds after observations begin, the second person arrives just 3 seconds later still, and so on.

In Table 10-5 the fourth row gives drawings from an exponential service distribution with a mean service time of 40 seconds. The first person, however, takes 136 seconds to be served, the next arrival takes 17 seconds to be served, and so on. The remaining data are calculated in the following fashion.

Table 10-5

1. Arrival no.	1	2	3	4	5	6	7	8	9	10	Σ
2. Inter-arrival time	38	3	41	20	57	10	46	99	87	221	
3. Arrival time	38	41	82	102	159	169	215	314	401	622	
4. Service time	136	17	23	4	70	55	36	17	12	62	
5. 'Into' time	38	174	191	214	218	288	343	379	401	622	
6. 'From' time	174	191	214	218	288	343	379	396	413	684	= Total time
7. Queueing time	0	133	109	112	59	119	128	65	0	0	725
8. s.p. idle time	38	0	0	0	0	0	0	0	5	209	
9. System time	136	150	132	116	129	174	164	82	12	62	1157

Arrival time of row (3) is the sum of the inter-arrival times up to and including the arrival in question. It is the time of arrival into the system (and the queue if there is one). If the whole process is started at $t = 0$, then person 4 arrives after 102 seconds $(= 38 + 3 + 41 + 20)$. The 'into' time of arrival n is the time that person n reaches the service point. This time will be either:

(a) the previous person's 'into' time plus service time (i.e., the 'from' time of person $n - 1$); or
(b) the arrival time of person n

whichever is the greater. This is (a) for all persons up to and including no. 8, who leaves the system at $t = 396$; but person 9 does not arrive until $t = 401$, thus 401 is person 9's into time. The queueing time will be the into time less the arrival time. Row 8 gives the service point (s.p.) idle time, being the difference, if any, between the into time of person n and the from time of $n - 1$. Row 9 gives the system process time for each individual and is queueing time plus service time.

Now from all of this we can produce estimates of the important system parameters:

1. *Average queueing time.* Total queueing time for all ten people is 725 seconds so that the average time spent queueing was $725/10 = 72.5$ *seconds*. This is the simulation estimate. In fact we know that the true average is

$$\frac{\lambda}{\mu(\mu - \lambda)} = \frac{60}{90(90 - 60)} \times 3600 = 80 \text{ seconds}$$

so that with only 10 observations the simulated sample estimate is remarkably close to the true value. Once again, simulation output is not normally checked in this fashion since there is no point in practice if analytical results can be obtained.

2. *Average system process time* (ASPT). This is the total of the system times (1157) divided by 10; giving 115.7. The true value is

$$\frac{1}{\mu - \lambda} \times 3600 = 120 \text{ seconds}$$

so that once again the simulation result is close.

3. *Average queue length.* This is obtained as

$$\frac{\text{total queueing time}}{\text{total time of problem}} = \frac{725}{684} = 1.06$$

On average (all times considered) there is a queue length of 1.06 persons. The ratio above is not obvious, but consider a much smaller example when total queueing time = 30 seconds and problem time (when the last person observed leaves the system) is 15 seconds. For total queueing time to be 30 seconds then in each of the 15 seconds of real time there must be an average of two persons in the queue. The true average queue length is

$$\frac{\lambda^2}{\mu(\mu - \lambda)} = 1.\overline{33}$$

4. *Average queue when there is a queue.* This statistic is rather more difficult to extract from the exercise. We need to prepare a separate table breaking down the total problem time into intervals when there were

Table 10-6

Time	No. in queue (X)	Seconds (S)	XS
0–41	0	41	0
41–82	1	41	41
82–102	2	20	40
102–159	3	57	171
159–169	4	10	40
169–174	5	5	25
174–191	4	17	68
191–214	3	23	69
214–215	2	1	2
215–218	3	3	9
218–288	2	70	140
288–314	1	26	26
314–343	2	29	58
343–379	1	36	36
379–401	0	22	0
401–684	0	283	0
		$\Sigma S = 684$	$\Sigma XS = 725$

particular queue lengths. This is done in Table 10-6. While there is only one person in the system there is no queue. The second person arrives after 41 seconds and the first person is still being served. The first person is still in service at $t = 82$ when the third customer arrives (row (3) of Table 10-4). Thus the length of queue has now risen to 2. When the fourth person arrives at $t = 102$ the first person is still in the queue. And so the queue length builds up (as shown in the X column of Table 10-6) until $t = 174$ when the first person leaves. The break points in the time column are moments when a person leaves or enters the system, thus affecting queue length. The average queue length is the weighted average of the numbers in the queue, the weights being the durations for which the particular lengths existed, viz.,

$$\text{average queue length (all times)} = \frac{\Sigma XS}{\Sigma S} = \frac{725}{684} = 1.06$$

which confirms the result previously obtained. To find the average queue length only where there is a queue, instead of taking the total $\Sigma S = 684$, add up only those times when there *is* a queue. Thus

$$\text{average queue length (when queue exists)} = \frac{\Sigma XS}{\Sigma X (\text{for } X > 0)}$$

$$= \frac{725}{338} = 2.14$$

whereas the true average is

$$\frac{\mu}{\mu - \lambda} = 3$$

5. *Average number in the system.* The simulated sampling estimate of this parameter is given by the ratio

$$\frac{\Sigma \text{ system process time}}{\text{total problem time}} = \frac{1157}{684} = 1.69$$

and the correct value is

$$\frac{\lambda}{\mu - \lambda} = 2$$

6. *System state probabilities.* Table 10-7, in similar fashion to Table 10-6, shows the numbers in the system over the length of the experiment. From the data in this form we can easily estimate the probability of having one person in the system (P_1) or the system being empty (P_0) or in general containing n people (P_n). The numbers in the system are called states and the P_n are *state probabilities.* Thus to find the simulation estimate of P_0 we use Table 10-7 to add the lengths of time for which the system is empty and divide by the total time. Thus

$$\text{estimate of } P_0 = \frac{38+5+209}{684} = 0.37$$

whereas in truth

$$P_0 = 1 - \frac{\lambda}{\mu} = 0.33$$

As a further example,

$$\text{estimate of } P_2 = \frac{41+26+36}{684} = 0.15$$

$$\text{true value} = \left(1 - \frac{\lambda}{\mu}\right)\left(\frac{\lambda}{\mu}\right)^2 = 0.15$$

As a further example of the use of Table 10-7, we can estimate

$$P(n \geqslant 5) = \frac{10+5+17}{684} = 0.05$$

whereas

$$P(n \geqslant 5) = \left(\frac{\lambda}{\mu}\right)^5 = 0.13$$

Table 10-7 can also be used to confirm the average number in system result of (5) above.

Table 10-7

Time	No. in system	Sec.
0–38	0	38
38–41	1	3
41–82	2	41
82–102	3	20
102–159	4	57
159–169	5	10
169–174	6	5
174–191	5	17
191–214	4	23
214–215	3	1
215–218	4	3
218–288	3	70
288–314	2	26
314–343	3	29
343–379	2	36
379–396	1	17
396–401	0	5
401–413	1	12
413–622	0	209
622–684	1	62

7. *Service point idle time.* The proportion of total time that the service point is idle is, from the eighth row of Table 10-4,

$$\frac{38+5+209}{684} = 0.37$$

so that the service point operative would have 37 per cent of their time available for interruptable tasks. Of course, the proportion of service point idle time is P_0.

On the whole the results of the simulation were in very good accord with the true values (which in general will be unknown). This with only 10 'runs'. Many more observations would be taken in a practical case and the results would, accordingly, be even more dependable.

10-5 GENERATING THE DATA

First consider the inter-arrival times: 38, 3, 41, etc. These were random drawings from a negative exponential distribution with mean 60 seconds (or, more conveniently, one minute). Now working here with a time unit of one minute, $\lambda = 1$. This is equivalent to the 60 per hour that we were working with earlier on. Now the negative exponential probability density function of inter-arrival time, T, is $f(T)$ where:

$$f(T) = \lambda e^{-\lambda T}$$

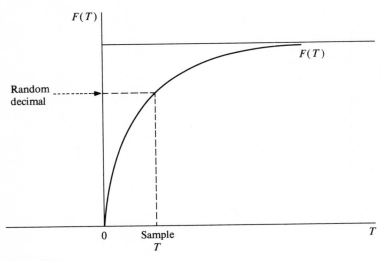

Figure 10-1

The probability that T minutes elapse between arrivals (i.e., that the inter-arrival time of T minutes occurs) is

$$\int_0^T f(T)dT = \int_0^T \lambda e^{-\lambda T}dT = [-e^{-\lambda T}]_0^T = 1 - e^{-\lambda T} = F(T) \quad (10\text{-}1)$$

The last term on the right of Eq. (10-1) is the *cumulative probability function.* It is this function which is most convenient for generating the simulation data. The appearance of $F(T)$ is shown in Fig. 10-1. To generate the sample data, random points in the 0–1 interval on the vertical axis are selected and, going through the function $F(T)$, sample values of T are read off the horizontal axis.

It is not actually necessary to use the graph to generate the data. Suppose that a table of random numbers (entered at an arbitrary point) yields the following string of digits:

$$471051491279613152539808764975$$

Use these in triplets (for sufficient accuracy) to generate random values of $F(T)$. These will be the random decimals shown in Table 10-8. Thus the first will be 0.471 so that we must now solve for T where

$$0.471 = 1 - e^{-T}$$

Use of a hand calculator or natural logarithms gives $T = 0.637$ minutes, i.e., 38 seconds (rounded). This is where the first inter-arrival time came from. Proceeding, the next triplet of random digits gives 0.051 and solving

$$0.051 = 1 - e^{-T}$$

gives $T = 0.052$ minutes or 3 seconds. The full workings are shown in Table 10-8.

Table 10-8

Random decimal ($=F(T)$)	T (min)	T (sec)
0.471	0.637	38
0.051	0.052	3
0.491	0.675	41
0.279	0.327	20
0.613	0.949	57
0.152	0.165	10
0.539	0.774	46
0.808	1.650	99
0.764	1.444	87
0.975	3.689	221

For practice the reader might like to generate the service time data of row (4) of Table 10-5. Setting $\mu = 1.5$ (per minute) and solving for service time, S, from

$$F(S) = 1 - e^{-\mu S}$$

using the following digits in triplets to generate values of $F(S)$

96735343708982674659235386178 9

10-6 TRAFFIC MANAGEMENT PROBLEM

It has already been mentioned that full-scale computer-based simulation methods have been used successfully (indeed there is little alternative) in inner-city traffic management problems. A full description of full-blown computer techniques is beyond the scope of this section (although certain relevant points are made later on). Similarly a whole volume could be devoted to traffic management problems. Here, mainly by way of a simple example, we aim to convey the style of approach.

QUESTION The installation of traffic lights at a T junction is under consideration. Two lanes of traffic are possible on each side of the roads. The possibility of vehicles crossing in front of each other is ruled out as too dangerous. This condition is to be stringently observed and the use of separate but adjacent lanes by traffic that otherwise may have crossed is also ruled out.

(a) Show that:
    (i) there are *six* routes through the junction;
    (ii) there are *four* possible combinations of routes that allow three distinct directions of traffic flow;
    (iii) it is not possible to have *four* distinct flows simultaneously;
    (iv) only *three* of the combinations are needed to include all routes at least once, and indicate the appropriate traffic light settings.
(b) Outline a procedure for using simulation to ascertain desirable timings for the lights (how long each light should show in each of the combinations). Explain what data would be required. What possible criteria might be considered for comparing alternative timings? In what directions must care be exercised in drawing conclusions?

ANSWER (a) (i) The form of the junction is as illustrated in Fig. 10-2 with the three approaches to the junction being labelled. The number of possible routes is the number of permutations of the letters ABC. Thus with the first letter representing the 'origin' and the second the 'destination' the routes are: AB, AC, BA, BC, CA, CB—six in all.
    (ii) This is not an easy question, bearing in mind the conditions that

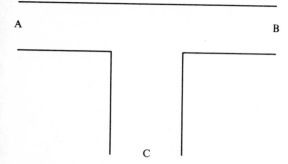

Figure 10-2

have to be observed. However, the problem size allows us to itemize for each route those routes on which traffic cannot be allowed simultaneously. In drawing up such lists it is helpful to sketch in some figures. The crossing-over prohibition obviously rules out the combining of BA and CB as shown in Fig. 10-3(a). But also ruled out by the 'adjacency' ban are such combinations as AB and CB of Fig. 10-2(b). The full results are given in Table 10-9. The most important column here is the one showing the routes that *are* allowed to operate in conjunction with any given route. Sorting out what *combinations* of routes are allowed can be tricky and time-consuming but fortunately there is a very helpful diagrammatic device. In Fig. 10-4 each route is represented by a point (at the corners of a regular hexagon for aesthetic reasons only). Any two points in the diagram are joined by a line if and only if they can operate simultaneously. Thus for AB we look at the 'allowed' list in Table 10-9 and join AB up with AC, BA, BC, and CA. Then AC will be joined up with AB (already done) and CA. Thus Fig. 10-4 is an alternative representation of Table 10-9, but it presents the information in a much more convenient way (rather as with critical path diagrams). The point is this: *a combination of routes* (say AB, BA, and BC) *can be operated simultaneously if*

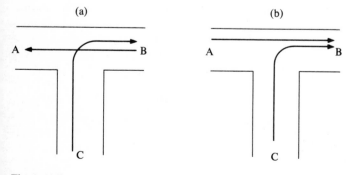

Figure 10-3

Table 10-9

Route	Prohibited	Allowed
AB	CB	AC, BA, BC, CA
AC	BA, BC, CB	AB, CA
BA	AC, CB, CA	AB, BC
BC	AC	BA, AB, CB, CA
CA	BA	BC, AC, AB, CB
CB	AB, AC, BA	BC, CA

and only if the corresponding points in Fig. 10-4 are ALL directly connected to each other.

Thus the combination AB, BA, and BC is permitted since each point is connected directly with a single straight line to every other in the combination. But AB, AC, and BA is *not* permitted because of the absence of a direct link between AC and BA. The reader may verify these results by drawing sketches as in Fig. 10-3.

It is now easy to see that there are precisely four triangles that can be extracted from Fig. 10-4. These are the four combinations of three routes referred to in the question. These combinations are:

$$
\begin{array}{cccc}
AB & AB & AB & BC \\
AC & BA & BC & CB \\
CA & BC & CA & CA \\
(1) & (2) & (3) & (4)
\end{array}
$$

Notice that CB appears only in (4) and that BA and AC appear only in (2) and (1) respectively. These three groups also include all the remaining routes. Thus arrangement (3) is not strictly necessary. Finally, it is easily seen from Fig. 10-4 that no quadrilaterals can be extracted. Thus no combination of four routes is possible. Of course, there are also smaller, essentially trivial, arrangements that include only two routes or even one. But each of these will be already included in (1), (2), (3), or (4) and must represent inferior

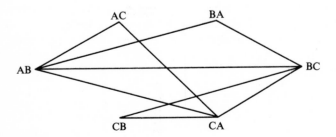

Figure 10-4

Table 10-10

Route	Arrangement		
	(1)	(2)	(4)
AB	G	G	R
AC	G	R	R
BA	R	G	R
BC	R	G	G
CA	G	R	G
CB	R	R	G

situations with the unnecessary closing of one or more routes. To complete part (a) of the problem we have simply to present the light settings appropriate to the arrangements (1), (2), and (4) above. These are shown in Table 10-10, in which G represents green (go) and red (stop) is indicated by R. Looking across the rows there must be at least one G in each row for feasibility.

Two questions now arise: (a) for how many seconds should each arrangement be shown and (b) can arrangement (3) be discarded altogether? To take the second question first—in fact we cannot say *a priori* that it is always going to be optimal to have only the minimum number of arrangements that include all routes at least once, especially so when connections with other sets of lights have to be considered. So, strictly speaking, we should include (3) in the simulation exercise *including some runs in which* (3) *is shown for zero seconds* (i.e., is excluded). However, it may be a traffic engineer's operating rule of thumb that the fewer the arrangements the better. This is always plausible, especially so in a simple isolated system such as we are considering. So we shall omit (3) from now on.

Now for the first question. One possibility would be to allow each arrangement an equal length of time, say, 90 seconds each. This would have the effect of giving routes AB, BC, and CA twice as much time as for the remaining three. This may be desirable if they are the busiest routes, but it is the main task of the simulation exercise to obtain the 'best' timings. We put the word 'best' in quotes for two reasons: (a) given a criterion (such as expected queueing time overall) there is no guarantee of reaching the global optimum by simulation and (b) there may be other possible criteria against which the system performance can be assessed (e.g., queue length or a priority system for certain routes). However, it is usual to try to minimize expected waiting time overall. This is the obvious statistic and the system performance will be judged according to this criterion.

The simulation would then *vary* the lengths of the settings and ascertain the effects on total waiting time. For instance, to begin with we might try (1) for 40 seconds, (2) for 110 seconds, and (4) for 50 seconds; these numbers being guesses at 'reasonable' values based on casual inspection of traffic flow

Table 10-11

1	2	3	4	5	6	7
Route	Average flow	(1) time	(2) time	(4) time	Total	%
AB	17	40	110		150	75
AC	8	40			40	20
BA	30		110		110	55
BC	7		110	50	160	80
CA	13	40		50	90	45
CB	10			50	50	25

rates. A number of runs would then be conducted (by computer!) with these timings, with average waiting time as the end product. Then the timings would be changed—in a direction which seems 'reasonable' or by some systematic automated procedure—some runs conducted, and again average waiting time ascertained. Then there would be more changes of timings and more sets of random drawings. The arrangement which provided the least overall waiting time would then be preferred.

The above initial values of timings might have resulted from the following flow data:

Route	Average number of vehicles per minute
AB	17
AC	8
BA	30
BC	7
CA	13
CB	10

BA being the busiest route and being represented only in (2) suggests that (2) must be given considerably longer time than (1) or (4). As a rough guide Table 10-11 gives the total time (per 200 seconds) that each route is open (column (6)) and the percentage of time in column (7). The figures suggest that increasing the proportion of time given to (2) might next be attempted. The simulation could also investigate the desirability of quick changes for the same proportionate times: viz., 20 s for (1), 55 s for (2), and 25 s for (3).

Clearly, the flow data is vital if the simulation is to be a good proxy for the real situation. One problem in gathering this data is that rates of flow will vary with time of day. Perhaps the data given above are for the early evening rush-hour with BA being the out-of-city route. A different pattern would be arrived at if 8 a.m. to 9 a.m. flow data were used. Clearly, if the settings can be varied according to time of day then perhaps four sets of timings could be provided (morning rush, day-time/evening, evening rush, night-time). At any rate the data would need to be compiled over a period of weeks (as there will be day-to-day as well as within-day variations) to ensure valid results. Recall the maxim GIGO. Further, in respect of data we have not considered the varying *nature* of traffic flows. If one route is much used by heavy commercial vehicles (taking longer to manoeuvre and causing obstruction) then the results may be questionable. If resources allow, it would be wise to monitor the system for a while after the simulation results have been implemented. Finally, recall that we have been considering the junction as an isolated system. Changes or unexpected events elsewhere may, in practice, significantly affect results.

10-7 ADVANTAGES AND DISADVANTAGES OF SIMULATION

Phillips, Ravindran, and Solberg (1976) give twelve reasons why simulation might be useful. They are:

1. Simulation makes possible the study of very complicated systems and subsystems.
2. The consequences for a system of possible changes in parameters or structural alterations can be investigated in terms of the model.
3. The knowledge of a system obtained in designing and conducting the simulation is often very valuable.
4. Simulation can be a useful teaching aid (e.g., business games).
5. Related to (3), the detailed observation of the simulated system can lead to better understanding of it.
6. The simulation of complicated systems can identify which variables are the most important influences on system performance.
7. Simulation can be used to experiment with novel and unfamiliar situations so as to prepare for many eventualities both routine and extreme (aircraft flight simulators are classic examples of this).
8. Simulation can provide a 'pre-service test' for possible new policies before the risk of actually implementing these policies is taken.
9. In some stochastic problems where the sequence of events is crucial, the ordinary statistical parameters (means, variances, etc.) may be inadequate to describe the process. Simulation is then the sole recourse.
10. Simulation can be used to confirm (or refute!) analytical solutions. (This is the reverse of the process described earlier in the chapter.)
11. Simulation enables a dynamic system to be studied in real time or in compressed (fast motion) or expanded (slow motion) time scales.
12. If new elements are introduced into a system possible bottlenecks or shortages can be identified.

There are, however, a number of possible dangers of which we should be aware. For example, Thierauf and Klekamp (1975) give seven limitations:

1. Simulation does not guarantee optimal solutions.
2. The simulation exercise can be time-consuming.
3. As the number of variables in the exercise increases the difficulty of finding near optimal values increases considerably.
4. A tendency may develop to rely on the technique too frequently because of its comparative ease of application (in contrast perhaps to analytical studies).
5. There may be serious errors of *omission* (important variables or relationships left out of the model).
6. There may be serious errors of *commission*, e.g., unnecessary constraints may have been included that look innocuous but in fact have dramatic effects.
7. Possible oversimplification. The true relationships between the variables may be so complex that they cannot be properly expressed in convenient mathematical relationships.

In addition, there are a number of drawbacks for business games (a form of simulation). They may be viewed as artificial and seen only as a game and not a learning experience and may produce a facile view of management.

In conclusion, the role of experience in usage should be emphasized. To quote Phillips, Ravindran, and Solberg (1976):

> a great deal of experience is desirable in order to adequately exploit the real powers of simulation. This background is often best gained through modelling experience, enabling a simulation analyst to create unique skills in this area. For this reason, simulation modelling is often more of an 'art' than a science. This art is best cultivated rather than taught, although the basic tools and modelling logic can be gained through diligent study of simulation methodologies.

EXERCISES

10-1 Why is simulation likely to prove useful in an operational research content? Very broadly, how does it work? Does the method optimize? Outline the major advantages and disadvantages of the method.

10-2 An investment requires an outlay of £12 000 and runs for three years. The discount rate is 10 per cent. Returns are independent between years and in each of the years are given by:

Probability	Return (£)
0.06	1500
0.17	2000
0.22	4500
0.29	6000
0.16	7500
0.10	9400

Given the following digits:

8 7 0 5 6 9 0 5 8 1 9 4 2 7 1 4 2 1 8 7 7 4 9 5 3 1 5 8 0 4

conduct a simulation exercise (five runs) to estimate ENPV. Use the information obtained to estimate the coefficient of variation.

10-3 Pisces Ltd trade in a perishable commodity. Each day Pisces receive supplies of the good from a wholesaler but the quantity supplied is a random variable as is subsequent retail customer demand for the commodity. Both supply and demand are expressed in batches of 50 units and over the past working year (300 days) Pisces have kept records of supplies and demands. The results are given in the table:

Wholesaler supplies	No. of days occurring	Customers' demand	No. of days occurring
50	60	50	60
100	90	100	60
150	90	150	150
200	60	200	30

Pisces Ltd buys the commodity at £6 per unit and sells at £10 a unit. At present unsold units at the end of the day are worthless and there are no storage facilities. Pisces estimate that each unit of unsatisfied demand on any day costs them £2. Using the following random numbers:

$$848033479615$$

   (i) Simulate six days' trading and estimate annual profit.

   (ii) Re-run the exercise to estimate the value of storage facilities.

   (iii) Briefly, what other information could be gleaned from the exercise and what qualifications should be made in respect of the results?

10-4 'There are two distinct approaches to problems arising from queueing situations. The more popular is simulation, but the formulae of queueing theory are equally useful. In fact, the choice of method is largely a matter of personal taste.'

Required:

Discuss and criticize this quotation. Your answer should also include the following:

   (a) an example of a problem to which queueing theory might be applied;

   (b) an example of a problem for which simulation is the more appropriate method;

   (c) an assessment of the relative strengths and weaknesses of each method.

(Association of Certified Accountants, Professional Examination: Section 2, paper 12, Management Mathematics, June 1976.)

10-5 Coltel Ltd is considering the introduction of a new product and has compiled the following information:

Variable	Expected value	Standard deviation
Sales quantity	5 000	400
Selling price per unit (£)	300	5
Fixed costs (£)	580 000	10 000
Variable costs per unit (£)	175	7.5

(For simplicity assume that all the random variables are independent and that the probability distributions are normal.)

Required:

   (a) Calculate, using break-even analysis and expected values, the break-even volume and the expected profit for the period.

(4 marks)

(b) Explain how you would carry out a simulation to arrive at an approximate distribution of profits. Illustrate your answer by using the cumulative normal distribution below and the following random numbers 20, 96, 68, 59 to obtain one simulated figure for profit.

(16 marks)

(c) What is the value to Coltel Ltd of having carried out a simulation rather than simply estimating profit using expected values?

(5 marks)

Cumulative normal distribution table

Random number	No. of deviations from mean	Random number	No. of deviations from mean	Random number	No. of deviations from mean
00	−2.5	22–24	−0.7	79–81	0.8
01	−2.3	25–27	−0.6	82–83	0.9
02	−2.0	28–31	−0.5	84–85	1.0
03	−1.9	32–34	−0.4	86–87	1.1
04	−1.8	35–38	−0.3	88–89	1.2
05	−1.7	39–42	−0.2	90–91	1.3
06	−1.6	43–46	−0.1	92	1.4
07	−1.5	47–53	0.0	93	1.5
08	−1.4	54–57	0.1	94	1.6
09–10	−1.3	58–61	0.2	95	1.7
11–12	−1.2	62–65	0.3	96	1.8
13–14	−1.1	66–68	0.4	97	1.9
15–16	−1.0	69–72	0.5	98	2.0
17–18	−0.9	73–75	0.6	99	2.3
19–21	−0.8	76–78	0.7		

(Association of Certified Accountants, Professional Examination: Section 2, paper 12, Management Mathematics, December 1977.)

10-6 For several years our local council's policy on housing has given widespread cause for concern. The main body of criticism has been levelled at the priority scheme operated by our council. This involves an allegedly crude classification of applicants as 'urgent' or 'non-urgent'. Urgent cases move directly to the head of the housing list provided no other urgent case is already there. The destitute fall into this category but similar accelerated treatment of other needy groups, e.g., the disabled, is being pressed.

Applications for housing are received at the rate of two per week. The following table details the rates at which houses are found for those reaching the head of the list:

Case type	Percentage of applicants	Time in days to find acceptable accommodation
Urgent	10	2
Non-urgent (a)	80	5
(b)*	10	7

* Applicants with 'special requirements', e.g., disabled applicants.
(Assume a 5-day working week.)

Required:

(a) Describe how you would carry out a simulation of the present policy clearly stating each logical step. Point out all the assumptions you make.

(15 marks)

(b) What further simulations would you want to carry out in order to advise the local council about extending its priority scheme?

(6 marks)

(c) How would you carry out the simulations to minimize the effect of chance creating differences between the existing scheme and any proposed new scheme?

(4 marks)

(Association of Certified Accountants, Professional Examination: Section 2, paper 12, Management Mathematics, December 1976.)

10-7 The Popage Company Ltd has a contract to supply 1 000 000 cans of spinach a year for three years to a major supermarket company. This is a new venture for the company and they need to purchase three new machines A, B, and C for the canning operation. The market situation is fluid however and the company cannot assume that the contract will be renewed after three years or that some other similar business will replace it. They are therefore reluctant to spend a substantial amount on the machines and the management has narrowed the possible choices of equipment to two manufacturers.

The less expensive equipment is built by Company X at a total cost of £60 000 and has an expected life of three years. All three types of machines are needed, and they all have to be purchased from the same company. The operating characteristics are as follows:

Company X

Machine type	A	B	C
Daily output when operating	4500	4500	4500
Probability of breaking down on any particular day	0.04	0.04	0.04
If broken down, probability of downtime duration			
1 day	0.40	0.40	0.35
2 days	0.35	0.30	0.40
3 days	0.25	0.30	0.25

The more expensive equipment is built by Company Y at a total cost of £120 000 and also has a life expectancy of three years. The operating characteristics which are more favourable, are as follows:

Company Y

Machine type	A	B	C
Daily output when operating	4500	4500	4500
Probability of breaking down on any particular day	0.035	0.035	0.035
If broken down, probability of downtime duration			
1 day	0.50	0.50	0.40
2 days	0.35	0.35	0.40
3 days	0.15	0.15	0.20

At the end of the three years the scrap value of the equipment from either company is estimated to be zero.

The contract requires 1 000 000 cans of spinach a year to be produced. The yearly total can however vary slightly from that figure but if 3 000 000 cans are not delivered in three years, a substantial penalty will be imposed. The number of working days in the year for the company is 300. You may assume that the three types of machine A, B, and C are all necessary for producing a can of spinach. Breakdown on any machine will stop all production for the duration of the breakdown.

Required:

Explain how you would carry out a simulation to evaluate the performance of each company's equipment in order to advise the management of Popage Company Ltd which, if either, should be purchased.

(Association of Certified Accountants, Professional Examination: Section 2, paper 12, Management Mathematics, June 1979.)

ELEVEN
TOPICS IN BRIEF

11-1 OVERVIEW

In this chapter we give brief presentations of five topics that have been of interest to professional accounting examiners from time to time. Except for the Game Theory section, for maximum efficiency the discussions are largely framed around examination-type questions, although the 'answers' are generally more comprehensive than could be achieved under actual examination conditions. Some suggestions for further reading are provided, but it would be unreasonable to expect the reader to be conversant with the subtleties of these problems.

11-2 'EXPECTED VALUES'

The type of problem that is envisaged under this head is best illustrated by a specimen question on which a full commentary is provided.

11-2-1 A problem

A boutique advertises fashion clothing from time to time in the press. Only one item is advertised on each occasion. Experience with clothing in the price range £30 to £40 leads the management to judge that the probabilities of demand at various levels, after each advertisement, are:

	After advertising in	
Demand (units)	One newspaper	Two newspapers
30	0.10	0.00
40	0.25	0.15
50	0.40	0.35
60	0.25	0.40
70	0.00	0.10

The next item to be advertised is to sell at £35, will cost £15 to buy in and can be disposed of to the trade, if unsold, for £10. There will be a charge of £37.50 for artwork and blockmaking for the advertisement and each newspaper will charge £50 for the insertion of the advertisement.

(i) How many units of the item should be bought in by the shop and in how many newspapers should advertisements be placed in order to maximize expected net profit?
(ii) Conduct a sensitivity analysis on the results.

The first step here is to construct a 'payoff matrix' showing gross profit for all possible combinations of purchases and sales. The gross profit per unit sold over the counter is £35 − £15 = £20 and the gross profit per unit disposed of otherwise is £10 − £15 = − £5. Table 11-1 shows the gross profits. If the shop purchases only 30 units then, since demand cannot be less than 30, exactly 30 units will be sold giving a gross profit of £20 × 30 = £600. If the shop buys in 40 units, if demand is for 40 or more, gross profits will be £800 (no more can be sold than have been purchased). If the shop buys 40 and demand is for only 30 units this means that 30 are sold at a gross profit of £20 per unit and 10 are disposed of at a loss per unit of £5, the net result is £550. It will be noted that entries below the main diagonal of Table 11-1 (top left to bottom right) are equal to the main diagonal entry in the same column and that those entries above the main diagonal reduce in steps of £250 from the main diagonal entry towards the top of the column.

Table 11-1

Demand (units)	Purchased by shop (units)				
	30	40	50	60	70
30	600	550	500	450	400
40	600	800	750	700	650
50	600	800	1000	950	900
60	600	800	1000	1200	1150
70	600	800	1000	1200	1400

Table 11-2

Demand	Purchased by shop					Probability (P)	
	30	40	50	60	70	One paper	Two papers
30	600	550	500	450	400	0.10	0.00
40	600	800	750	700	650	0.25	0.15
50	600	800	1000	950	900	0.40	0.35
60	600	800	1000	1200	1150	0.25	0.40
70	600	800	1000	1200	1400	0.00	0.10
Σpx (one)	600	775	887.5	900	850		
Σpx (two)	600	800	962.5	1037.5	1012.5		

Now to calculate the expected gross profits the information in Table 11-1 (which will represent 'x' values) is combined with the probability data (the p values) and Σpx, the expected gross profit, is calculated for each possible level of purchases. A convenient layout is shown in Table 11-2. In Table 11-2 expected gross profit of £887.5 corresponding to a purchase of 50 units and advertisement in one newspaper is the sum of products of elements in the 50 column multiplied by the 'one paper' probabilities, viz., 887.5 = 500(0.1) + 750(0.25) + 1000(0.4) + 1000(0.25) + 1000(0). From the Σpx values produced it is evident that sixty units should be bought *irrespective of the number of newspapers in which the advertisement is placed.*

The expected net profit figures are now readily obtained. If the advertisement is placed in one newspaper the costs of this will be:

Cost of block	£37.5
Cost of one insert	£50
Total	£87.5

Thus (assuming the optimal purchase of sixty units is made) expected net profit will be £(900 − 87.5) = £812.5. For two newspapers the advertising costs would be:

Cost of block	£37.5
Cost of two inserts	£100
Total	£137.5

So that the expected net profit in this case would be (again assuming 60 units purchased) (£1037.5 − 137.5) = £900. Thus the optimal course of action is the purchase of 60 units and advertisement in two newspapers.

11-2-2 Alternative layout

There is an alternative layout for the calculations of expected gross profit. For each possible level of purchase, the expected revenue can be found and the cost subtracted. For instance for an advertisement in one newspaper and 40 units purchased the expected gross profit is given by

$$0.10(1050+100)+0.25(1400)+0.40(1400)+0.25(1400)-600 = 775$$

where the bracketed figures are the revenues achieved at each possible level of demand, so that if demand is at 30 units then 30 of the 40 items are sold at £35 giving £1050 revenue and 10 are sold at £10 giving £100 revenue. Expected gross profit with 60 units purchased by the store would be

$$0.10(1050+300)+0.25(1400+200)+0.40(1750+100)+0.25(2100)-900$$

$$= 900$$

The correct answer can be obtained by proceeding in this fashion.

However, it is *not* correct to work with the expected level of demand. For one newspaper advertisement this would be obtained as 48, viz.

D	P	PD
30	0.10	3
40	0.25	10
50	0.40	20
60	0.25	15
70	0	0
		48

Working with 50 (to the nearest multiple of 10) or, even worse, with 48 itself will produce the wrong result with an expected gross profit of under £900. This approach would work only if profit was always strictly proportional to the value of D, which is not the case here.

11-2-3 Sensitivity analysis

We begin the sensitivity discussion with the following question: *Given a decision to advertise in two newspapers, for what range of values of selling price is it optimal to purchase 60 units?*

Working with a selling price of £p instead of £35, the expected gross profit, $E(\pi)$, with 60 units purchased is $53(p-15)-32.5$. The workings are

$$E(\pi) = 0.15[40(p-15)-100]+0.35[50(p-15)-50]$$
$$+0.4[60(p-15)]+0.1[60(p-15)]$$
$$= 53.5(p-15)-32.5$$

For instance, there is a 0.15 chance of demand being only 40 units. In this event 40 are sold at a margin of $p-15$ and 20 are sold at a loss of £5, thus giving the bracketed term $[40(p-15)-100]$. By a similar process the expected gross profit on 70 units bought $E(\pi)70$, is

$$E(\pi)70 = 0.15[40(p-15)-150]+0.35[50(p-15)-100]$$
$$+0.4[60(p-15)-50]+0.1[70(p-15)]$$
$$= 54.5(p-15)-77.5$$

and also in similar fashion we obtain

$$E(\pi)50 = \underline{48.5(p-15)-7.5}$$
$$E(\pi)40 = \underline{40(p-15)}$$
$$E(\pi)30 = \underline{30(p-15)}$$

Note that the purchase of 30 units can never be optimal in the two-paper case.

Now for 60 units to give at least as much expected profit as 70 we require

$$53.5(p-15)-32.5 \geqslant 54.5(p-15)-77.5$$

which re-arranges to give $p \leqslant 60$. *This is the upper bound on price.* In comparison with the 50 unit alternative, again there must be no less expected profit with 60 bought. Therefore

$$53.5(p-15)-32.5 \geqslant 48.5(p-15)-7.5$$

giving $p \geqslant 20$.

Comparing the 60 and 40 alternatives

$$53.5(p-15)-32.5 \geqslant 40(p-15)$$

i.e., $p \geqslant 17.\overline{407}$.

Thus, *given* a decision to use two newspapers the policy of buying 60 units is optimal provided that

$$20 \leqslant p \leqslant 60$$

This is a broad range and the original value of $p = 35$ falls near the middle. So even if there is some uncertainty about the final price to be charged, the shop can be confident that the correct purchasing decision has been made.

Now the 'artwork and blockmaking' cost is common to all cases and so does not affect the final decision. However, the newspaper insertion charge might. The insertion charge, I, cannot influence the number of units that the shop buys in but it *might* cause a switch to one-newspaper advertising. With one newspaper the expected net profit is

$$E\pi(60) = 900 - 37.5 - I$$

and with two newspapers

$$E\pi(60) = 1037.5 - 37.5 - 2I$$

Thus two newspapers will only be chosen if

$$1037.5 - 37.5 - 2I \geqslant 900 - 37.5 - I$$

that is if

$$I \leqslant 137.5$$

Thus, provided that the insertion charge remains below £137.50 per paper, then it is best to use two papers.

Finally, consider again the question of the selling price, p; by an extension of the earlier workings to allow for a switch in the number of newspapers (given the original insertion charge) we obtain the following results:

Price range	Optimal decisions
$p \leqslant 15.556$	30, one paper
$15.556 \leqslant p \leqslant 17.692$	40, one paper
$17.692 \leqslant p \leqslant 22.5$	50, one paper
$22.5 \leqslant p \leqslant 60$	60, two papers
$p \geqslant 60$	70, two papers

In fact, it is better not to do business at all if $p < 17.372$ as the expected profit is negative. On this account it would *never* be worth buying 30 units. Note that the switch from two to one newspaper would occur at $p = 22.5$ and that the original, composite, decision of 60 bought *and* two newspapers is optimal if $22.5 \leqslant p \leqslant 60$.

EXERCISES

11-2-1 Each day a department store purchases for £30 per unit a product which it sells for £55 per unit. For each item sold a 'selling cost' of £5 is incurred. Units unsold at the end of the day are returned to the supplier who refunds £20 for each returned item. Daily customer demand experienced by the store is a random variable described by the probability distribution

Units demanded	Probability
1	0.1
2	0.4
3	0.3
4	0.2

    (i) What amount should the store order each day?
    (ii) Given the order size determined in (i) and with all other data unchanged, what is the minimum selling price that the store can set without sustaining a loss?
    (iii) A newspaper advertisement costing £10 per day would alter the probabilities of each level of demand to 0.1, 0.1, 0.4, 0.4 respectively. Would this be worth while?

(iv) As an alternative to the newspaper advertisement the store is considering a price-cut to £50. This would cause the probabilities to alter to 0, 0.1, 0.3, 0.6. Would this policy be preferable to the advertisement?

11-2-2 Once each year, Chaos Limited buys a quantity of perishable commodity. It processes and packages the commodity immediately and holds the cartons for sale one year later. Purchases have to be made in units of 100 kg; the current buying price is £30 per 100 kg. Each 100 kg yields sufficient output for a batch of 100 cartons and the processing and packaging of each batch costs £70. Storage costs, excluding interest, amount to £25 per 100 cartons per annum, payable at the end of the year. Chaos incurs fixed operating costs, i.e., costs which arise independently of the output level, of £70 000 per annum, payable at the end of the year.

Market conditions are such that Chaos takes its selling price as fixed by competitive considerations. Sales are made in cases of 100 cartons. The selling price, next year, for current output is estimated at £200 per 100 cartons. The probabilities of different volumes of sales have been estimated as follows:

Cases of 100 cartons	Probability
2000	0.2
2500	0.5
3000	0.3
	1.0

The directors are considering what quantity of the commodity should now be purchased for sale next year. Assume that the quantity to be purchased will be 200 000 kg, 250 000 kg, or 300 000 kg. Any output that is not sold next year will have to be scrapped and will have no scrap value. The cost of capital is 25 per cent per annum.

You are required to:

(a) calculate the quantity which should be purchased in order to maximize the expected value of cash flows from the year's operations, and

(b) comment on the limitations of the criterion that the expected value of cash flows from operations should be maximized.

Ignore taxation.

(Institute of Chartered Accountants in England and Wales, Professional Examinations: Part II, Elements of Financial Decisions, July 1975.)

11-2-3 Every day a shop purchases for £2 per unit, a product which it sells for £4 per unit. For every unit of product sold, a wrapping cost of £0.20 is incurred. Since the product is perishable, units remaining unsold at the end of the day are returned, without wrapping, to the supplier who refunds £1 for each returned item. The probability distribution for daily demand is as follows:

Possible number of units demanded daily	Probability that X units will be demanded daily
(X)	P(X)
0	0.1
1	0.4
2	0.3
3	0.2

Required:

(a) Draw up a table showing the profit earned for different order and demand levels. Your profit table should be in the form:

Order level

	Q 0	1	2	3
N				
0				
1				
2				
3				

Demand level

where Q is the order level.

(8 marks)

(b) Let the profit figures in your table be the elements of a matrix **A**. If the probability vector **P** is given by (0.1, 0.4, 0.3, 0.2) calculate the matrix product **PA**.

(4 marks)

(c) Interpret the entries in the matrix **PA** and hence determine the optimal order level that the shop should place each day.

(8 marks)

(d) If the wrapping cost per unit increases dramatically to £1, write out the additional cost matrix and determine the effect upon the order level policy.

(5 marks)

(Association of Certified Accountants, Professional Examination: Section 2, paper 12, Management Mathematics, December 1976.)

11-2-4 That well-known author D. C. Fields who wrote: *There's no Accounting for Mathematics* is about to publish his new book on computers called *The Calculating Accountant.* Due to the rapid change in technology in the computer industry, he does not expect his book to sell any copies after three years.

His publishers have carried out a market survey attempting to forecast demand for his new book and have produced the following probability estimates:

Year 1		Year 2		Year 3	
Likely sales	Probability	Likely sales	Probability	Likely sales	Probability
5 000	0.2	5 000	0.4	5 000	0.8
10 000	0.5	10 000	0.6	10 000	0.2
20 000	0.3				

Required:

(a) Calculate the expected total sales (i.e., number of books) over the three years.

(5 marks)

(b) The book's price is fixed at £10 and the variable cost of producing each book will be £2 in year 1, £3 in year 2 and £4 in year 3. Calculate the present value of the contribution as at the beginning of the first year, using a discount rate of 10 per cent per annum. (Assume that all cash flows take place at the end of the year concerned.)

(10 marks)

(c) There is a possibility of an updated soft-backed version of the book being published at the beginning of year 2 (the original hard-backed version would then be taken off the market at the end of year 1) with the following estimates of sales:

Year 2		Year 3		Year 4	
Likely sales	Probability	Likely sales	Probability	Likely sales	Probability
20 000	0.5	10 000	0.8	5 000	0.9
30 000	0.5	20 000	0.2	10 000	0.1

(The sales will be extended by one year due to the updating.)

The soft-backed book will be priced at £5 and the variable cost of producing each book will be £1 in year 2, £2 in year 3, and £3 in year 4. Advise D. C. Fields whether to take up the option to produce a soft-backed version of his book.

(10 marks)

(Association of Certified Accountants, Professional Examination: Section 2, paper 12, Management Mathematics, December 1977.)

11-3 GAME THEORY

11-3-1 Introduction

All the problems that we have so far described have involved *one* decision maker. In Game Theory the value of the objective function of one decision maker will depend not only upon his own actions but also upon the actions of others. Game Theory is the study of such situations and in general both *conflict* and *co-operation* are involved.

The rapidly expanding body of knowledge came to be called Game Theory because in mathematical form the multi-decision maker situations are in many respects similar to those presented by parlour games of strategy. These essentially frivolous associations may, in part, have accounted for the comparatively few areas of application in business decision making. Apart from some of the more general strategic considerations of the theory which are useful guides at the policy level, the main area of application in business has been in *marketing* models. Game Theory plays an important role in modern theories of *imperfect competition* and leads into consideration of *voting systems*, with important political implications.

A *game* has been defined as a collection of rules, known to all players, which determine what players may do and the outcomes and payoffs resulting from their choices.

11-3-2 Two-person zero-sum games

Consider as an example the following *zero-sum* game between two players A and B. The *payoff matrix* is

		Player B		
		Action 1	Action 2	Action 3
Player A	Action 1	6	3	4
	Action 2	1	2	7

The numbers (which can be thought of as money) are the gains to A. Each player has alternative *actions*. If A plays his Action 1 and B plays his Action 1 then A wins 6 and B loses 6. 'Plays' of the game are *simultaneous*. A's gains are B's losses. This is what is meant by *zero sum*—there is no net gain or loss to both players taken together. If B plays Action 2 and A plays Action 2 then B pays A 2 units (think of B as the taxpayer!). Which action should each player adopt? Brief consideration shows that B should never play his Action 3. Whatever A does B is worse off with Action 3 than his Action 2. Action 3 is said to be *dominated* and can be scratched out.

In what remains of the payoff matrix there are strong logical arguments for A always playing Action 1 and B always playing Action 2. This is because the payoff 3 represents a *saddle point*. It is at once the minimum of its row and the maximum of its column. This being the case, one player *will only lose* by altering his choice of action provided that his opponent sticks resolutely to his saddle point action. Verify this from the matrix. The reader should also verify that *dominance* considerations also force the saddle point solution (this does not work, in general, for more than two actions per player). The reader should now find the saddle point in the following payoff matrix

$$\begin{matrix} -7 & 6 & 1 & -2 \\ 0 & -5 & -1 & 4 \\ 6 & 4 & 2 & 3 \\ 3 & -3 & -7 & 5 \end{matrix}$$

What happens when there is no saddle point? Here the players must be *unpredictable*. Where a saddle point exists the players adopt *pure strategies*; the selection of just one course of action that is always played. When there is no saddle point, as in the payoffs of the following matrix, if either player plays the same action

$$\begin{matrix} 2 & 4 \\ 5 & 3 \end{matrix}$$

consistently, or follows a predictable pattern of plays, the opponent can take advantage of this information. The players, if they desire the best average or *expected return*, randomly select their actions in a *mixed strategy*. Player A attaches probabilities p and $1-p$ to the choice of his actions 1 and 2 respectively. What is the best value of p from player A's point of view? It is that value which gives him the largest expected payoff. If B always played *his* action one, then A's payoff would be (reading down the first column) E_1 where

$$E_1 = 2p + 5(1-p) = 5 - 3p$$

On the other hand if B played his action 2 then A would expect E_2 where

$$E_2 = 4p + 3(1-p) = 3 + p$$

In repeated plays of the game, B might be expected to select his action that produced the *lower* of the E_1 and E_2 values. Consequently it is best for A to select the value of p that makes this least value *as large as possible*. The solution can be found by solving the equation

$$5 - 3p = 3 + p$$
$$\therefore \quad p = 0.5 \quad \text{and so} \quad (1-p) = 0.5$$

Thus A should make equiprobable his selection of actions—in this case. The situation is graphed in Fig. 11-1. In turn, player B should attach probabilities q and $1-q$ to the selection of his actions such that

$$2q + 4(1-q) = 5q + 3(1-q)$$
$$4 - 2q = 3 + 2q$$
$$q = \tfrac{1}{4}$$
$$(1-q) = \tfrac{3}{4}$$

In which case B will keep A's gain down to 3.5. Note that this figure, 3.5, the *value of the game*, is what can be expected from A's calculations; 3.5 is the highest *expected* return that A can achieve. When there is a saddle point A's return (the saddle point value) was guaranteed.

When there are more than two undominated actions for each player,

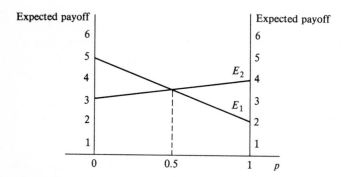

Figure 11-1

and where there is no saddle point, the calculation of optimal probabilities can involve extensive workings. There are a variety of solution techniques and also approximation methods. The problems can also be expressed as linear programming problems and solved via the simplex method! When the game is not zero sum but the sum of the payoffs to A and B in each case is constant, the game is said to be *constant sum*. Constant sum games can be easily reduced to zero-sum games and the same strategic considerations apply.

11-3-3 More advanced games

When there are more than two players (still zero sum) the situation becomes much more complicated and less clear cut. The talk is then of *solution concepts* rather than 'solutions'. One of the best solution concepts is that of the *Shapley value*, in which the final disbursement to a player reflects the contributions that he would make to coalitions which he might join.

When the games are not constant sum but variable (depending on the actions that the players choose) the situation also becomes much more involved. For the first time an element of *co-operation* enters the picture (zero-sum games are ones of pure conflict) which at once becomes richer, more realistic, and more complicated. Bargaining situations are frequently of this character and much work has been done applying the theory to this area. Again the talk is of solution concepts. The Shapley value again comes into the picture as may the concept of the *core* and numerous other solution concepts.

Let us specifically consider some of these solution concepts. The payoff matrix in non-zero-sum games has to state separately the gain to each player for each combination of actions, viz.:

		Player B	
		Action 1	Action 2
Player A $\Big\{$	Action 1	(4, 4)	(0, 5)
	Action 2	(5, 0)	(2, 2)

where the first element in any bracketed pair is A's gain and the second is B's gain. We can use this matrix to illustrate some of the simpler solution concepts.

1. *Equilibrium points.* An equilibrium point represents a pair of actions such that no player can improve his own position by a *unilateral* change of action. Examine the matrix and see that (2, 2) is the only equilibrium point in this case.
2. *Max-min.* Each player maximizes his own minimum payoff. This again gives (2, 2) as the solution.
3. *Min-max.* Here each player seeks to minimize the *opponent's maximum*

payoff. This is a more 'bloody minded' philosophy but again $(2,2)$ would be the solution arrived at.

4. *Max-diff.* This is another uncharitable outlook. Here a player seeks to maximize the difference between his own and his opponent's payoffs. Thus A would choose Action 2 (hoping for $(5,0)$) and B would choose Action 2 (hoping for $(0,5)$). They both 'fail' and $(2,2)$ again results.

5. *Altruism.* There are various ways in which this outlook could be defined. Here we mean that a player seeks to ensure the welfare *of his opponent* by attempting to maximize his opponent's minimum payoff. This results in the solution $(4,4)$. Since this is the 'best' solution from the society $(A+B)$ point of view there may be a moral paradigm here for contemporary bargaining behaviour.

6. *Max-sum.* This involves co-operation between the players. They should select their actions so as to maximize total payoffs. This again results in $(4,4)$ but says nothing about how the total of 8 will in fact be divided up.

7. *Asceticism. Minimize* one's own:
    (a) maximum payoff (resulting in $4,4$);
    (b) minimum payoff (resulting in $4,4$).

How many of these approaches can the reader see elements of in day-to-day industrial, commercial and international bargaining solutions? What other solution concepts could there be?

We should also mention, in this section, that a *Theory of Teams* has now been developed (mainly by Radner in the USA). This emphasizes the co-operative elements in a situation.

However, we wish to finish on a much simpler and rather more practical note with the study of a rather special sort of two-person game, set in a marketing context.

11-3-4 Games against nature: a marketing exercise

In a *game against nature* there is only one rational player or decision maker, but the outcomes depend not only upon his decisions but also upon the 'state of nature'. The payoff matrix has the same structure as in an ordinary two-person game but player B is 'nature' and his courses of action are the states of nature. These states are, of course, not selected on a known, rational criterion, but are determined by some unknown process. Obvious examples of games against nature are agricultural—where nature would represent factors such as weather, pests, etc. Less obviously, player A could be the firm and player B, nature, 'the market'. Consider an example.

A company is about to launch a new product and considers itself to have three essentially different possible 'actions'.

1. To undertake a television-based advertising campaign which would bring rich rewards if successful, but big bills and poor rewards if the product is not well accepted (A_1).

2. To undertake a pilot study—a trial launch in a comparatively self-contained and representative community—say a town in the North East of England. This would be expected to give better prior knowledge of the product, so less widespread outcomes, but 'lack punch at the top end' (A_2).
3. Instead of the TV campaign, undertake a magazine- and poster-based programme of sales promotion. This might be expected to produce results somewhere between the other alternatives (A_3).

Market reaction to the product has been classified into three states, and estimated profits (in £10 000 units) are as given in the payoff matrix below:

	Market reaction		
	Good	Moderate	Poor
A_1	110	45	-30
A_2	80	40	10
A_3	90	55	-10

How can a decision be arrived at? What course of action should be adopted? First let it be clear that there is *no definitive answer* to this kind of problem that is always right for all decision makers at all times. Nevertheless there are a number of very helpful strategic possibilities.

There is the *maximin* strategy. This is suitable for the 'play safer'—those of a sure and steady disposition. The maximin strategy, which we have already encountered, says: select that course of action for which the *worst* outcome is better than the worst outcome of all other actions. Thus the maximin strategy maximizes the minimum possible gain. Thus A_2, with a worst outcome of $+10$, would be selected and the trial launch duly undertaken.

Then there is the *maximax* strategy. This is suitable for those of a venturesome disposition—to put it politely. Maximax says: select that course of action for which the *best* outcome is better than the best outcomes of all other actions. Thus maximax would indicate A_1 and the TV campaign would get underway.

Both maximin and maximax ignore two-thirds of the information in the payoff matrix. In general they ignore a proportion $(n-1)/n$ of the information when nature has n states. They are also *extreme* strategies. In some presentations of game theory the impression is given that anything except maximin is illogical. This is not the case in games against nature.

The *Hurwicz criterion* encapsulates the extremes of maximax and maximin as special cases and doubles the information used. The Hurwicz criterion is: select that course of action with the greatest Hurwicz number.

For each action the Hurwicz number is a proportion α of the best outcome plus a proportion $(1-\alpha)$ of the worst $(0 \leqslant \alpha \leqslant 1)$. Note that if $\alpha = 0$ we have the maximin strategy and if $\alpha = 1$ the maximax strategy results. The investor must choose α to best reflect his psychology. We shall see shortly that sensitivity analysis can help in this respect. For the moment set $\alpha = 0.3$. The Hurwicz numbers produced are:

$H(\alpha = 0.3)$
12
31
20

In this event A_2 would be selected. On the other hand, if $\alpha = 0.7$

$H(\alpha = 0.7)$
68
59
60

in which event the TV campaign would be indicated. One fact strikes us. So far the magazine and poster campaign has not emerged as the favoured alternative. Could it ever be chosen? This question can be answered by a sensitivity analysis on α.

For A_1 the Hurwicz number for arbitrary α will be H_1 where

$$H_1 = 110\alpha - 30(1-\alpha) = 140\alpha - 30$$

For A_2 we have

$$H_2 = 80\alpha + 10(1-\alpha) = 70\alpha + 10$$

and for A_3

$$H_3 = 90\alpha - 10(1-\alpha) = 100\alpha - 10$$

Now A_1 will be preferred to A_3 if $H_1 > H_3$. That is if

$$140\alpha - 30 > 100\alpha - 10$$

$$40\alpha > 20$$

$$\alpha > \tfrac{1}{2}$$

and A_2 will be preferred to A_3 if

$$70\alpha + 10 > 100\alpha - 10$$

$$20 > 30\alpha$$

$$\alpha < \tfrac{2}{3}$$

So action three will not be selected at all. To decide which actions are selected compare H_1 and H_2. Action 1 will be chosen if $H_1 > H_2$, i.e.,

$$140\alpha - 30 > 70\alpha + 10$$

$$70\alpha > 40$$

$$\alpha > \tfrac{4}{7}$$

So, if α is less than $\tfrac{4}{7}$ the trial launch should be adopted and if $\alpha > \tfrac{4}{7}$ the TV campaign should be used. This clarifies the issues considerably. Although the decision maker may not be able to pin down a precise value of α he may be able to make the statement: 'In my opinion no less emphasis should be placed on the worst result than on the best'. In other words $0 \leqslant \alpha \leqslant 0.5$. Throughout this range A_2 is preferred, so the trial launch it is.

Are there any grounds on which the magazine and poster campaign *would* be accepted? The answer is definitely 'yes'. So far we have not considered the moderate outcomes in any way. A_3 has the best of these results and any device that gave sufficient emphasis here would select A_3. One criterion that so happens to do this is the *Laplace criterion* or the *principle of insufficient reason*. Other descriptions of the same device are *Bayes criterion* (not to be confused with Bayes' theorem in probability theory) and the 'equi-probability of the unknown'. The approach is similar to expected value. It is simply said that if we have no information then there is no reason to think that any one state of nature is more probable than any other, and to give all states equal weights. Thus with three states of nature a weight of 1/3 is attached to each payoff in any row and the results summed. We obtain

$$L_1 = 110/3 + 45/3 - 30/3 = 125/3$$
$$L_2 = 80/3 + 40/3 + 10/3 = 130/3$$
$$L_3 = 90/3 + 55/3 - 10/3 = 135/3$$

and Action 3 with the greatest 'Laplace number' would be preferred. When (as is the case here) it so happens that all the worst outcomes are in one column, all the second worst in another, and so on, the Laplace criterion can be viewed as a particular extension of the Hurwicz criterion. Otherwise the two principles are quite different.

Finally, there is the criterion of *minimax regret*. This is in some ways the most subtle approach and is akin to the ideas of opportunity cost in economic theory. For each state of nature and payoffs are subtracted from the best payoff in that state (column). For the reaction 'Good' this gives the results:

	'Good'
A_1	0
A_2	30
A_3	20

The entries here can be thought of as 'regrets' in the following sense. If A_1 had been selected and *if* the market response was good, then the decision maker would have 'no regrets'. On the other hand if A_2 had been selected and the market response turned out to be good, then there would have been 30 less profit made than for the optimum decision in this state. There are regrets to the tune of 30. If A_3 had been selected then the regrets would have been $110 - 90 = 20$. Below is given the full regret matrix, where in the 'poor' state the regret of 40 for A_1 is $10 - (-30)$. Minimax regret then selects that action which has the *least maximum regret figure*. The maximum entry in the A_1 row is 40, in the A_2 row it is 30, and in the A_3 row it is 20. So with A_3 we guarantee that regrets are not excessive.

	Regret matrix		
	Good	Moderate	Poor
A_1	0	10	40
A_2	30	15	0
A_3	20	0	20

After all of this, what decision is to be made? The answer is that it is up to the decision maker. The technique will select an answer (or at least facilitate the selection) but the decision maker must first *select the technique*. The reader might examine some of the larger financial decisions that he has made. The writer suggests that minimax regret—or something not too far removed—will have cropped up once or twice. But not by that name of course. Example: 'I won't buy the Ferrari because if it breaks down I shan't be able to afford the repairs'. Translation: 'If the state of nature "car breaks down" arises the regrets would be "too large".'

EXERCISES

11-3-1 Why is game theory so called? What characteristic distinguishes game theory from most other OR topics? In what areas has game theory provided useful insights?

11-3-2 What is meant by the terms
   (i) payoff matrix,
   (ii) zero-sum,
   (iii) action,
   (iv) dominance,
   (v) pure strategy.

11-3-3 Find the saddle points in the following payoff matrix:

$$\begin{matrix} 4 & -2 & -6 & 6 & -3 \\ 7 & 5 & 3 & 4 & -1 \\ 1 & -4 & 0 & 5 & 0 \\ -6 & 7 & 2 & -1 & -2 \\ 2 & 6 & 4 & 3 & 0 \end{matrix}$$

11-3-4 Find the optimal mixed strategy probabilities for player A in the following game:

$$\text{player A} \quad \begin{pmatrix} -1 & 2 \\ 1 & 0 \end{pmatrix}$$

player B

What is the value of the game to player A?

11-3-5 For the following non-zero-sum two-player game:

		Player B	
		Action 1	Action 2
Player A	Action 1	(1, 1)	(4, −1)
	Action 2	(−1, 4)	(3, 3)

Find

    (i) the equilibrium point,
   (ii) the max-min solution,
  (iii) the min-max solution,
  (iv) the max-diff solution,
   (v) the max-sum solution,
  (vi) an altruistic solution,
 (vii) an ascetic solution.

11-3-6 An agricultural research station has estimated that for a 50-acre farm with standard soil conditions and husbandry, the annual profits to be obtained from planting the land solely with each of four varieties of wheat depend on rainfall in the following way:

		Rainfall		
		Low	Medium	High
Seed variety	A	11 200	9 100	7000
	B	10 100	14 000	5600
	C	6 800	10 800	7300
	D	9 900	13 500	5500

For a farmer with a standard 50 acres, and for *one season only*, ascertain which variety should be sown under each of the following decision rules:

  (a) maximax;
  (b) maximin;
  (c) Hurwicz and criterion for $\alpha = 0.6$;
  (d) the Laplace criterion;
  (e) minimax regret.

11-3-7 What is Game Theory?
Required:
Attempt to answer this question by explaining what a 'game' is in this context and illustrate by considering simple zero-sum, two-person games. Include in your explanation and examples the terms 'dominance' and 'saddle point'.
Give an example of a non-zero-sum game, and say why it is not a zero-sum game.
(Association of Certified Accountants, Professional Examination: Section 2, paper 12, Management Mathematics, June 1977.)

11-4 SEQUENCING

11-4-1 Introduction

Sequencing-type problems are also known by the fuller, more descriptive title of *job shop sequencing* problems. In a factory shop-floor situation the sequencing problem is that of determining the order in which several jobs shall be done on several machines. The problems are not limited to the factory production line setting. For instance, a building firm may have contracts at a number of sites, all of which call for the use of excavators, cement mixers, and the like—of which there are only a limited number. How should the contracts be worked on to minimize completion time or to secure good equipment utilization?

Before starting on a shop-floor scheduling example, we should mention the allied, but more substantial *dispatching problem*, that of deciding which of several clashing jobs shall be worked on next. Pity the poor foreman! New jobs may arrive each day (on which completion dates may already have been promised). Quite apart from the inventory problems that this situation presents, what is the foreman to optimize? Sasieni, Yaspan, and Friedman (1959) give seven plausible, *alternative* objectives:

1. Minimize the *average* amount of time by which delivery dates are missed.
2. Minimize the *maximum* amount by which any of the delivery dates are missed.
3. Minimize set-up costs (in some time period).
4. Maximize production (in some time period).
5. Minimize production costs.
6. Meet certain priorities assigned by management (e.g., the XYZ corporation job *must* be delivered in time).
7. Minimize machine idle time.

Workable approaches to this problem involve *priority rules*, e.g., process that job first with the shortest processing time, or with the earliest late start time. These are *empirical* rules which have been tested and compared in simulations. There is no workable technique that finds the global optimum.

The same is true in sequencing problems. Wild (1971) gives the example of a problem in which five jobs must be processed on each of six machines. In the absence of precedence requirements there are $(5!)^6$ alternative solutions. This is the number

$$2\,985\,984\,000\,000$$

The problems are *combinatorial* in the extreme. Although this kind of problem is long standing, formal analysis has only been undertaken in the last 25

Table 11-3

	Job						
	(1)	(2)	(3)	(4)	(5)	(6)	(7)
Cutting m/c (min)	8	9	14	12	6	10	7
Polishing m/c (min)	14	6	6	9	5	7	8

years. There are no globally optimizing methods of any value in the general case. Nor are there likely to be such in the foreseeable future even with today's powerful computers.

11-4-2 Johnson's method

Some simpler cases (which do crop up quite frequently!) have been profitably studied. The method developed in 1953 and published in 1954 by S. M. Johnson was originally designed to work with any number of jobs but only two machines. It was later extended to the three-machine case (still any number of jobs) provided that there is no bottleneck on the middle machine. This procedure will be described later on. Johnson's original method is best illustrated by example.

A firm has seven jobs which must be processed by two machines, a cutting machine and a polishing machine. For all jobs, cutting precedes polishing. The jobs differ in specification and the times taken by each job on each machine are as shown in Table 11-3. In what sequence should the jobs be put through the two machines so as to minimize the total time taken to complete all of the jobs? Now suppose that numerical order was used to determine the sequencing, i.e., job (1) first, job (2) second, and so on. The results are shown in Table 11-4. Job (1) goes onto the cutting machine at

Table 11-4

Job	Cutting m/c		Polishing m/c	
	Time in	Time out	Time in	Time out
(1)	0	8	8	22
(2)	8	17	22	28
(3)	17	31	31	37
(4)	31	43	43	52
(5)	43	49	52	57
(6)	49	59	59	66
(7)	59	66	66	74

time $t = 0$ and is finished at time $t = 8$. It goes straight onto the polishing machine and is finished after $8 + 14 = 22$ minutes. Meanwhile the cutter became free at $t = 8$ and job (2) can go on at that time. Cutting is finished at $t = 17$ but job (2) now has to wait until $t = 22$ for the polishing machine to be free. Again, job (3) can be started on cutting at $t = 17$ and, since it is not finished until $t = 31$ it can go straight onto the polisher (job (2) has finished polishing at $t = 28$). And so on. The time out of polishing for the last job is the total time of the problem. Thus the arrangement takes 74 minutes.

Now let us find the optimal sequence. Johnson's method, which is guaranteed to produce an optimal sequence, can be presented as a four-step procedure:

1. Select the shortest time on any (remaining) job.
2. (a) If this is a first machine (i.e., cutting here) time place the job (nearest) first.
   (b) If this is a second machine (i.e., polishing here) time place the job (nearest) last.
3. Delete the job so dealt with from further consideration.
4. Return to step (1).

The process terminates when all jobs have been dealt with. So job (5) crops up first of all having the shortest overall time of 5 minutes. This is a 'second-machine' time so (5) goes to the end of the list. Next come jobs (2) and (3) each with six minutes' polishing time. We shall put job (3) in next to last place and job (2) above it. The reader should verify that the same total time is arrived at if the order of jobs (3) and (2) is reversed. This is true in general, 'ties' do not matter—they can be resolved arbitrarily. This is true for ties of all kinds, e.g., if a job takes the same time on both machines it does not matter whether the job is treated as a first-machine case or a second-machine case. The two resulting sequences will usually differ but both will have the same total time.

Table 11-5

Job	Cutting m/c		Polishing m/c	
	Time in	Time out	Time in	Time out
(7)	0	7	7	15
(1)	7	15	15	29
(4)	15	27	29	36
(6)	27	37	37	44
(2)	37	46	46	52
(3)	46	60	60	66
(5)	60	66	66	71

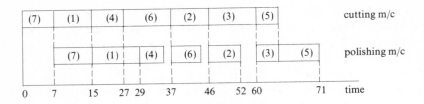

Figure 11-2

Continuing with the sequencing, next are jobs (7) and (6) each with a seven-minute time. Job (7) goes to the top of the list and (6) goes above (2). Then comes job (1) which goes beneath (7) and finally job (4) goes in the last remaining place. The sequence is then: (7), (1), (4), (6), (2), (3), (5) and the times in and out are shown in Table 11-5. Thus the completion time has been reduced to 71 minutes total. The result of Table 11-9 can also be presented as a bar chart with the horizontal axis being time in minutes. This is done in Fig. 11-2.

11-4-3 Three Machines: Special Cases

While there is no solution for the *general* three-machine case, we mentioned that Johnson's method can be extended to the three-machine, n-job case if there was no bottleneck on the middle machine. To be more specific if the three machines are A, B, and C, Johnson's method can be used if one or both of the following conditions are satisfied: (a) the lowest job time for machine A is at least as large as the largest job time for machine B; and (b) the lowest job time for machine C is at least as large as the largest processing time for machine B.

The extension is quite simple. Let the individual job times be A_i, B_i, and C_i for the jobs $i = 1, \ldots, n$. Reduce the problem to a *two*-machine case by defining new times D_i and E_i where

$$D_i = A_i + B_i$$
$$E_i = B_i + C_i$$

and apply Johnson's method as if there were only two machines D and E.

Consider an example where there are six jobs to be sequenced through the three machines A, B, and C. The job times are given in Table 11-6. It will be seen that condition (a) above is satisfied since the least of the times on machine A is eight and the greatest of the machine B times is also eight. The D_i and E_i values produced are shown in Table 11-7 and Johnson's method rapidly gives the optimal sequence (4), (2), (1), (3), (5), (6).

Table 11-6

Job	A_i	B_i	C_i
(1)	13	8	14
(2)	8	6	11
(3)	12	8	10
(4)	8	5	10
(5)	10	8	7
(6)	11	8	4

Table 11-7

Job	D_i	E_i
(1)	21	22
(2)	14	17
(3)	20	18
(4)	13	15
(5)	18	15
(6)	19	12

11-4-4 Other Approaches

Another special case that has received attention is the m-machine two-job case for which an optimizing solution procedure is available. There is not space to present the method here, but the interested reader is referred to Sasieni, Yaspan, and Friedman (1959). In this section we shall briefly review some very different lines of approach to the formidable sequencing problem.

1. Enumeration Enumeration (considering all possibilities) is not *always* out of the question. We saw earlier that the number of *prima facie* possibilities would soon become enormous. However, Giffler and Thompson devised an algorithm to enumerate only 'active' schedules (those for which unnecessary idleness of machines is eliminated). Heller also studied the problem using graph theory. These are rather advanced approaches on which work is continuing. Here we shall discuss a scheduling problem of a slightly different character in which enumeration is possible.

Floss and Crackwell make a line of five tinned food-products. They are made in batches ('jobs') using one process ('machine'). When one job has been done the equipment must be cleaned and re-set for the next job. The 'set-up times' between each pair of jobs are shown below. For technical reasons job (2) *must* be done first and job (4) must be the last to be done. With these restrictions in mind:

(a) What sequence minimizes total set-up times?
(b) The processing times for each job (not given) are widely different—could this affect the answer?
(c) Although it is not essential, management would prefer job (1) to be done before job (3). Can this desire be accommodated without undue time penalty?
(d) As a result of a time and motion study it is found that the (2) to (1) set-up time could be substantially reduced. What size reduction would be needed to cause a change in the optimal sequence?

Set-up times (minutes)
To job

		(1)	(2)	(3)	(4)	(5)
	(1)	—	18	13	21	12
	(2)	32	—	16	17	14
From job	(3)	18	25	—	20	11
	(4)	12	21	19	—	41
	(5)	27	16	20	40	—

(a) Since job (2) must come first and job (4) last, the possible sequences differ only in the ordering of jobs (1), (3), and (5). There are just $3! = 6$ different arrangements. Simply add up the times for each sequence, viz.:

$$(2)(1)(3)(5)(4) \quad 32+13+11+40 = 96 \text{ min}$$
$$(2)(1)(5)(3)(4) \quad 32+12+20+20 = 84 \text{ min}$$
$$(2)(3)(1)(5)(4) \quad 16+18+12+40 = 86 \text{ min}$$
$$(2)(3)(5)(1)(4) \quad 16+11+27+21 = 76 \text{ min}$$
$$(2)(5)(1)(3)(4) \quad 14+27+13+20 = 74 \text{ min}$$
$$(2)(5)(3)(1)(4) \quad 14+20+18+21 = 73 \text{ min}$$

Thus the sequence $(2)(5)(3)(1)(4)$ is optimal with total set-up times of 73 minutes.

(b) The actual processing times would make no difference to the sequence that minimizes total time (processing + set-up) since the sum total of the processing times will be the same in any sequence (remember that it is a one-machine problem).

(c) Yes. Only one minute would be lost by switching to the sequence $(2)(5)(1)(3)(4)$.

(d) The saving would need to be at least 12 minutes ($32 \to 20$) to make a change positively worth while. This time saving could come down to 11 minutes if the (1) before (3) preference is adopted.

2. Priority or 'loading' rules We have already mentioned these guidelines. Some of these operating rules of thumb may work quite well; others (such as random selection) may be bad. The rules can be compared in simulations or, more expensively, by varying the rule adopted in the practical situation and keeping a record of the results. Some general impressions may be gained from study of the record.

3. 'Heuristic' procedures Here procedures are developed which ape the methods of experienced operators who have developed 'good hunches'. Thus priority rules may fall into this category but experienced operators may use more abstruse methods. Heuristic methods sometimes smack of desperation but in the last analysis if they *improve* performance (rather than find the unobtainable optimum) they are justified.

4. Sampling Here a large number of feasible schedules are randomly selected and the schedule giving the shortest time is adopted. If the sample size is made large enough the probability of having included an optimal schedule can be made as high as desired. Of course there is a trade-off here as computation costs rise with the size of sample. This method compares favourably with many of the commonly used priority rules although performance varies with the detail of problem specification.

5. Learning techniques In this approach *combinations* of loading rules are tried in simulated situations. It has been shown that learning is possible — but of course is time-consuming — but it does not give great improvements over randomly selected combinations of priority rules.

6. Programming methods There are a number of 'programming'-type approaches to the job shop scheduling problem. Under this head we are thinking of integer programming, dynamic programming, and 'branch and bound' methods (although the latter may have heuristic elements). The scheduling problem can be precisely formulated using integer programming. This is intellectually satisfying but as yet the formulations are not computationally practicable.

EXERCISES

11-4-1 Cite some instances where sequencing problems arise in industry, and illustrate the combinatorial nature of these problems. Can all such problems be solved by the use of Johnson's method?

11-4-2 (i) What are the steps involved in Johnson's method?

(ii) A company has 10 jobs which must each be processed on two machines. For all jobs the machine A operation precedes the machine B operation. The times required by each job are shown below. In what sequence should the jobs be put through the two machines so as to minimize the total time taken to complete all of the jobs?

	Job									
	(1)	(2)	(3)	(4)	(5)	(6)	(7)	(8)	(9)	(10)
Machine A (min)	23	21	15	19	16	17	17	24	18	17
Machine B (min)	14	16	17	22	20	13	20	18	17	23

11-4-3 (i) Under what conditions can Johnson's method be extended to the case of n jobs to be processed on three machines?

(ii) Eight jobs are to be sequenced through three machines: A, B, and C. The job times on each machine are given below. Find an optimal sequence.

	Time required on machine		
Job	A	B	C
(1)	25	17	20
(2)	17	17	18
(3)	20	16	23
(4)	15	18	24
(5)	13	14	21
(6)	21	15	19
(7)	22	13	25
(8)	12	18	26

11-4-4 A company makes a range of five products in batches. It has to decide in what order to run off the batches. Machine re-set times (hours) between manufacture of each pair of products are:

	To product				
	(1)	(2)	(3)	(4)	(5)
From product (1)	—	5.8	3.8	3.4	3.5
(2)	5.9	—	3.7	3.9	3.0
(3)	2.9	3.8	—	4.3	3.6
(4)	3.2	3.5	3.4	—	5.0
(5)	3.0	3.9	3.1	3.6	—

It is necessary that job (5) is the last to be done. Because of tight delivery schedules job (4) must not be later than second to be done and job (3) must be no later than third.

(i) Find a time minimizing sequence. Is it unique?

(ii) What would be the time penalty involved in starting with product three?

11-4-5 In a sequencing context explain briefly what is meant by the following terms:

(a) Enumeration.

(b) Priority rules.

(c) Heuristic procedures.

(d) Solution sampling.

(e) Learning techniques.

11-4-6 Sequencing is a special case of a combinatorial model. It is used when one is trying to find an optimal solution from a large number of alternatives. At this point in time the literature on sequencing is not exhaustive and it is only possible at present to solve a limited range of problems.

Required:

(a) Give a numerical example of a sequencing problem and determine the total time for one non-optimal sequence.

(b) Determine, by any standard method you know, the optimal sequence for your problem in (a) above giving a clear and concise description of your method.

(*c*) To your knowledge, what is the current state of the art? Describe types of problems for which we have solution algorithms. What non-optimizing methods can we use to help us solve sequencing problems? What problems can we not solve at present?
(Association of Certified Accountants, Professional Examination: Section 2, paper 12, Management Mathematics, December 1977.)

11-5 DYNAMIC PROGRAMMING

11-5-1 Introduction

Rather than being a specific, single technique that can be used to solve all the problems of a particular kind (as is the case for the simplex method) dynamic programming is more a style of approach. It uses the idea of *recursion* to solve a complex problem that has been broken down into a series of easier sub-problems. Sometimes dynamic programming is about the only sensible approach to a problem. At other times it is but one of a number of possible approaches.

Dynamic programming developed mainly as the work of Richard Bellman (1957) in the nineteen-fifties. It is structurally related to *control theory* and has found many engineering applications. In operations research proper it has found application in network flows, capital budgeting, stock control, scheduling, and diophantine (integrality) problems. Dynamic programming overlaps virtually all types of mathematical programming areas and is not easily compartmentalized.

Advanced work in the area is, naturally, not easy to grasp, but even the elementary material has been rendered obscure by a rather opaque notation. As far as is possible we shall avoid the use of symbols in this presentation and attempt to convey the essential notions by way of examples.

11-5-2 The Routing Problem

One of the best illustrations of the value of dynamic programming is in *routing problems*, in physical terms relating to electrical power transmission or to the construction of gas or oil pipelines. Figure 11-3 represents a pipeline routing problem. From a storage reservoir, S, a pipeline is to be routed through intermediate stations to a delivery point or terminal, T. Five intermediate stations are required (for pumping, inspection, etc.) but there are a number of alternative locations for each station. Costs of constructing links between possible stations are shown. The only feasible linkages are as illustrated. What is the cheapest route for the pipeline?

We shall solve the problem by the *backward solution*. The reader will already be familiar with the notion of a backward pass through a network from the process of obtaining late start or late event times in critical path method. Consider first the choice of location for station (5). There are three

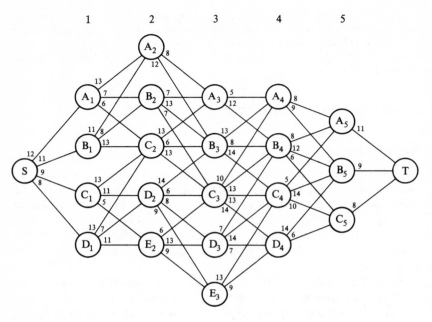

Figure 11-3

possibilities: A_5, B_5, or C_5. In each of the circles enter the *least cost* of getting to the terminus, T, from that location. In fact there is no choice. It costs 11 from A_5, 9 from B_5, and 8 from C_5. We would put this as in Fig. 11-4, nothing having been decided so far. Now consider the choice of location for station (4). There are four possibilities: A_4, B_4, C_4, and D_4. For *each* of these stations we want to determine the least cost of completing the journey to T. Consider A_4. From here we can go, at a cost of 8, to A_5 and from there we know it costs 11 to get to T. Thus the cost would be 19. But there is another possibility. We can go from A_4 to B_5 and thence to T. This means of completing the journey from A_4 would cost 9 (from A_4 to B_5)+9 (from B_5 to T), a total of

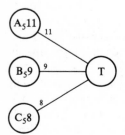

Figure 11-4

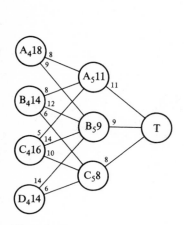

Figure 11-5

Figure 11-6

18. These are the only possibilities. Enter the *lower* figure in the circle for A_4 thus:

Now do the same for B_4, C_4, and D_4. From B_4 there are three choices: via A_5 costing $8 + 11 = 19$; via B_5 costing $12 + 9 = 21$; or via C_5 costing $6 + 8 = 14$. So in the B_4 circle enter 14. Applying the same simple procedure to C_4 and D_4 gives the picture as in Fig. 11-5. Now apply the same ideas to the station three locations as shown in Fig. 11-6. And similarly for stations (2) and (1). The complete picture is shown in Fig. 11-7. The first thing that is found is that the cheapest pipeline would cost 44. The actual route is then 'unrolled' quite simply since it was D_1 that gave rise to the 44 at S, it was D_2 that gave rise to the 36 at D_1 and so on. It will be seen that there are *two* optimal routes marked ——╫——. They diverge at D_3 and consist of

$$D_1, D_2, D_3, B_4, C_5 \quad \text{and} \quad D_1, D_2, D_3, D_4, C_5$$

This *non-uniqueness* is usually welcomed in practice as some flexibility is introduced, although it is minimal here.

The reader may confirm that the solution is correct by repeating the exercise going *forwards* from S. The principle is the same. At first glance the methods may seem rather close to enumeration—a lot of possibilities seem to have been considered. But this is not so. Once the structure is given it takes only a few minutes to solve the problem. Enumerating every possible route would take much longer and be extremely tedious. As the number of

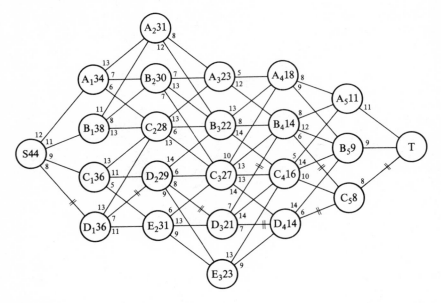

Figure 11-7

connections increases and the number of choices at each stage increases, the total number of possible routes rises *combinatorially*. Even in the present, small example, there are 272 routes. By enumeration each path would have to be (a) identified, (b) recorded, and (c) evaluated by adding up six figures. If we allowed 20 seconds or so to do each path, over $1\frac{1}{2}$ hours of intense effort would be required to solve the problem by complete enumeration. There would also be much greater likelihood of error. The reader might like to verify that there are 272 paths through the network. This can be done by a method not dissimilar to the one we have just used. Go through the network but at each station enter not the least cost to that point, but the *number of paths to that point*. The number of paths to A_3 (from S) for instance is the *sum* of the number of paths to A_2, B_2, and C_2. This result can be confirmed by a backward pass.

11-5-3 The Principle of Optimality

If you have understood the workings of the pipeline example and have grasped, in your own mind, the idea of why it works, then you have all that is needed to solve any (fully spelt out) simple numerical example. In the next section we spell out what has been involved and what the general principles are. The writer is not aware of a simpler, less technical exposition. But if it succeeds only in confusing you—pass on. It will not mean that you do not really understand what is involved, nor that you will not be able to solve numerical problems.

We have seen that the problem involves five *stages*. At each of these stages the system may be on any one of a number of *states*. In our example a 'state' is a choice of location. For instance at the *first* stage we are concerned with the choice of location for the fifth station. The states possible here are 'being at A_5', 'being at B_5', and 'being at C_5'. The *second* stage in the problem solution relates to the location of station four. The possible states here are being at A_4, at B_4, at C_4, or at D_4. And so on. For each of these states we need a *state description*. This is a presentation of all relevant information for future decision. Here, we are concerned with costs. The state description at A_4, for instance, is the cost of 18. Working back from T we have seen that 18 is the lowest cost that we can arrive at. Put another way, 18 is the least cost of completing the journey from A_4. The sequence of states that gave rise to the optimal cost of 18 was A_4, B_5, T. In technical jargon this sequence of states constitutes an optimal *sub-policy*. In the system as a whole we look for the optimal *policy* which is a sequence of states from start to finish. Now the fundamental concept in dynamic programming is the *principle of optimality*. This can be stated in numerous ways. In respect of a least-cost routing problem we can express it thus:

> *Principle of optimality:* 'The overall least cost route from origin to destination (i.e., from S to T) contains the least-cost route between any two stations on the overall least-cost route.'

By 'station' here we intend to include both S and T. So that the overall least-cost route gives, for example, the cheapest route between B_4 and T, or between S and D_3, or between D_1 and C_5.

One final thing. In all the workings we had no idea which stations would figure in the optimum. We did not know whether A_3 or D_3 would be part of the optimal sequence. The full sequence—and hence the optimal states of which it is comprised—is only revealed at the 'unrolling'. All the bridges have to be properly built: we do not know, when we are building them, which ones the army will pass over.

11-5-4 The Warehousing Problem

We have already studied one well-known problem in dynamic programming—the routing problem. Now we consider another famous case—the *warehousing problem*. This is a simplified and stylized version of the wholesaler's situation in which it is desired to decide on purchases and sales of a single commodity to take best advantage of known price variations.

A wholesaler stocks a single item. The ex-factory price (c_t) at which he buys and the wholesale price (p_t) at which he sells vary from month to month. Lead time on his purchases is 14 days, i.e., an order placed on 18

March arrives in stock on 1 April. Each month he buys an amount, q_t, around mid-month so that it arrives in stock on the first day of the following month. Sales volume in any month, v_t, will not exceed the stock available at the start of that month. Total storage capacity is K. Ignore storage and transactions costs. The prices are expected to be

Month (t)	Ex-factory price (c_t)	Wholesale price (p_t)
Jan. ($t = 1$)	70	90
Feb. ($t = 2$)	64	82
Mar. ($t = 3$)	72	70
Apr. ($t = 4$)	70	85
May ($t = 5$)	65	90
June ($t = 6$)	65	85

The wholesaler holds an initial stock of 300 units on 1 January. What should be the pattern of purchases and sales to maximize profit over the six-month period?

Again a backward working method will be employed. Consider the situation in June. Let this be stage one. Profit in this stage, Π_1, is revenue from sales less cost of purchases. Namely

$$\Pi_1 = p_6 v_6 - c_6 q_6$$

which we wish to maximize with respect to v_6 and q_6; the June sales and purchases. Clearly

$$v_6 \leqslant I_6$$

since by the specification of the problem sales in any month cannot exceed the inventory at the start of the month. Now purchases in June are limited by storage capacity

$$q_6 \leqslant K - I_6 + v_6$$

i.e., storage capacity is K; there was already I_6 in stock to start with but v_6 have already been sold. Naturally v_6 and q_6 cannot be negative. So what we are faced with is a linear programming problem! In full it is to

Maximize $\quad \Pi_1 = p_6 v_6 - c_6 q_6$

subject to $\quad\quad v_6 \leqslant I_6$

$\quad\quad\quad\quad\quad q_6 \leqslant K - I_6 + v_6$

where $\quad\quad\quad q_6 \geqslant 0, v_6 \geqslant 0$

Now this problem is trivial. We shall assume that no terminal stocks are required (this *could* be incorporated) and June is the last month being considered; thus it is pointless making purchases, so $q_6 = 0$. Also v_6 is made as large as possible (all stock is sold) so $v_6 = I_6$. Thus

$$\text{Maximum} \qquad \Pi_1 = p_6 I_6$$

and we should note, for use in a moment, that

$$I_6 = I_5 + q_5 - v_5$$

Now consider transactions in May. This is stage two. In keeping with the principle of optimality we want the profit *from here on* (i.e., May *plus* June's) to be as large as possible. So we write the profit function at stage (2) as

$$\Pi_2 = p_5 v_5 - c_5 q_5 + \Pi_1$$

in which the *maximum* value of Π_1 would be used, i.e., $p_6 I_6$. But if we now substitute for I_6 we get

$$\text{Maximum} \qquad \Pi_1 = p_6 I_6 = p_6 I_5 + p_6 q_5 - p_6 v_5$$

and substituting into Π_2 gives

$$\Pi_2 = p_5 v_5 - c_5 q_5 + p_6 I_5 + p_6 q_5 - p_6 v_5$$
$$\therefore \quad \Pi_2 = (p_5 - p_6) v_5 + (p_6 - c_5) q_5 + p_6 I_5$$

which is the expression to be maximized with respect to the two variables v_5 and q_5. The constraints are

$$v_5 \leqslant I_5$$
$$q_5 \leqslant K - I_5 + v_5$$

so that the linear programming problem is

$$\text{Maximize} \quad \Pi_2 = (p_5 - p_6) v_5 + (p_6 - c_5) q_5 + p_6 I_5$$
$$\text{subject to} \qquad v_5 \leqslant I_5$$
$$q_5 \leqslant K - I_5 + v_5$$
$$v_5 \geqslant 0, q_5 \geqslant 0$$

Figure 11-8 graphs the feasible region (shaded). The optimum will be at one of the corners OABC depending on the slope of the objective function contours.

This whole procedure is repeated for each month until January (stage (6)). The solution is then unrolled. Let us now use the actual figures and carry out the workings.

For stage (1) we can straightaway write

$$\text{Maximum} \qquad \Pi_1 = p_6 I_6 = \boxed{85 I_6}$$

Now the LP problem for stage (2) is

$$\text{Maximize} \quad \Pi_2 = (90 - 85) v_5 + (85 - 65) q_5 + 85 I_5$$
$$\text{subject to} \qquad v_5 \leqslant I_5$$
$$q_5 \leqslant K - I_5 + v_5$$

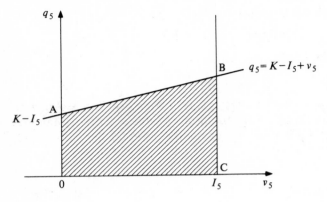

Figure 11-8

Now thinking in terms of Fig. 11-8, the objective function contours have negative slope ($= -5/20$) so B will be the optimal point. Thus $v_5 = I_5$ and $q_5 = K$. So that

$$\text{Maximum} \quad \Pi_2 = 5v_5 + 20q_5 + 85I_5$$
$$= 5I_5 + 20K + 85I_5$$
$$= \boxed{90I_5 + 20K}$$

Now for April (stage (3), $t = 4$) we must maximize Π_3, that is

$$\text{Maximize} \quad \Pi_3 = p_4v_4 - c_4q_4 + \text{maximum } \Pi_2$$
$$= 85v_4 - 70q_4 + 90I_5 + 20K$$

but $I_5 = I_4 + q_4 - v_4$ so that

$$\Pi_3 = 85v_4 - 70q_4 + 90(I_4 + q_4 - v_4) + 20K$$
$$= -5v_4 + 20q_4 + 90I_4 + 20K$$

and the linear programming problem is to

$$\text{Maximize} \quad \Pi_3 = -5v_4 + 20q_4 + 90I_4 + 20K$$
$$\text{subject to} \quad v_4 \leqslant I_4$$
$$q_4 \leqslant K - I_4 + v_4$$
$$v_4 \geqslant 0, q_4 \geqslant 0$$

Now again thinking in terms of Fig. 11-8, AB has a slope of $+1$ and the objective function contours here have a slope of $+1/4$. So that B is again optimal. Thus

$$v_4 = I_4 \quad \text{and} \quad q_4 = K$$

and maximum $\qquad \Pi_3 = -5I_4 + 20K + 90I_4 + 20K$

so maximum $\qquad \Pi_3 = \boxed{85I_4 + 40K}$

Now for the fourth stage (March)

$$\Pi_4 = p_3 v_3 - c_3 q_3 + \max \Pi_3$$

So

$$\Pi_4 = 70v_3 - 72q_3 + 85I_4 + 40K$$
$$= -15v_3 + 13q_3 + 85I_3 + 40K$$

and in this case the objective function contours (slope $= 15/13$) are steeper than the constraint line AB so that point A is optimal. At this point $v_3 = 0$ and $q_3 = K - I_3$. This results in

$$\text{Maximum} \quad \Pi_4 = 72I_3 + 53K$$

By similar processes we obtain

$$\text{Maximum} \quad \Pi_5 = 82I_2 + 61K \qquad (v_2 = I_2, q_2 = K)$$

and

$$\text{Maximum} \quad \Pi_6 = 90I_1 + 73K \qquad (v_1 = I_1, q_1 = K)$$

and the fully unrolled results sequence (recalling that $I_1 = 300$) and setting $K = 1000$) is

$$
\begin{aligned}
v_1 &= 300 \\
q_1 &= 1000 \\
\text{So} \quad I_2 &= 1000 \\
\therefore \quad v_2 &= 1000 \\
q_2 &= 1000 \\
I_3 &= 1000 \\
v_3 &= 0 \\
q_3 &= 0 \\
I_4 &= 1000 \\
v_4 &= 1000 \\
q_4 &= 1000 \\
I_5 &= 1000 \\
v_5 &= 1000 \\
q_5 &= 1000 \\
I_6 &= 1000 \\
v_6 &= 1000 \\
q_6 &= 0
\end{aligned}
$$

and the total profit made is

$$\Pi_6 = 90I_1 + 73K = 27\,000 + 73\,000 = 100\,000$$

In retrospect the optimal policy is fairly obvious but we have gained a little more than this. For instance we have seen that the optimal level of profit (the 100 000) is a *linear* function of initial stock and warehouse capacity (the coefficients 90 and 73 depend upon the pattern of prices) and various further results can be proved. The main point of the exercise was to illustrate a classic dynamic programming problem which turns out to be a sequence of simple linear programming problems.

11-5-5 A Marketing Problem

This problem is similar to one set by a professional accounting body. It is a good example in that it is of obvious business interest (involving a marketing problem) and does not at first sight appear to be a dynamic programming problem. However, dynamic programming turns out to be a good solution procedure. Here is the question.

A chain of retail chemists is thinking of introducing its own brand of shampoos. There would be three types: Gold (dry hair), Silver (greasy hair) and Green (medicated). The maximum sales promotion (sp) budget is £45 000 and the relationship between the various possible sp levels and subsequent contributions is

	Type														
	Gold				Silver				Green					
Sp expenditure (£000's)	10	15	20	30	10	15	20	30	10	15	20	25	30
Contribution (£000's)	25	35	40	48	25	28	30	48	30	35	38	40	48

It is necessary that each product receive some expenditure and the alternatives above represent distinct 'packages' and are neither divisible nor repeatable. The entire budget need not be spent. What should be the level of sales promotion expenditure on each product in order to maximize total contribution? How does dynamic programming improve on complete enumeration in this type of problem?

As a rule it is a good idea to spend a few moments checking for any obvious simplifications or reductions in problem size that can be made at once. A little reflection reveals that the most expensive alternative (sp = 30) can be ruled out in each case since even if the cheapest package was used in the other cases (10 each) the budget limit would be exceeded.

This done, we come to the questions of stages and states. There is a fairly obvious sequence of stages. The first stage will be the consideration of *one product alone*. Stage (2) will be the joint consideration of two products and stage (3) will incorporate all three products. We shall see that it does not matter which product is taken first. The process is like the consideration of the months in the warehousing problem: first June, then May and June together, and so on.

But what are we to mean by 'state' in this problem? As Taha (1976) points out, 'The definition of "state" is usually the most subtle concept in dynamic programming formulations.' Taha goes on to suggest two helpful questions:

1. What relationships bind the stages together?
2. What information is needed to make feasible decisions at the current stage without checking the feasibility of decisions made at previous stages?

These questions point very strongly towards 'sp expenditure so far' as the 'state'. This links the stages and is one of the two feasibility considerations.

Now for the workings. Let stage (1) be consideration of Green expenditures (states). So, in tabular form we have

Stage (1) (Green)

State	Π_1
10	30
15	35
20	38
25	40

That is all that is done for the moment in this stage—no more than a recording of the possibilities. The objective function Π_1 simply records the contributions from Green alone. There is no way of telling at the moment which 'state' will be selected. This will become clear only at the unrolling

Table 11-8 Stage (2): (Green + Silver)

State	Silver sp		Stage (1) state	Π_2
20	10	+	10	55
25	15	+	10	58
	10	+	15	60*
30	20	+	10	60
	15	+	15	63*
	10	+	20	63*
35	20	+	15	65
	15	+	20	66*
	10	+	25	65

phase. Now for stage (2). Here we shall consider Green and Silver *taken together*. The function Π_2 will consist of Silver *and* Green returns. Now there are only four distinct states (representing total sp expenditure on Green and Silver) made up as shown below. But for the states 25, 30, and 35 these can be made up in different ways and, of course, only the *best* value of Π_2 for these states could ever be relevant. Details are shown in Table 11-8. This completes stage (2) at the moment. Again, there is no indication as to what the best decision is. The asterisk indicates the best value of Π where there is more than one possibility. Now on to stage (3). This brings in Gold as well, so that Π_3 will represent the total contributions from all three products.

Table 11-9 Stage (3):
(Green + Silver + Gold)

State	Composition			
	Gold sp		Stage (2) state	Π_3
30	10	+	20	80
35	15	+	20	90*
	10	+	25	85
40	20	+	20	95
	15	+	25	95
	10	+	30	98*
45	20	+	25	100*
	15	+	30	98
	10	+	35	91

Now the solution can be unrolled. Obviously the best value of Π_3 is 100. This is the greatest total contribution from all three products. As in the warehousing problem the value of the objective at the last stage represents the total position, not just what is added at that stage. The 100 corresponded to 20 for Gold and the state of 25 from stage (2). Referring to the stage (2) workings we see that the 25 is best made up by 10 from Silver and the state of 15 from stage (1). This completes the solution.

To demonstrate that the same optimum would be arrived at if the products had been brought together in a different order, Table 11-10(a)–(c) gives the workings when Gold is taken first and then Green introduced at the second stage. Thus all products are included in a different order to the original workings. The optimal decision (choice of state) at each stage has been boxed. There are three important points to note when comparing the workings. The first is that the *best* value of Π_3 for each state of stage (3) in either set of workings is the same. But some of the inferior values may not be (examine state (40)). Why? Since the best values are the same this must include the optimal state. The best values of states at pre-final stages may be

Table 11-10(a) Stage (1): Gold

State	Π_1
10	25
15	35
20	40

Table 11-10(b) Stage (2): (Gold + Green)

State	Composition		Stage (1) state	Π_2
	Green sp			
20	10	+	10	55
25	15	+	10	60
	10	+	15	65*
30	20	+	10	63
	15	+	15	70*
	10	+	20	70*
35	25	+	10	65
	20	+	15	73
	15	+	20	75*

Table 11-10(c) Stage (3): (Gold + Green + Silver)

State	Composition		Stage (2) state	Π_3
	Silver sp			
30	10	+	20	80
35	15	+	20	83
	10	+	25	90*
40	20	+	20	85
	15	+	25	93
	10	+	30	95*
45	20	+	25	95
	15	+	30	98
	10	+	35	100*

quite different between the two sets of workings (why?). Finally the list of possible states for the final stage must be the same in any workings, but the list of states at earlier stages may differ between workings.

How does the procedure improve on complete enumeration? We see that in both sets of workings (as it happens) we have evaluated 21 combinations of three, two, or one product sp expenditures. Excluding the sp levels of 30 there are 36 ($= 3 \times 3 \times 4$) combinations of the remaining possibilities (three at a time). Thus we got away with (roughly) $[100 \times \frac{21}{36}]$ per cent $= 58$ per cent of the work involved in enumeration calculations. This is quite a high percentage, but this would rapidly drop as problem size becomes more realistic (consider the routing problem again in this respect). It could easily turn out that dynamic programming workings occupy less than 1 per cent, or less than one-tenth of 1 per cent, or less than one-hundredth part of 1 per cent, of the time needed for complete enumeration.

11-5-6 Conclusions

We have illustrated the dynamic programming style of approach with three fairly representative problems from one side of the subject. Of course, in so doing we have by no means exhausted the possible range of problems. All the cases we examined were *discrete* examples in which the state variable took on integral values and a tabular (or equivalent) method could be employed. There is also *continuous-state dynamic programming* where the state variable can take any value in an allowable range. There are also some fearsome *multiple-state dynamic programming* problems in which there is more than one state variable.

Various areas of application were mentioned in the introduction. We would only add here that the shampoo marketing problem has a capital budgeting structure. Taha gives the following example of a capital budgeting problem with the same structure. A company has a number of factories each of which could be expanded. The number of expansion alternatives differs between factories. The cost of plan i for factory j is c_{ij} and the present value of return from this plan is n_{ij}. The total budget is k. Which plan should be adopted at each factory so as to maximize NPV overall?

Although dynamic programming is not a panacea for all problems it has a broad range of applications. As Phillips, Ravindran, and Solberg (1976) put it, 'any optimization problem that can be decomposed by the principle of optimality is a candidate for efficient solution via dynamic programming. If the problem can also be formulated with three or less state variables, spectacular computational savings can often be realised.'

EXERCISES

11-5-1 What is dynamic programming? In what areas of operational research has dynamic programming found application?

11-5-2 Below is shown a routing problem.

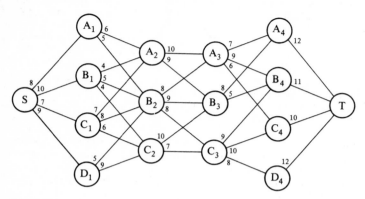

Figure 11-9

    (i) Find the cheapest route using a backward pass.

    (ii) How many different routes are there through the system?

11-5-3 A wholesaler stocks a single item. The ex-factory price (at which the wholesaler buys) and the wholesale price (at which the wholesaler sells) both vary from one month to the next, but all prices are constant within the month. The lead time on the wholesaler's purchases is two weeks. Each month an order is placed 13 days before the last day of the month. The wholesaler's sales take place around mid-month. The maximum warehouse capacity is 500 units and the warehouse is half full at the beginning of January. With the prices given below, what should be the pattern of purchases and sales to maximize profits over the six-month period?

Month	Ex-factory price	Wholesale price
Jan. ($t = 1$)	35	45
Feb. ($t = 2$)	37	35
Mar. ($t = 3$)	36	41
Apr. ($t = 4$)	38	36
May ($t = 5$)	34	46
June ($t = 6$)	39	43

What is the maximum profit attainable in the six-month period? Also, work out the month-by-month cash flows.

11-5-4 The Gassington Mineral Water Company is an old-established firm with modern ideas. At this moment three new product proposals are being investigated by the company's market research department. Under the working titles of Perraigne, Top-Pop, and Slim Fizz these materials are to be promoted as high-class non-alcoholic party drink, teenage jet-set refresher, and slimming aid beverage respectively. Having an extensive knowledge of rival ventures in all three fields as well as long experience of its own, the department has compiled a comprehensive table relating each product's expected contribution before advertising for the year 1977/78 to three different levels of expenditure on advertising as follows:

Product	Perraigne			Top-Top			Slim Fizz			
Advertising (£000's)	1.0	1.5	2.0	1.0	2.0	3.0	1.0	1.5	2.0	2.5
Expected contribution (1977/78) (£000's)	15	25	30	15	20	35	20	25	27.5	30

Current controls on promotional expenditure are particularly stringent, however, and the company will allocate no more than £4500 to the total advertising budget for Perraigne, Top-Pop, and Slim Fizz.

Required:

Assuming that the short-term aim is to maximize the total expected contribution before advertising of the three products, use a three-stage dynamic programming technique to determine the initial expenditure on advertising to be devoted to each.

(*Note:* Only the expenditure given in the table should be considered and each product must receive some promotional expenditure.)

To what extent is your method shorter than a complete enumeration method?

(Association of Certified Accountants Professional Examination: Section 2, paper 12, Management Mathematics, June 1976.)

APPENDIX: Discounting and present values

A number of the questions in the exercises have involved a little knowledge of present value methods, and the same have been occasionally referred to in the text. Here, the most basic elements of discounted cash flow are presented in order that OR questions involving discounting can be fully understood. A full description of the methods can be found in Samuels and Wilkes (1980a, Chapters 11 and 12).

First consider the basics of compound interest. The most familiar example of compound interest is that of the bank deposit account. If interest is paid annually at 10 per cent then £1 deposited at the start of the year will have produced £1.10 by the year's end. If this entire sum is left on deposit then all the £1.10 earns interest in the second year. Interest in the second year is paid not only on the principal sum but on the first year's interest also. Second year's interest is 10 per cent of £1.10, that is £0.11, so that the total sum in the account after two years is £1.21. The 'pound's progress' is shown below:

Year 0	Year 1	Year 2	Year 3
1	$\rightarrow$ $1+0.1\times1$ $=1.1$	$\rightarrow$ $1.1+0.1\times1.1$ $=1.1(1+0.1)$ $=(1+0.1)^2$ $=1.21$	$\rightarrow$ $1.21+0.1\times1.21$ $=1.21(1+0.1)$ $=(1+0.1)^3$ $=1.331$ $\rightarrow$

In general, after n years the original £1 would have become £$(1+0.1)^n$ at 10 per cent interest. By a similar process we can see that £1 invested for n years at 100 per cent would have become £$(1+r)^n$.

In compound interest calculations it is frequently necessary to find what amount must be set aside at present to produce £1 at a later date. This sum is called the *present value* of £1 and of course depends upon the number of years and rate of interest involved. The relationship is

$$PV = \frac{1}{(1+r)^n}$$

For if this sum, PV, is invested now its future value after n years compound interest at 100 per cent will be $PV(1+r)^n = 1$.

The present value of a stream of receipts (or payments) can be found by summing the present values of the individual components. Thus if receipts of £100, £150, and £200 are to occur at the end of each of three consecutive years then the present value of this income stream at 10 per cent interest will be

$$PV = \frac{100}{(1+0.1)} + \frac{150}{(1+0.1)^2} + \frac{200}{(1+0.1)^3}$$

Or, more conveniently, using *discount factors*

$$PV = 100 \times 0.9091 + 150 \times 0.8264 + 200 \times 0.7513$$
$$= 364.93$$

where $0.9091 = 1/(1.1)$, $0.8264 = 1/(1.1)^2$, $0.7513 = 1/(1.1)^3$. In these calculations it is convenient to use pre-prepared tables of discount factors. As an example of a convenient layout for workings, at a 15 per cent rate of discount, determine the present value of the cash flow:

$t = 0$	$t = 1$	$t = 2$	$t = 3$
-600	750	-150	1050

Workings are

Year	Sum	Discount factor (15 per cent)	PV
0	-600	1	-600
1	750	0.8696	652.20
2	-150	0.7561	-113.42
3	1050	0.6575	690.38
		Total $PV =$	629.16

Note that in the stream of returns the 'return' of -600 (which would be the *initial outlay* of 600 on the project) has a discount factor of unity. Being assigned year zero it is assumed payable at once and so is its own present value. The loss of 150 in the second year might be caused by a cyclical recession in the market, the entry of a competitor or overhaul of equipment. The figure 629.16 is the *net present value*.

In general, if S_1 represents the first-year return of S_2 the second-year return and so on, we can write:

$$\text{Present value} = \frac{S_1}{(1+r)} + \frac{S_2}{(1+r)^2} + \frac{S_3}{(1+r)^3} + \frac{S_4}{(1+r)^4} + \cdots + \frac{S_n}{(1+r)^n}$$

which can be put more concisely in summation or 'sigma' notation as

$$\text{Present value} = \sum_{t=1}^{n} S_t(1+r)^{-t}$$

The symbol Σ is read as 'sigma' and tells us to sum all terms which follow it (the general form of these terms being $S_t(1+r)^{-t}$) over the range of values t from $t = 1$ up to and including $t = n$. The terms S_t being considered as returns to an investment project would typically be positive, although in general they might not *all* be positive. In order to secure them it will be necessary to invest money in one or more years and if an investment of £K now is required to secure the return S_t then the above present value is said to be the *gross present value (GPV)* of the investment and the *GPV* minus K (the *initial outlay*) is the net present value *(NPV)* that is

$$NPV = \sum_{t=1}^{n} S_t(1+r)^{-t} - K$$

In relation to an individual investment opportunity the single project *NPV decision rule* is: Invest in the project if the *NPV* is positive. Do not invest if the *NPV* is negative. In the case where $NPV = 0$ the result is ambiguous but this is unimportant; unless there were extraneous considerations no action would normally be taken in such a case.

As an illustration of the use of *NPV* consider the following problem. A company has the opportunity to purchase a machine at the price of £2200. It will have a productive lifetime of three years, and the net additions to cash flows (after tax and including scrap value at the end of the third year) at the end of each of three years are respectively £770, £968, and £1331. The company has sufficient funds to buy the machine without recourse to borrowing and the best alternative is investment elsewhere at an annually compounded interest rate of 10 per cent. Should the machine be bought? Workings are

Year	Sum	Discount factor	PV
0	− 2200	1	− 2200
1	770	0.9091	700.0
2	968	0.8264	800.0
3	1331	0.7513	1000.0
			$NPV = +300$

So that the investment is worth while, that is, the machine should be bought.

The discount rate is very important to the *NPV* decision rule. For example, if the discount rate employed to evaluate the investment in the machine had been 20 per cent ($r = 0.2$) instead of 10 per cent ($r = 0.1$), then the *NPV* of the project would have been considerably reduced. Specifically:

Year	Sum	Discount factor	PV
0	− 2200	1	− 2200
1	770	.0.8333	641.6
2	968	0.6944	672.2
3	1331	0.5787	770.2
		NPV =	116.0

and the project should have been rejected.

Now consider the special case of an income stream where the sum to be received is the same in each year. This is called an *annuity*. Examples of annuities in business life are: hire-purchase contracts, leases, 'consols', endowment policies (neglecting the lump sum), and mortgages (with constant interest rate). Clearly the present value of an annuity could be found as for an 'irregular' income stream, but there is a short-cut. Consider an annuity of £100 for four years at 10 per cent interest. Assume that the first payment will be made after one year. Using discount factors the present value is

$$100 \times 0.9091 + 100 \times 0.8264 + 100 \times 0.7513 + 100 \times 0.6830$$

$$= 100(0.9091 + 0.8264 + 0.7513 + 0.6830)$$

$$= 100 \times 3.1699$$

$$= 316.99$$

The significant line of workings above is the second. All that has to be done is to multiply the amount involved, £100, by the sum of the first four discount factors: 3.1699. (The last digit of this sum is nine rather than eight due to rounding in the discount factors.) Tables of annuity factors are available to facilitate working of annuity problems (see Samuels and Wilkes, 1980a). For instance suppose we were asked to find the present value of an annuity of £125 lasting for six years with an interest rate of 11 per cent. An annuity table for 11 per cent and six years would give the factor 4.2305; thus the present value is $4.2305 \times £125 = £528.81$. It is usually assumed that the first payment in an annuity is made after one year. This is strictly called an *immediate annuity*. Where the first payment is due at once, this is called an *annuity due* and all the annuity factors must be increased by one in this case.

A special case of annuity is where a contract runs indefinitely—there being no end to the payments. This is called a *perpetuity*. Perpetuities are rare phenomena in the private sector, but certain government securities are undated, for instance, consols and war loan. There is a very simple formula for calculating the present value of a perpetuity being simply the sum involved divided by the interest rate as a decimal. If the annual sum is £S and the interest rate is $100r$ per cent, then

$$PV = \frac{S}{r}$$

Note that although the income stream is infinite the present value is finite. At a 10 per cent rate of interest a perpetuity of £50 has a present value of £500 and if the security is negotiable we might expect it to change hands at around this price. For instance, what should be the price of a unit of $3\frac{1}{2}$ per cent war loan stock if the current market rate of interest for this kind of very low risk security is 12 per cent? War loan is quoted in units of £100 nominal value and the annual interest payment is $3\frac{1}{2}$ per cent of this figure, i.e., £3.50. Assuming for simplicity a single annual payment the price should be PV given by

$$PV = \frac{3.5}{0.12} = £29.17$$

There are also available tables of *annual equivalent annuities*. Such tables show the size of annuity required to give a present value of one pound. Of course, the sum required depends upon the prevailing interest rate and the number of years for which the annuity would run. For instance, to give a present value of £1 a sum of £0.1490 would be required at the end of each of 10 years if the interest rate was 8 per cent.

To illustrate the use of annual equivalents suppose that the capital cost of a machine tool is £25 000 and that the expected life of the equipment is 10 years. At an interest rate of 8 per cent the lump sum is equivalent, in present value terms to an annual charge of £25 000 × 0.1490 = £3725. The figure of £3725 could be compared with an annual charge resulting from alternative financing arrangements and also would represent the gross amount of the depreciation which would be charged on the equipment using the annuity method of depreciation. Annual equivalents are very useful in repair–replace problems (see Samuels and Wilkes, 1980a).

Finally, the annuity related concept of a *sinking fund* can be useful (for tables see Samuels and Wilkes, 1980a). A sinking fund table shows how much must be set aside each year in order to achieve a sum of one pound at the end of a set number of years. These tables are helpful in loan repayment problems. For instance, it turns out that with a 12 per cent rate of interest, £0.0813 would need to be set aside annually in order to give a total of £1 after eight years. Consider an example. A company has loan stock of £750 000 due to mature in seven years' time. The company does not wish to make an issue of fresh stock at this time but rather to pay off the debt. At an interest rate of 10 per cent, how much should be set aside annually to meet the liability when it falls due? To give a 'terminal value' of £1 after seven years at 10 per cent £0.1054 must be put aside each year; thus to finish with £750 000 the amount required annually is £750 000 × 0.1054 = £79 050.

Table A Area under the standard normal curve up to z standard units above the mean

z	0.00	0.01	0.02	0.03	0.04	0.05	0.06	0.07	0.08	0.09
0.0	.5000	.5040	.5080	.5120	.5160	.5199	.5239	.5279	.5319	.5359
0.1	.5398	.5438	.5478	.5517	.5557	.5596	.5636	.5675	.5714	.5753
0.2	.5793	.5832	.5871	.5910	.5948	.5987	.6026	.6064	.6103	.6141
0.3	.6179	.6217	.6255	.6293	.6331	.6368	.6406	.6443	.6480	.6517
0.4	.6554	.6591	.6628	.6664	.6700	.6736	.6772	.6808	.6844	.6879
0.5	.6915	.6950	.6985	.7019	.7054	.7088	.7123	.7157	.7190	.7224
0.6	.7257	.7291	.7324	.7357	.7389	.7422	.7454	.7486	.7517	.7549
0.7	.7580	.7611	.7642	.7673	.7704	.7734	.7764	.7794	.7823	.7852
0.8	.7881	.7910	.7939	.7967	.7995	.8023	.8051	.8078	.8106	.8133
0.9	.8159	.8186	.8212	.8238	.8264	.8289	.8315	.8340	.8365	.8389
1.0	.8413	.8438	.8461	.8485	.8508	.8531	.8554	.8577	.8599	.8621
1.1	.8643	.8665	.8686	.8708	.8729	.8749	.8770	.8790	.8810	.8830
1.2	.8849	.8869	.8888	.8907	.8925	.8944	.8962	.8980	.8997	.9015
1.3	.9032	.9049	.9066	.9082	.9099	.9115	.9131	.9147	.9162	.9177
1.4	.9192	.9207	.9222	.9236	.9251	.9265	.9279	.9292	.9306	.9319
1.5	.9332	.9345	.9357	.9370	.9382	.9394	.9406	.9418	.9429	.9441
1.6	.9452	.9463	.9474	.9484	.9495	.9505	.9515	.9525	.9535	.9545
1.7	.9554	.9564	.9573	.9582	.9591	.9599	.9608	.9616	.9625	.9633
1.8	.9641	.9649	.9656	.9664	.9671	.9678	.9686	.9693	.9699	.9706
1.9	.9713	.9719	.9726	.9732	.9738	.9744	.9750	.9756	.9761	.9767
2.0	.9772	.9778	.9783	.9788	.9793	.9798	.9803	.9808	.9812	.9817
2.1	.9821	.9826	.9830	.9834	.9838	.9842	.9846	.9850	.9854	.9857
2.2	.9861	.9864	.9868	.9871	.9875	.9878	.9881	.9884	.9887	.9890
2.3	.9893	.9896	.9898	.9901	.9904	.9906	.9909	.9911	.9913	.9916
2.4	.9918	.9920	.9922	.9925	.9927	.9929	.9931	.9932	.9934	.9936
2.5	.9938	.9940	.9941	.9943	.9945	.9946	.9948	.9949	.9951	.9952
2.6	.9953	.9955	.9956	.9957	.9959	.9960	.9961	.9962	.9963	.9964
2.7	.9965	.9966	.9967	.9968	.9969	.9970	.9971	.9972	.9973	.9974
2.8	.9974	.9975	.9976	.9977	.9977	.9978	.9979	.9979	.9980	.9981
2.9	.9981	.9982	.9982	.9983	.9984	.9984	.9985	.9985	.9986	.9986
3.0	.9987	.9987	.9987	.9988	.9988	.9989	.9989	.9989	.9990	.9990
3.1	.9990	.9991	.9991	.9991	.9992	.9992	.9992	.9992	.9993	.9993
3.2	.9993	.9993	.9994	.9994	.9994	.9994	.9994	.9995	.9995	.9995
3.3	.9995	.9995	.9995	.9996	.9996	.9996	.9996	.9996	.9996	.9997
3.4	.9997	.9997	.9997	.9997	.9997	.9997	.9997	.9997	.9997	.9998
3.5	.9998	.9998	.9998	.9998	.9998	.9998	.9998	.9998	.9998	.9998
3.6	.9998	.9998	.9999	.9999	.9999	.9999	.9999	.9999	.9999	.9999

Table B Poisson probabilities $(T = 1)$; $\lambda^n e^{-\lambda}/n!$

λ \ n	0	1	2	3	4	5	6	7	8	9	10	11	12
.1	.9048	.0905	.0045	.0002	.0000								
.2	.8187	.1637	.0164	.0011	.0001	.0000							
.3	.7408	.2222	.0333	.0033	.0002	.0000							
.4	.6703	.2681	.0536	.0072	.0007	.0001	.0000						
.5	.6065	.3033	.0758	.0126	.0016	.0002	.0000						
.6	.5488	.3293	.0988	.0198	.0030	.0004	.0000						
.7	.4966	.3476	.1217	.0284	.0050	.0007	.0001	.0000					
.8	.4493	.3595	.1438	.0383	.0077	.0012	.0002	.0000					
.9	.4066	.3659	.1647	.0494	.0111	.0020	.0003	.0000					
1.0	.3679	.3679	.1839	.0613	.0153	.0031	.0005	.0001	.0000				
1.1	.3329	.3662	.2014	.0738	.0203	.0045	.0008	.0001	.0000				
1.2	.3012	.3614	.2169	.0867	.0260	.0062	.0012	.0002	.0000				
1.3	.2725	.3543	.2303	.0998	.0324	.0084	.0018	.0003	.0001	.0000			
1.4	.2466	.3452	.2417	.1128	.0395	.0111	.0026	.0005	.0001	.0000			
1.5	.2231	.3347	.2510	.1255	.0471	.0141	.0035	.0008	.0001	.0000			
1.6	.2019	.3230	.2584	.1378	.0551	.0176	.0047	.0011	.0002	.0000			
1.7	.1827	.3106	.2640	.1496	.0636	.0216	.0061	.0015	.0003	.0001	.0000		
1.8	.1653	.2975	.2678	.1607	.0723	.0260	.0078	.0020	.0005	.0001	.0000		
1.9	.1496	.2842	.2700	.1710	.0812	.0309	.0098	.0027	.0006	.0001	.0000		
2.0	.1353	.2707	.2707	.1804	.0902	.0361	.0120	.0034	.0009	.0002	.0000		
2.2	.1108	.2438	.2681	.1966	.1082	.0476	.0174	.0055	.0015	.0004	.0001	.0000	
2.4	.0907	.2177	.2613	.2090	.1254	.0602	.0241	.0083	.0025	.0007	.0002	.0000	
2.6	.0743	.1931	.2510	.2176	.1414	.0735	.0319	.0118	.0038	.0011	.0003	.0001	.0000
2.8	.0608	.1703	.2384	.2225	.1557	.0872	.0407	.0163	.0057	.0018	.0005	.0001	.0000
3.0	.0498	.1494	.2240	.2240	.1680	.1008	.0504	.0216	.0081	.0027	.0008	.0002	.0001
3.2	.0408	.1304	.2087	.2226	.1781	.1140	.0608	.0278	.0111	.0040	.0013	.0004	.0001
3.4	.0334	.1135	.1929	.2186	.1858	.1264	.0716	.0348	.0148	.0056	.0019	.0006	.0002
3.6	.0273	.0984	.1771	.2125	.1912	.1377	.0826	.0425	.0191	.0076	.0028	.0009	.0003
3.8	.0224	.0850	.1615	.2046	.1944	.1477	.0936	.0508	.0241	.0102	.0039	.0013	.0004
4.0	.0183	.0733	.1465	.1954	.1954	.1563	.1042	.0595	.0298	.0132	.0053	.0019	.0006
5.0	.0067	.0337	.0842	.1404	.1755	.1755	.1462	.1044	.0653	.0363	.0181	.0082	.0034
6.0	.0025	.0149	.0446	.0892	.1339	.1606	.1606	.1377	.1033	.0688	.0413	.0225	.0113
7.0	.0009	.0064	.0223	.0521	.0912	.1277	.1490	.1490	.1304	.1014	.0710	.0452	.0263
8.0	.0003	.0027	.0107	.0286	.0573	.0916	.1221	.1396	.1396	.1241	.0993	.0722	.0481
9.0	.0001	.0011	.0050	.0150	.0337	.0607	.0911	.1171	.1318	.1318	.1186	.0970	.0728
10.0	.0000	.0005	.0023	.0076	.0189	.0378	.0631	.0901	.1126	.1251	.1251	.1137	.0948

ANSWERS TO NUMERICAL QUESTIONS

2-6 This problem can be solved using either the semi-graphical method or the simplex method. Noting first that unit profit on the Prima product is 6 and on the Seconda product it is 4, and letting x_1 be the number of Primas made and x_2 be the number of Secondas made the simplex workings are:

			6	4	0	0	0
			x_1	x_2	S_1	S_2	S_3
0	S_1	390	2	1	1	0	0
0	S_2	810	3	3	0	1	0
0	S_3	200	0	1	0	0	1
		0	-6	-4	0	0	0
6	x_1	195	1	$\frac{1}{2}$	$\frac{1}{2}$	0	0
0	S_2	225	0	$\frac{3}{2}$	$-\frac{3}{2}$	1	0
0	S_3	200	0	1	0	0	1
		1170	0	-1	3	0	0
6	x_1	120	1	0	1	$-\frac{1}{3}$	0
4	x_2	150	0	1	-1	$\frac{2}{3}$	0
0	S_3	50	0	0	1	$-\frac{2}{3}$	1
		1320	0	0	2	$\frac{2}{3}$	0

So that the anwers are:
(a) 120 Primas, 150 Secondas (giving total profit 1320).
(b) The dual values are: cutting hours; 2, finishing hours; 2/3.
(c) Opportunity loss on third product:

$$2 \text{ at } 2 + 2 \text{ at } \tfrac{2}{3} - 5 = \tfrac{1}{3}$$

So do not produce the third product.
(d) Letting the Prima unit profit be Π_1 the range is

$$4 \leqslant \Pi_1 \leqslant 8$$

2-7 A peculiar feature in this problem is that the second constraint is *redundant*. This will be evident from the graph. However, it will not spoil the simplex workings if this constraint is left in. The optimal solution is $x_1 = 20$, $x_2 = 4$ giving $F = 800$. In simplex workings the slack variables for the x_2 upper bound will be at the level 16. Incidentally, the dual value for the first constraint is 25/3. Note that the upper bound on x_1 has a dual value, since it is a binding constraint at the optimum. This dual value is 5/3 and is provided *gratis* in the simplex workings.

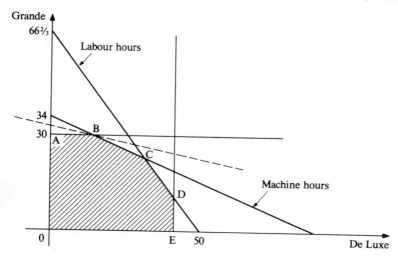

Figure A2-8

2-8 A graph of the problem is shown in Fig. A2-8.

(a) The feasible region is OABCDE and the optimum is at B, where 10 De Luxes and 30 Grandes are made, giving a total profit of 400. Note that the optimum is *not* point C which gives only 380 profit. In this case it is not profitable to use up all the available labour hours.

(b) It would not be worth having since the dual value is only £4.

(c) With Π_1 as the unit profit on the De Luxe model then the range emerges as: $0 \leqslant \Pi_1 \leqslant 4.8$.

(Note that it follows from this that if there is *any* profit to be had on De Luxes ($\Pi_1 > 0$) they will be produced at the optimum. If $\Pi_1 > 4.8$ then the optimum moves to point C at which more De Luxes and fewer Grandes are made.)

2-9 This problem can be divided into two sub-problems. Letting the amounts produced by $x_A, x_B, x_C,$ and x_D the two problems are:

$$\text{Maximize:} \quad 3x_A + 9x_B$$
$$\text{subject to} \quad 2x_A + 5x_B \leqslant 8000$$
$$4x_A + x_B \leqslant 4000$$
$$x_A \geqslant 0, x_B \geqslant 0$$

and

$$\text{Maximize:} \quad 5x_C + 8x_D$$
$$\text{subject to} \quad 3x_C + 4x_D \leqslant 6000$$
$$x_C \geqslant 0, x_D \geqslant 0$$

The answers are:

(a) $x_A = 0$, $x_B = 1600$, $x_C = 0$, $x_D = 1500$. The profit made is 26 400.

(b) This selling price is given by the unit profit such that the objective function contours have a slope of (minus) 4. This is the slope of the second constraint to which the objective function contours would then be parallel. We have

$$\frac{\Pi_A}{\Pi_B} = \frac{3}{\Pi_B} = 4 \qquad \therefore \quad \Pi_B = \frac{3}{4}$$

So with other data unchanged, the selling price that would give this level of unit profit is $18\frac{3}{4}$. This is the requisite minimum price.

(c) The dual value of skilled labour is £2. Thus the maximum overtime wage rate is £3 + £2 = £5.

2-10 The problem can be solved without using the simplex method.

(a) The opportunity loss on the existing plan is found by first finding the opportunity loss per unit of each product and multiplying by the current production levels and then summing. Given the dual values the opportunity losses are:

product A: 1 at 4 + 1.5 at 9 − (40 − 26) = 3.5
product B: 1 at 4 + 2.5 at 9 − (38 − 14) = 2.5
product C: 1.5 at 4 + 1 at 9 − (35 − 20) = 0
product D: 0.5 at 4 + 2 at 9 − (32 − 12) = 0

So that the total opportunity loss on the original plan is 3.5(1000) + 2.5(900) = 5750.

Clearly, products A and B should be discontinued and products C and D produced since they show no opportunity losses. To find the new production levels of C and D we need to know the total machine hours and materials available. Since we are told that the original plan uses up all available machine hours and materials, the total amounts must be the sum of the products of the original production levels and the per unit requirements of the products. Thus machine hours available are

$$1(1000) + 1(900) + 1.5(750) + 0.5(250) = 3150$$

and materials available are

$$1.5(1000) + 2.5(900) + 1(750) + 2(250) = 5000$$

We can now solve for the production levels

$$1.5x_C + 0.5x_D = 3150$$
$$x_C + 2x_D = 5000$$

Thus $x_C = 1520$ and $x_D = 1740$.

(b) At such prices that made their opportunity losses zero. The price of A must go up by 3.5 and the price of B must go up by 2.5. The resulting prices are then 43.5 for A and 40.5 for B.

2-11 (a) In formulating the objective it is soon discovered that the questioner assumes that assembly time labour is paid the rate of £1 per hour *whether it is used or not*. This is probably a reasonable assumption for practical cases, at least in the short term. We shall follow the questioner and assume that assembly time labour is a fixed cost in this case. The objective is stated to be profits maximization. With the assumption given about costs, the unit profit figures are

$$\text{for } x_1, \text{ unit profit} = 45 - 15 = 30$$
$$\text{for } x_2, \text{ unit profit} = 110 - 60 = 50$$
$$\text{for } x_3, \text{ unit profit} = 120 - 80 = 40$$

Thus the objective function is

$$\text{Maximize} \quad F = 30x_1 + 50x_2 + 40x_3$$

There are four constraints in this problem. The first relates to the circuits. Since each product requires one circuit per unit

$$x_1 + x_2 + x_3 \leqslant 350$$

Incidentally, we are here consistent with the questioner in designating this constraint as the 'first', since slack variable no. 1, S_1, relates to unused circuits. The second constraint is for assembly time.

$$x_1 + 3x_2 + 2x_3 \leqslant 380$$

Finally there are the two upper bounds on sales

$$x_2 \leqslant 20 \quad \text{and} \quad x_3 \leqslant 10$$

The full problem, with sign requirements and slacks included is therefore to

$$
\begin{aligned}
\text{Maximize:} \quad & F = 30x_1 + 50x_2 + 40x_3 \\
\text{subject to} \quad & x_1 + x_2 + x_3 + S_1 = 350 \\
& x_1 + 3x_2 + 2x_3 + S_2 = 380 \\
& x_2 + S_3 = 20 \\
& x_3 + S_4 = 10 \\
& x_1 \geqslant 0, x_2 \geqslant 0, x_3 \geqslant 0, \\
& S_1 \geqslant 0, S_2 \geqslant 0, S_3 \geqslant 0, S_4 \geqslant 0
\end{aligned}
$$

(b) It is apparent from the tableau that there is no unique best mix of products. The solution shown gives $x_1 = 335$ and $x_2 = 15$ with $x_3 = 0$. However, the index row number under x_3 is zero. Since x_3 is not 'in the solution' this means that there is another solution, in which x_3 is included, which is just as good. In the solution given, the usual convention of showing optimal index row numbers as non-negative has *not* been followed. In the notation of this text and most others, the index row numbers under S_1 and S_2 would be shown as $+20$ and $+10$ respectively. This change will be made in the workings shown below. One further iteration produces the alternative best plan involving x_3. With x_3 as the pivotal column and S_4 as the pivotal row the solution is:

			30	50	40	0	0	0	0
			x_1	x_2	x_3	S_1	S_2	S_3	S_4
30	x_1	330	1	0	0	$1\frac{1}{2}$	$-\frac{1}{2}$	0	$-\frac{1}{2}$
50	x_2	10	0	1	0	$-\frac{1}{2}$	$\frac{1}{2}$	0	$-\frac{1}{2}$
0	S_3	10	0	0	0	$\frac{1}{2}$	$-\frac{1}{2}$	1	$\frac{1}{2}$
40	x_3	10	0	0	1	0	0	0	1
		10 800	0	0	0	20	10	0	0

Thus 330 car vacuums, 10 standard vacuums, and 10 de luxe vacuums could equally well have been produced. In fact, of course, any non-basic solution *between* the two basic optima would also have served as well. The reader should verify that 334 car vacuums, 14 standard vacuums, and 2 de luxe vacuums would be just as profitable.

(c) The dual value for assembly time labour is found in the index row under slack variable S_2. This is $+10$. Since we are assuming that assembly time labour represents a fixed charge [for LP purposes the variable costs of standard rate assembly time labour are zero] the $+10$ represents the *total* amount that could be paid, in the extreme, for one hour's overtime. The overtime wage rate is much less than this (at £3) so it is certainly well worth having. But how much overtime should the company use? This is an important question to answer, but it is technically tricky and mistakes are all too easy. One way to proceed is as follows. Using more assembly labour is mathematically equivalent to leaving the total available at 380 but allowing slack variable S_2 to be *negative*. Thus if $S_2 = -1$ then this is equivalent to having 381 hours of labour. When a variable is brought in to negative level, positive index row numbers (in our notation) mean improvement. If overtime labour was *free*, if S_2 was set at -1 the objective function would go up by 10. If S_2 was set at -2 it would increase contribution by 20, and so on. So we shall bring in S_2 to negative level. But which one of the non-unique bases shall we start from? It turns out to be more convenient to start from the basis involving x_3 (given above). You can still start from the basis involving S_4 but one extra iteration is required in this event. Now overtime labour is *not* free, it costs £3 per hour. To accommodate this give S_2 an objective function coefficient of 3. This will do the trick technically, but care must then be exercised in interpreting the resulting dual values (for further discussion see Wilkes, 1977, pages 124–30). The workings below show the result:

ANSWERS TO NUMERICAL QUESTIONS **277**

			30	50	40	0	(3)	0	0
			x_1	x_2	x_3	S_1	S_2	S_3	S_4
30	x_1	320	1	0	0	1	0	-1	-1
50	x_2	20	0	1	0	0	0	1	0
(3)	S_2	-20	0	0	0	-1	1	-2	-1
40	x_3	10	0	0	1	0	0	0	1
		10 940	0	0	0	27	0	14	7

So far as the S_2 row is concerned, with the heretical -20, all that needs to be said is that the -20 means that 20 hours overtime would be optimal. Otherwise this row can be ignored. The new production levels are 320 car vacuums, 20 standard vacuums, and 10 de luxe vacuums. Total contribution is 10 940. (Note: naive scrutiny of the original tableau might suggest that only 10 hours overtime was desirable. This is incorrect. The figure of 10 is only the upper bound for feasibility of the original solution involving S_4.)

(d) There are two ways in which this new provision can be met. A new variable, x_4, could be introduced into the problem: x_4 would represent the sale of the circuits and would have an objective function coefficient of 28. If this was done there would be no need to start the problem all over again (see Wilkes, 1977, pages 128–30). A simpler method is to alter the S_1 objective function coefficient to 28 (again care would be required in interpreting index row numbers (see Wilkes, 1977)). The reader may verify that the resulting optimal solution is as shown below. The fact that $S_1 = 20$ at the new optimum simply means that 20 of the circuits would be re-sold. Total contribution would be £10 960.

			30	50	40	28	0	0	0
			x_1	x_2	x_3	S_1	S_2	S_3	S_4
30	x_1	300	1	0	0	0	1	-3	-2
50	x_2	20	0	1	0	0	0	1	0
28	S_1	20	0	0	0	1	-1	2	1
40	x_3	10	0	0	1	0	0	0	1
		10 960	0	0	0	0	2	16	8

2-12 Assume that the company's objective is profits maximization. There are numerous other possible criteria, notably those based upon 'growth'. However, no data is provided that would allow of such a formulation. Given the data, one of the few alternative objectives would have been maximization of turnover. Economic justification for such a criterion is weak, however. In general, a company's ability to do things will depend ultimately upon profitability. Politics has been described as the art of the possible; in the same spirit business is the art of the profitable.

In order to maximize profits, the greatest possible sum should be made available to set against overheads. Thus contribution should be maximized.

In the problem data this means that fixed overheads will not be included in the unit 'costs'. Let X_a be the number of units made of product A. Unit contribution will be $48 - (15 + 18) = 15$. Following similar notation and procedure for the other products the objective function is

$$\text{Maximize} \quad F = 15X_a + 12X_b + 16X_c + 12X_d + 7X_e$$

$$\text{subject to:} \quad
\begin{aligned}
X_a &\leqslant 1500 \\
X_b &\leqslant 1200 \\
X_c &\leqslant 900 \\
X_d &\leqslant 600 \\
X_e &\leqslant 600
\end{aligned}$$

and for the component constraint:

$$X_a + X_b + 3X_c + 4X_d + 5X_e \leqslant 5800$$

For the labour constraint the requirements per unit of each product will be the direct labour costs divided by 1.5. Thus

$$12X_a + 10\tfrac{2}{3}X_b + 4X_c + 2\tfrac{2}{3}X_d + 2\tfrac{2}{3}X_e \leqslant 20\,000$$

and for material expenditures

$$15X_a + 14X_b + 16X_c + 15X_d + 16X_e \leqslant 30\,000$$

and the sign requirements

$$X_a \geqslant 0,\ X_b \geqslant 0,\ X_c \geqslant 0,\ X_d \geqslant 0,\ X_e \geqslant 0$$

(b) There are many 'practical' problems. There are the problems of deciding what the objective is to be, identifying the constraints, and obtaining the data. Then there may be non-linearities (usually dealt with by an approximating device), random influences, and whole-number problems. However, recall that sensitivity analysis would be of great value in assessing the consequences of possible inaccuracies and changed conditions.

2-13 (a) (i) In general, the idea of maximum utilization of capacity will not lead to profits maximization. When it so does, however, this is merely fortuitous.

All costs except materials are fixed. The problem is then to maximize contribution:

$$\text{Maximize} \quad F = 14X_a + 6X_b$$

(Note: the '14' and '6' here are only coincidentally equal to the standard product costs. In the objective function they represent the unit contributions.)

The capacity constraint is

$$X_a + X_b \leqslant 1200 \qquad\qquad \text{(A2-2)}$$

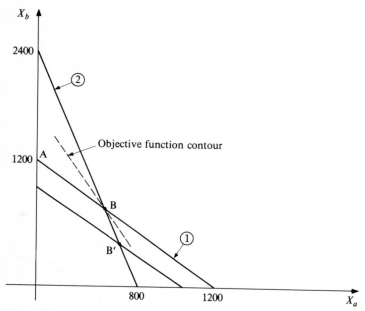

Figure A2-13(ai)

and the finishing labour hours constraint is

$$3X_a + X_b \leqslant 2400 \tag{A2-2}$$

The graph of the problem is shown in Fig. A2-13(ai) from which it is seen that the feasible region is OABC and that point B is optimal ($X_a = 600$, $X_b = 600$) so that it happens that both resources *are* fully used at the optimum.

(ii) During the overhaul the optimum moves to B′ at which point $X_a = 700$, $X_b = 300$.

(b) (i) Net profit for product A is $16 - 14 = 2$ and for product B is $8 - 6 = 2$. Thus with 600 units of each product manufactured the standard net profit is $600 \times 2 + 600 \times 2 = 2400$.

(ii) Maximum contribution at B′ is 11 600. With 500 units of each product made the contribution is 10 000. Thus 1600 would be lost.

2-14 The model will be (slack variables included):

$$\text{Maximize} \quad F = 1500x_1 + 1300x_2 + 2500x_3$$
$$\text{subject to} \qquad x_1 + S_1 = 500$$
$$x_2 + S_2 = 750$$
$$x_3 + S_3 = 400$$
$$0.5x_1 + 0.5x_2 + x_3 + S_4 = 1400$$
$$0.5x_1 + 0.5x_2 + 2x_3 + S_5 = 1200$$

and sign requirements on all variables.

In the style of layout adopted in part (b) of the question, the first two tableaux would be:

1500	1300	2500	0	0	0	0	0		
x_1	x_2	x_3	S_1	S_2	S_3	S_4	S_5		
1	0	0	1	0	0	0	0	500	S_1
0	1	0	0	1	0	0	0	750	S_2
0	0	1	0	0	1	0	0	400	S_3
0.5	0.5	1	0	0	0	1	0	1400	S_4
0.5	0.5	2	0	0	0	0	1	1200	S_5
1500	1300	2500	0	0	0	0	0	0	

1	0	0	1	0	0	0	0	500	S_1	
0	1	0	0	1	0	0	0	750	S_2	
0	0	1	0	0	1	0	0	400	x_3	2500
0.5	0.5	0	0	0	-1	1	0	1000	S_4	
0.5	0.5	0	0	0	-2	0	1	400	S_5	
1500	1300	0	0	0	-2500	0	0	1 000 000		

The writer has added a column identifying the variables in the solution and to the right of this column the objective function coefficient (when not zero) has been placed. Note that since optimal index row numbers are shown as *negative* in part (b), for consistency there will be positive numbers entered in the index row to start with (they will be just *minus* the usual index row numbers).

(b) In tableau layouts that (irritatingly) do not have a column labelling the solution variables, the variable concerned can be found by reading across the row of rates of exchange until a unit entry is found in a column which otherwise contains zeros. Thus the first entry in the column headed b_{ij} refers to x_1, the second entry refers to S_3 and so on. The full solution is (in units of 1000)

$$x_1 = 500, x_2 = 750, x_3 = 287.5, S_1 = 0, S_2 = 0,$$
$$S_3 = 112.5, S_4 = 487.5, S_5 = 0.$$

The total contribution made (in £'s) is 2 443 750. The fact that S_3 is in the solution simply means that the upper bound on x_3 is not reached. The fact that S_4 is in the solution means that there are unused machine hours.

The dual values are interpreted as follows. If the upper bound on x_1 could be relaxed by 1000 units an extra £875 contribution would be made. Similarly, if the bound on x_2 could be relaxed by 1000 units an extra £675 contribution could be made. Finally, if an additional 1000 hours of assembly time were available *at the existing price* then £1250 would be added to contribution.

3-2

	1	2	3	4	
1	18	(5) ^{16}	(95) ^{8}	13	100
2	14	(30) ^{14}	6	(95) ^{10}	125
3	20	(70) ^{15}	17	15	70
4	(55) ^{8}	(25) ^{12}	19	11	80
	55	130	95	95	

Figure A3-2

3-3 The VAM solution is degenerate. Place the epsilon assignment in the first independent location found. This is square 1,1.

	$v_1=10$	$v_2=16$	$v_3=12$	
$u_1=0$	(ε) ^{10}	(12) ^{16}	(13) ^{12}	25
$u_2=-3$	(20) ^{7}	11	11	20
$u_3=-7$	7	(15) ^{9}	8	15
	20	27	13	

VAM solution with degeneracy resolved

Figure A3-3(i)

Square 2,2 now shows real improvement and 12 units can be shipped round the closed path. The resulting solution is optimal (and, incidentally, no longer degenerate).

(12) ^{10}	16	(13) ^{12}	25	
(8) ^{7}	(12) ^{11}	11	20	
7	(15) ^{9}	8	15	
20	27	13		

Figure A3-3(ii)

3-4 (i) The VAM solution costs £606.

(ii) The unique optimum, following one iteration from the VAM solution, is shown in Fig. A3-4(ii), and the cost of this solution is £586. Note that a dummy customer is required with demand of 12.

	$v_1=6$	$v_2=8$	$v_3=10$	$v_4=9$	$v_5=0$	
$u_1=0$	7	8 (28)	11	10	0 (2)	30
$u_2=-5$	10	12	5 (17)	4 (28)	0	45
$u_3=0$	6 (20)	10	11	9 (5)	0 (10)	35
	20	28	17	33	12	

Figure A3-4(ii)

(iii) The evaluation of square B1 at the optimum is $-5+6-10=-9$. To make the square just worth while the evaluation would have to be zero. To achieve this the transportation cost would have to be reduced by 9 to only 1 per unit.

(iv) £5. The u_i+v_j value is $-5+6=1$ and to find the total increase in cost this per unit increase of 1 must be multiplied by the number of units involved (5). The new optimum would be degenerate.

3-6 (i) The unique optimum is shown below:

	$v_1=20$ A	$v_2=15$ B	$v_3=25$ C	$v_4=26$ D	$v_5=20$ E	$v_6=2$ F	
$u_1=0$; 1	20 (11)	15 (13)	23	25	13	0	24
$u_2=1$; 2	19	12	25	27 (22)	21 (8)	0	30
$u_3=-2$; 3	17	13 (11)	22	21	18 (7)	0 (5)	23
$u_4=+2$; 4	22 (5)	12	27 (20)	23	18	0	25
	16	24	20	22	15	5	

Figure A3-6(i)

The total profit made is £2096. Note that manufacturer three is only called on to supply 18 units.

(ii) The contract would mean having to place an assignment of 7 in square 1,E. The evaluation of this square shows that profit would be reduced by 7 (this is a maximization problem) for every unit located here. Thus the total drop in profit would be £49 (the closed path for this square could just accommodate an assignment of 7 in 1,E). Thus £49 is the maximum sum that the firm would be prepared to pay.

(iii) Take more from manufacturer four and less from manufacturer one (remember that this is a maximization problem).

(iv) £96.

3-7 (a) The original policy followed by the Rental Company is shown below:

	$v_1=13$ Sidmouth	$v_2=15$ Liverb'ne	$v_3=16$ Centapool	$v_4=0$ Dummy	
East Sidmouth $u_1=0$	13 (80)	15 (60)	15	0 (70)	210
West Liverbourne $u_2=2$	18	17 (140)	18	0	140
Martrent $u_3=0$	15	18	16 (200)	0 (90)	290
	80	200	200	160	

Figure A3-7(a)

The costs in each square represent the variable distribution costs per unit *plus* the production costs per unit. It follows at once from the stated arrangements that East Sidmouth and Martrent have unused capacities of 70 and 90 respectively. The cost of this original solution is 7520 (£000's).

(b) The original solution is not optimal as both square 1,3 and 2,4 show improvement. Routing 70 round the 2,4 closed path gives the solution below which is optimal. The cost of the solution is 7380 so that a saving of 140 could be effected.

	$v_1=13$	$v_2=15$	$v_3=14$	$v_4=-2$	
$u_1=0$	13 (80)	15 (130)	15	0	210
$u_2=2$	18	17 (70)	18	0 (70)	140
$u_3=2$	15	18	16 (200)	0 (90)	290
	80	200	200	160	

Figure A3-7(bi)

The solution is not unique as square 3,1 has zero evaluation. 70 units can be shipped round this closed path to give the alternative solution (Fig. 3-7(bii)).

⑩	⑳⓪			
			⑭⓪	
⑦⓪		⑳⓪	⑳	

Figure A3-7(bii)

(c) The alternative optimum of (b) does not involve usage of the West Liverbourne factory, so that there would be *no* increases in variable production and distribution costs on account of the closure. Of course, in reality, closure can be very expensive on other grounds.

3-8 (i) The sources are the categories into which the applicants fall. In the optimal tableau (Fig. A3-8(i)), B represents those qualified in both specialist areas, A in accounting only, D in data processing only, and G with general experience only.

	$v_1=50$ A	$v_2=48$ D	$v_3=46$ G	$v_4=0$ Dummy	
$u_1=0;$ B	50 *	48 *	48	② 0	2
$u_2=0;$ A	② 50	M	① 46	① 0	4
$u_3=-1;$ D	M	③ 47	② 45	0	5
$u_4=-2;$ G	M	M	③ 44	0	3
	2	3	6	3	

Figure A3-8(i)

It will be seen that a dummy column is needed to balance the rim conditions. The 'transportation costs' represent the higher of the two relevant salary figures in each case. The figure M is an unspecified *arbitrarily large* number inserted as the cost to prevent assignments in squares where the applicants are unqualified. M is so large that any square with an M cost *always has a negative evaluation*. Some safely large (say 1000) number can be used in place of M if desired.

The cost of the optimal solution is seen to be 509 (£00). This is the least figure that can be submitted. Of course the solution does not tell us which *person* gets which job, only that, for instance, of the four people qualified in accounting only, any two should be assigned to the accounting jobs.

The solution is not unique. Those squares with zero evaluations are starred. There are three other basic solutions with the same cost corresponding to the placing of assignments in squares 1,1 and 1,2. The assignments are:

2	0	0	0		0	1	0	1		1	1	0	0
0	0	1	3		2	0	0	2		1	0	0	3
0	3	2	0		0	2	3	0		0	2	3	0
0	0	3	0		0	0	3	0		0	0	3	0

There is also one non-basic solution involving assignment of one at square 1,1. The pattern in this case is:

1	0	0	1
1	0	1	2
0	3	2	0
0	0	3	0

(ii) Consider a 'two-by-two' problem in which the shipments are represented by x's. The amount to be shipped from source i to destination j is represented by x_{ij}. The cost per unit is shown by c_{ij}. Thus in tableau form:

Destination

		1	2	
Source	1	c_{11} x_{11}	c_{12} x_{12}	S_1
	2	c_{21} x_{21}	c_{22} x_{22}	S_2
		D_1	D_2	

The objective is to minimize costs overall. Thus

$$\text{Minimize} \quad F = c_{11}x_{11} + c_{12}x_{12} + c_{21}x_{21} + c_{22}x_{22}$$

Since rim conditions are balanced ($S_1 + S_2 = D_1 + D_2$) to satisfy the demands *all* available supplies must be used (there can be nothing remaining at either source). Thus

$$x_{11} + x_{12} = S_1 \quad \text{and} \quad x_{21} + x_{22} = S_2$$

The demands also will be precisely met

$$x_{11}+x_{21} = D_1 \quad \text{and} \quad x_{12}+x_{22} = D_2$$

and negative shipments are disallowed

$$x_{11} \geqslant 0, x_{12} \geqslant 0, x_{21} \geqslant 0, x_{22} \geqslant 0$$

Thus the problem is clearly one of linear programming with the special features that all constraint coefficients of the x_{ij} are zero or one and that since rim conditions are balanced if any *three* of the constraints are satisfied then the fourth is automatically satisfied. In general with m origins and n destinations there will be $m+n$ such equations of which any one can be dropped. This is why basic solutions to transportation problems contain only $m+n-1$ assignments. It is important to realize that transportation problems are linear programming problems; thus anything that is true for LP in general is true for transportation. Also, it follows that *some* LPs are transportation problems. If this special feature can be spotted, then the highly efficient transportation solution procedures can be adopted.

3-9 Notwithstanding the injunction of the last sentence, space permits only the optimal solution to be presented here! However, it should be pointed out that in obtaining a VAM solution there are several 'ties' and some VAM solutions require several iterations. The problem is one of maximization. The entries in the top right of the squares are unit profits (selling price minus transportation, material, and labour costs).

	$v_1=7$ 1	$v_2=9$ 2	$v_3=13$ 3	$v_4=5$ 4	$v_6=0$ Dummy	
$u_1=0;$ A	6	8	(30) 13	(110) 5	0	140
$u_2=0;$ B	5	7	12	2	(100) 0	100
$u_3=3;$ C	(80) 10	(70) 12	6	4	0	150
$u_4=0;$ D	6	(50) 9	(100) 13	1	(10) 0	160
	80	120	130	110	110	

Figure A3-9

The total profit made is £4330. Note that the evaluation of square 1,5 is zero, so that the solution is not unique.

4-5 The unique optimal assignment pattern is shown in Fig. A4-5 with one version of the opportunity cost matrix. If you have the same assignment pattern but differing opportunity cost elements, cost out a few alternative complete solutions as a check.

1	0	⊡	3	2
0	⊡	3	4	0
⊡	1	4	2	0
5	2	0	⊡	2
4	1	1	9	⊡

Figure A4-5

4-6 The solution here is non-unique but all optima cost 36. One optimal arrangement, with one version of the opportunity cost matrix, is shown in Fig. A4-6.

6	6	⊡	3	4	8
5	6	M–5	⊡	0	5
3	4	3	5	2	⊡
⊡	0	0	M–8	1	5
0	0	2	3	⊡	5
4	⊡	4	6	0	M–6

Figure A4-6

4-7 All 24 possible arrangements are optimal. All cost 17. The opportunity cost matrix is unique and consists entirely of zeros. In the original effectiveness matrix the rows can be made the same by addition of suitable constants throughout three of the rows (e.g., add 5 throughout the second row, 6 to the third, and 2 to the fourth). A similar result could be obtained for the columns.

4-8 A 'dummy' fifth product is needed to balance up the problem. This is added in; the profit data are shown in Fig. A4-8. Applying the maximization process it is soon evident that plant (3) should be closed (it gets assigned the dummy product in the unique optimum).

9	12	7	9	0
11	12	13	11	0
8	10	11	9	0
7	10	14	7	0
15	6	8	13	0

Figure A4-8

5-2 (i), (ii), (iii)

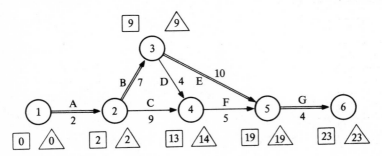

Figure A5-2

The critical path joins events 1-2-3-5-6 and consists of activities A, B, E, and G. It is shown as ⇒ above.

(iv)

Activity	Total float	Free float
A	0	0
B	0	0
C	3	2
D	1	0
E	0	0
F	1	1
G	0	0

(v) One day. A B D F G becomes uniquely critical.

5-3 (i) The network is as shown in Fig. A5-3.

The critical path consists of jobs A B E F G J K.

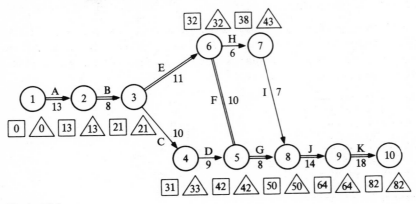

Figure A5-3

(ii)

Job	Total float	Free float
C	2	0
D	2	2
H	5	0
I	5	5

(iii) By changes of logic (repositioning jobs) or speedings up. In either case the critical path must be affected. In the case of speedings-up, this usually requires further resources to be applied to the job. If these resources are drawn from outside the system, then there is only cost to consider. If the resources have to be drawn from other—presently non-critical—jobs, thus slowing them down, the problem is more complex. If time on job G is halved, the original path remains critical, 4 days are saved overall, and node 8 is reached after 46 days. However, if, in order to speed up G, resources are drawn from *I* with the effect that it is slowed down by 2 days, then the critical path switches to include EHI and only 3 days are saved overall, node (8) being reached after 47 days.

5-5 (a) 17 days. Cost £1910 + £400 penalty = £2310.

(b) Two days to be saved from critical path. CP consists of activities 1–2, 2–4, 4–6, 6–7. The *cost per day saved* is least (£70) in 4–6 and both days can be saved here. Check with the network to see that no other path becomes critical. Revised cost = £1910 + 140 = £2050.

(c) Here a trade-off must be made between the bonus payments on the one hand and the costs of time savings on the other. Overall time reductions that can be achieved for less than £100 per day will be worth while. It is soon evident that the optimal arrangement is 4–6 in 4 days and 6–7 in 1 day, other jobs at normal times. Duration 11 days, cost £2410 − £400, bonus = £2010.

(d) Save 4 days in 6–7, cost = 360
2 days in 4–6, cost = 140
1 day in 5–6, cost = 70
—————
570

∴ Total cost here = £1910 + 570 = £2480

5-6   (a)

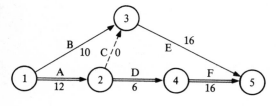

Figure A5-6(a)

The critical path consists of A, D, F and takes 34 days at normal times.
   (b) Prepare a table showing cost per day saved.

Job	Cost/day saved	Max. saving
A	1000	4
D	500	2
E	1500	2
F	600	8

All paths must be completed in 30 days. The only non-critical paths are BE and ACE which take less than 30 days even at normal times. Thus we need only be concerned with the critical path. The cheapest way of saving 4 days here is to save 2 days in D and 2 in F at an additional cost of £2200. Thus cost is now £31 200 + £2200 = £33 400.
   (c) One would wish to know the probability distributions (in full if discrete; type, mean, and variance if continuous) of the job times. A confidence interval for completion of the whole project could then be found. Statements would have to be in terms of probabilities and expected values. The second part of the question is vague. The meaning is unclear and no probabilities are given. However, the problematical path is ACE which *could* take 32 days if E took 20 days. As no probabilities are given, no expected value calculations are possible. However, assume that it is desirable to avoid lateness with probability one. The cheapest way to do this is by saving 2 days in job A at a cost of £2000.

5-7 (a) The two variants of the network diagram are shown below. The arrow or more correctly the arc–node diagram is the earlier form and is still more widely used. The activity-on-the-node or precedence diagram form has advantages (dummies are never required, easier to construct networks from dependency tables) but has not really caught on. For a full description of this form see Wilkes (1977, Chapter 8).
   (b) There are only two paths. If *average* times are used both are critical. After the event, of course, only one will have transpired to be critical. It is

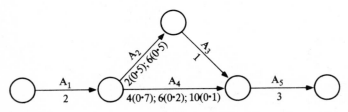

Figure A5-7(ai)

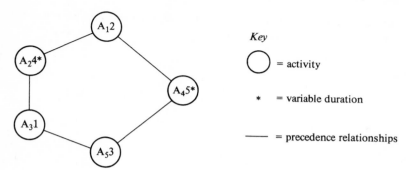

Figure A5-7(bii)

somewhat more likely that the $A_1A_4A_5$ path will be critical. The full range of possibilities is

Path	Time	Probability
$A_1A_2A_3A_5$	8	0.5
$A_1A_2A_3A_5$	12	0.5
$A_1A_4A_5$	9	0.7
$A_1A_4A_5$	11	0.2
$A_1A_4A_5$	15	0.1

The only occasions when the $A_1A_2A_3A_5$ path can be critical are when the 12-day time occurs and the $A_1A_4A_5$ path takes 9 or 11 days. The chance of this is $0.5(0.7+0.2) = 0.45$. Thus the probability that $A_1A_4A_5$ is critical is 0.55. The average or expected completion time for the network is 11.15 days. The workings are as follows:

(1) $A_1A_2A_3A_5$ time	(2) prob	(3) $A_1A_4A_5$ time	(4) prob	(5) Max(1),(3)	(6) (2) × (4)	(7) (5) × (6)
8	0.5	9	0.7	9	0.35	3.15
8	0.5	11	0.2	11	0.10	1.10
8	0.5	15	0.1	15	0.05	0.75
12	0.5	9	0.7	12	0.35	4.20
12	0.5	11	0.2	12	0.10	1.20
12	0.5	15	0.1	15	0.05	0.75
					mean time =	11.15

Column (5) gives the larger of the times for the two paths and column (6) is the chance of the particular situation arising. As to cost, the costs of A_1, A_3, and

A_5 are fixed and total 23. The average cost of A_2 and A_4 is 65 as shown below. Thus the average cost for the whole project is $65 + 23 = 88$.

(1) A_2 time	(2) A_4 time	(3) prob	(4) A_2, A_4 cost	(5) (3) × (4)
2	4	0.35	40	14
2	6	0.10	50	5
2	10	0.05	70	3.5
6	4	0.35	80	28
6	6	0.10	90	9
6	10	0.05	110	5.5
				65

(c) From the above workings the minimum time is 9 days with probability 0.35 and the maximum time is 15 days with probability 0.10.

5-8 The network for this project is shown in Fig. A5-8.

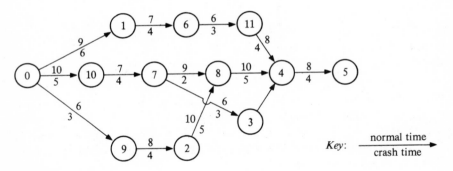

Figure A5-8

Key: $\dfrac{\text{normal time}}{\text{crash time}}$

(a), (b) There are just four paths, the longest of which at normal durations is 0–10–7–8–4–5 taking 44 days. The normal cost of the project is just the sum of the entries in the normal cost column; £8280.

(c) When crash times are used on all jobs the minimum completion time is 21 days. Two paths are now jointly critical: 0–9–2–8–4–5 and 0–1–6–11–4–5. Note that it is not necessary to crash both of 7–3 and 3–4; one of these could be left at the normal duration saving £300.

(d) Use of a bar chart (as in Fig. 5-7(a)) shows that the maximum number of men required at any one time is 19.

5-9 (a) The network for the project is as shown in Fig. A5-9(a). Note that two dummies are required. J is required because, by convention in this format, two nodes are joined by only one arc. K is required to ensure the correct

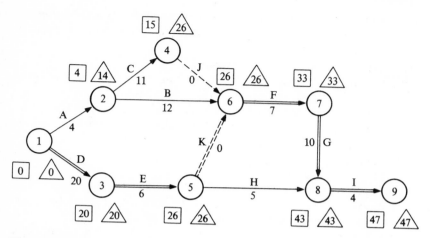

Figure A5-9(a)

precedence relationships. The critical path joins nodes 1 3 5 6 7 8 9 and comprises jobs D E (K) F G I.

(b) A bar chart for the project is shown in Fig. A5-9(b). In this case the lengths of the activities (bars) correspond to duration. The figures in brackets after C, B, and H represent free float in those jobs. Note that no dummy activities are required in this format.

(c) Three. At no time are more than three activities being worked upon simultaneously. This is evident from the bar chart.

(d) One day's delay (48 now required). C can be worked on after B or B after C. This would delay the start of F by only one day.

6-1 (i) Production cannot be exactly tailored to fit erratic demand, but the company does not wish to lose custom by being unable to fill orders promptly.

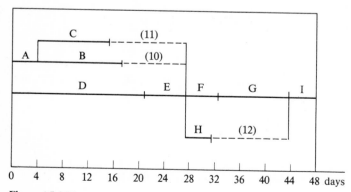

Figure A5-9(b)

(ii) The 'fixed charge' component of re-ordering or 'set-up costs' means that frequent re-ordering or re-starting production is uneconomical.

(iii) Supplies of materials may be erratic.

(iv) Breakdowns at one stage of production need not bring the whole process to a stop if in-process inventory is held.

(v) In times of rising prices early buying of supplies can be economical. If supplies are subject to complete stoppage or disruption, this is another reason for inventory.

(vi) There are sometimes other reasons too. A speculator may attempt to 'corner the market' to force up prices. A country may hold 'strategic' stocks of commodities in the event of emergency.

(vii) Good inventory management is essential in view of the high proportion of assets tied up in stock.

(viii) Inventory management overlaps production control, pricing, costing, capital budgeting, and financial control more generally.

6-2 The principal results are: the square root formula; the irrelevance of unit costs to optimal lot size; the robustness of the EOQ model; the fact that the basic EOQ can be built upon.

6-3

$$EOQ = \sqrt{\frac{2 \times 400 \times 2500}{8}} = 500$$

$$\therefore \text{ no. of replenishments} = \frac{2500}{500} = 5$$

6-4
$$EOQ = \sqrt{\frac{2 \times 75 \times 1000}{6}} = 158.11$$

This calls for $1000/158.11 = 6.32$ orders per annum (view this as a *rate* of ordering). Total costs are

$$\tfrac{1}{2} \times 158.11 \times 6 + \frac{75 \times 1000}{158.11} = 474.33 + 474.35$$

$$= 948.68.$$

With only five re-orders p.a., re-order size would be 200. Putting this value into the cost expression gives

$$\tfrac{1}{2} \times 200 \times 6 + \frac{75 \times 1000}{200} = 600 + 375$$

$$= 975.$$

The absolute maximum that the company would pay is £975 − £948.68 = £26.32

6-5
$$EOQ = \sqrt{\frac{2 \times 25 \times 250\,000}{0.125}} = 10\,000$$

$\therefore$ 25 investments to be made per annum.

Total costs here are

$$C = \tfrac{1}{2} \times 10\,000 \times 0.125 + \frac{25 \times 250\,000}{10\,000} + 0.01 \times 250\,000$$

$$= \quad 625 \quad + \quad 625 \quad + \quad 2500$$

$\therefore \quad C = £3750$

With the revised scheme a new optimal size of investment is needed.

$$EOQ \text{ (revised scheme)} = \sqrt{\frac{2 \times 100 \times 250\,000}{0.125}}$$

$$= 20\,000$$

Costs would then be

$$C = \tfrac{1}{2} \times 20\,000 \times 0.125 + \frac{100 \times 250\,000}{20\,000} + 0.0075 \times 250\,000$$

$$= \quad 1250 \quad + \quad 1250 \quad + \quad 1875$$

$\therefore \quad C = £4375$

So that the company would prefer the original scheme.

6-6 Expected weekly demand is 5 units, so annual demand is 250 on average. Thus:

$$EOQ = \sqrt{\frac{2 \times 50 \times 250}{40}} = 25$$

$\therefore$ 10 re-orders p.a.

Now find expected shortages for the different levels of buffer stock. For $B = 0$ the re-order level is 5 so that expected shortage is 0.89 (workings below).

X	S	P	PX
6	1	0.17	0.17
7	2	0.12	0.24
8	3	0.08	0.24
9	4	0.06	0.24
		$\Sigma = 0.89$	

Similar workings for other values of B produce the ESPC data in the table below:

B	ESPC	ESPA	SOC	BSCH	Total
0	0.89	8.9	178	0	178
1	0.46	4.6	92	40	132
2	0.20	2.0	40	80	120*
3	0.06	0.6	12	120	132
4	0.00	0.0	0	160	160

Hence the optimum size of buffer stock is two units. This gives a re-order level of 7. Now if the shortage cost was S the Total column would read

B	Total
0	8.9S
1	4.6S + 40
2	2S + 80
3	0.6S + 120
4	160

For $B = 2$ to be optimal we must have

$$2S + 80 \leqslant 4.6S + 40$$
$$\therefore \quad S \geqslant 15.38 \quad \text{(greatest lower bound)}$$
$$2S + 80 \leqslant 8.9S$$
$$\therefore \quad S \geqslant 11.59$$
$$2S + 80 \leqslant 0.6S + 120$$
$$\therefore \quad S \leqslant 28.57 \quad \text{(least upper bound)}$$
$$2S + 80 \leqslant 160$$
$$\therefore \quad S \leqslant 40$$

So, *ceteris paribus*, the solution is optimal for

$$15.38 \leqslant S \leqslant 28.57$$

A sensitivity analysis *can* be conducted on the holding cost figure but it is rather more complicated than the above analysis on S as the EOQ depends on H.

6-7
$$EOQ = \sqrt{\frac{2 \times 160 \times 4000}{8}} = 400$$

so that there will be 10 cycles per annum. The total cost at present is:

$$4Q + \frac{640\,000}{Q} + 48\,000 = 51\,200$$

So that the alternative scheme should be rejected.

Now weekly demand is $4000 \div 50 = 80$ with variance 156.25 (i.e., standard deviation = 12.5). For a $97\frac{1}{2}$ per cent service level

$$\begin{aligned}
R &= LW + 1.96\,\sigma\sqrt{L} \\
&= 4 \times 80 + 1.96 \times 12.5 \times 2 \\
&= 369.
\end{aligned}$$

At $97\frac{1}{2}$ per cent service level the probability of a stock out each cycle is 0.025 so that the expected number of stock outs per annum is $0.025 \times 10 = 0.25$. The buffer stock is 49 here. At 80 per cent service level the buffer stock is

$$\begin{aligned}
B &= 0.84\,\sigma\sqrt{L} \\
&= 21.
\end{aligned}$$

The expected number of stock outs per annum is $0.2 \times 10 = 2$. So, at the 80 per cent level

$$\begin{aligned}
\text{BSHC} &= 21 \times 8 &= 168 \\
\text{SOC} &= 2 \times 120 &= 240 \\
&\qquad \text{Total} & \overline{408}
\end{aligned}$$

Whereas at the $97\frac{1}{2}$ per cent service level

$$\begin{aligned}
\text{BSHC} &= 49 \times 8 &= 392 \\
\text{SOC} &= 0.25 \times 120 &= 30 \\
&\qquad \text{Total} & \overline{422}
\end{aligned}$$

So that the reduction in service level is advisable on grounds of cost. Since stock out cost is difficult to estimate a sensitivity analysis of the result is worth while. Instead of £120 let the stock out cost be S. For the 80 per cent service level to be preferable we require that

$$168 + 2S \leqslant 392 + 0.25S$$
$$\therefore \quad S \leqslant 128$$

Thus only a $6\frac{2}{3}$ per cent increase in S is tolerable. The result should therefore be regarded with caution.

6-8 The optimum size of run will be the economic lot size, ELS (ELS $\equiv$ EOQ) or at one of the 'break points' *above* the ELS. Now:

$$\text{ELS} = \sqrt{\frac{2 \times 500 \times 5000}{5}} = 1000$$

For this value of Q unit cost is 1.9 so that

$$C = 2500 + 2500 + 9500 = 14\,500$$

whereas at the 2000 breakpoint

$$C = 5000 + 1250 + 8500$$
$$= 14\,750.$$

However, at the 3000 breakpoint

$$C = 7500 + 833\tfrac{1}{3} + 6000$$
$$= 14\,333\tfrac{1}{3}$$

So that the optimum size of production run is 3000 units.

6-9
$$\bar{q} = \sqrt{\frac{2 \times 25\,000 \times 600 \times 10\,000}{5(25\,000 - 10\,000)}}$$
$$= 2000$$

So that one production run will satisfy ten weeks' demand and, with annual demand at 10 000, there will be five runs required per annum.

6-10 Annual demand is 5000. The fixed costs per batch are the set up costs, 9 hours at £4 per hour = £36. The holding costs are properly viewed on an opportunity cost basis. Each unit stored reduces sub-letting revenue by £3 × 3 = £9. Other holding costs are £7. Thus the holding costs figure is £16. So the economic batch size is given by

$$\text{EBS} = \bar{q} = \sqrt{\frac{2 \times 36 \times 5000}{16}} = 150$$

The rationale of the basic square root formula is explained in section 6.2. Review if necessary. The labour costs are invariant with respect to q. In fact they are totally fixed. Thus they cannot affect the EBS decision. In terms of warehouse space although the 'over-the-counter' payment is only £2 per square foot the company would lose money over the year if it employed this figure. Each square foot used to store the Cyclops reduces rental revenues by £3. People who have difficulty accepting the reality and relevance of opportunity costs might imagine that the full rental moneys are *actually received* and a *refund* (of £3) has then to be paid for every square foot occupied by Cyclops. This question contained much redundant information, which is characteristic of real situations.

6-11 Annual demand = 40 000. Fixed costs per replenishment are £32. This is made up of the £12 materials cost plus £20 labour costs. In the labour costs 20 hours are required and although the wages are £2 per hour the true cost is only £1. This arises from the fact that the £2 per hour is paid no matter what.

But if they are not employed on Zand costs of £1 per hour can be saved. Thus the opportunity cost is £2 − £1 = £1. Annual holding costs come in two forms. With the existing single warehouse there are the inescapable maintenance costs of £120 p.a. This figure has nothing to do with the value of $i \cdot C_m$. The best estimate we can make of the holding cost per unit per annum is from the cost of capital. It costs £40 to make a unit of Zand. If this £40 was not spent on Zand it could be invested elsewhere, *or* used to retire debt, *or* reduce overdraft saving interest charges at 10 per cent. Thus the holding cost is again an opportunity cost figure, and is 0.1 × £40 = £4. Now, we are given a figure for hourly production but unless we assume a number of hours worked per day and days worked per year we cannot obtain all the data required in the build-up model formula.

Furthermore, the formula given in the question (suppressed here) was the standard EOQ formula. So, with the reservation that the production rate formula would have been used if data had been available, we shall proceed with the basic square root expression. This gives the result

$$EOQ = \sqrt{\frac{2 \times 32 \times 40\,000}{4}} = 800$$

However, there is a limit on storage of 500 with only one warehouse. The shape of the cost function gives no alternative to setting the batch size at 500. Total annual costs will then be

$$C = \tfrac{1}{2} \times 500 \times 4 + \frac{32 \times 40\,000}{500} + 40 \times 40\,000 + 120$$

$$= \quad 1000 \quad + \quad 2560 \quad + \quad 1\,600\,000 + 120$$

in which the 1 600 000 figure swamps virtually everything else. Clearly in this case inventory is a minor contributor to costs overall. However, the costs of £1 600 000 are incurred regardless of inventory, so leaving these out and calling the remainder C^* we have

$$C^* = 1000 + 2560 + 120$$
$$= 3680$$

Now if the second warehouse is obtained the EOQ of 800 can now be stored but the maintenance costs now total £240 so C^* here is

$$C^* = \tfrac{1}{2} \times 800 \times 4 + \frac{32 \times 40\,000}{800} + 240$$

$$= \quad 1600 \quad + \quad 1600 \quad + 240$$
$$= 3440.$$

So that in operating terms there would be a saving of £3680 − £3440 = £240 per annum. However, in order to secure this saving, capital of £5000 must be invested. This represents the initial outlay on an investment for which the returns are cost savings. Due to the indefinite life of the warehouse the investment is a perpetuity having a net present value of:

$$\text{NPV} = \frac{240}{0.1} - 5000 = -2600$$

So that the second warehouse is *not* worth while. This question illustrates nicely the linkage between inventory and capital budgeting decisions.

6-12 (a)   optimal order size $= \sqrt{\dfrac{2 \times 200\,000 \times 32}{8 \times 0.1}} = 4000$

$\therefore$ order frequency $= 200\,000/4000 = 50$ times a year.

(b)   order cost $=$ order frequency $\times$ order cost per unit

$= £50 \times 32$

$= £1600$

holding cost $= \frac{1}{2} \times 4000 \times 0.1 \times 8 = £1600$

total relevant inventory cost per annum $= £1600 + 1600$

$= £3200.$

(c) Maintaining the same order level of 4000, the new order frequency $=$ $242\,000/400 = 60.5$ times a year.

Now order cost per annum $= £60.5 \times 32 = £1936$

Holding cost per annum as before $= £1600$

Therefore total relevant inventory costs per annum

$= £1936 + 1600 = £3536$

New optimal EOQ $= \sqrt{\dfrac{2 \times 242\,000 \times 32}{8 \times 0.1}} = 4400$

So new order frequency $= 242\,000/4400 = 55$

Order cost $= £55 \times 32 = £1760$

Annual holding cost $= £\frac{1}{2} \times 4400 \times 0.1 \times 8 = £1760$

So total relevant cost per annum $= £1760 + £1760 = £3520$

A decrease of just £16

(d) This example, in which an underestimate of demand of over 17 per cent gave a cost penalty (over the minimum value of 3520) of under $\frac{1}{2}$ per cent illustrates the robustness of the square root model.

6-13 (a) Storage costs are only a part of total holding cost. Here we must include the opportunity cost of money tied up in physical stock. This will be 20 per cent of £4 per thousand screws. So holding cost per unit per annum $= 0.001 + 0.0008$. So

$$\text{EOQ} = \sqrt{\frac{2 \times 125\,000 \times 5}{0.0018}} = 26\,352$$

(b) Instead of ordering when stock level is zero, order when two weeks' supply remain, $R = 5000$. The EOQ is unchanged.

(c) Here the build-up model applies. The working year is inferred to be 50 weeks (from the first sentence of the question) so that $P = 1\,250\,000$. Note that holding costs will now be £1.4 per thousand. $C_0 = 5 + 10 = 15$.

$$\text{EBQ} = \sqrt{\frac{2 \times 125\,000 \times 15 \times 1\,250\,000}{0.0014(1\,125\,000)}} = 54\,554$$

In practice this might be rounded to 11 days' production (55 000) or even 2 weeks' production (50 000).

(d) When demand is deterministic the re-order level and periodic review approaches come to the same thing. When demand is stochastic a decision has to be taken as to which system to adopt. If the re-order level model was retained then the level of buffer stock would have to be decided on. How this was done would depend on the information available.

(e) Presumably 'no problem' means that a buffer stock of 2500 is being carried $(2500 = 2(3750 - 2500))$. The re-order level would be 7500. 'Tolerated' presumably means that stock outs can be ignored in the calculations. (Note: if stock outs are costless (e.g., if demand is merely backlogged) then advantage can be taken of this in determining the re-order level.)

7-4 The probability of n arrivals in a T minute interval with mean rate of arrivals λ per minute is given by

$$P(n \text{ in } T) = \frac{(\lambda T)^n e^{-\lambda T}}{n!}$$

Table B tabulates these Poisson probabilities and is constructed for $T = 1$.

(i) Looking in the $\lambda = 0.4$ row and $n = 0$ column gives $p = 0.6703$. For the same row, with $n = 1$, $p = 0.2681$ and if $n = 2$, $p = 0.0536$. Note that the sum of the probabilities in any row is one since there must be *some* number of arrivals.

(ii) The probability that more than one customer arrives is one minus the chance that one or no customers arrive (using the fact that the probabilities in any row sum to one).

$$\begin{aligned}
\text{Thus } P(n > 1 \text{ in } 1) &= P(2) + P(3) + P(4) + \dots \\
&= 1 - [P(0) + P(1)] \\
&= 1 - [0.6703 + 0.2681] \\
&= 1 - 0.9384 \\
&= 0.0616.
\end{aligned}$$

(iii) This has already been found in answering (ii). $P = 0.9384$.

(iv) $P(2) = 0.0536$, $P(3) = 0.0072$. Thus since two or three arrivals are mutually exclusive events the probabilities may be added: $P(2 \text{ or } 3 \text{ in } 1 \text{ min}) = 0.0536 + 0.0072 = 0.0608$.

(v) Now here we have to find some information where $T = 3$. A glance at the formula above shows that the same result is obtained for $\lambda = 0.4$ and $T = 3$ as is the outcome when $\lambda = 1.2$ and $T = 1$. Thus using the $\lambda = 1.2$ row of the table: $P(2 \text{ in } 3) = 0.2169$.

7-5 $\lambda = 20$ per hour, $\mu = 30$ per hour

(i) $\dfrac{1}{\mu - \lambda}$ hours $= \dfrac{1}{10}$ hour $= 6$ minutes

(ii) $\dfrac{\lambda}{\mu(\mu - \lambda)} = \dfrac{20}{30(30 - 20)}$ hours $= \dfrac{1}{15}$ hour $= 4$ minutes

(Note that this result could have been obtained by subtracting the mean service time (two minutes) from the 6 minute ASPT already obtained.)

(iii) λ now $= 22$. Queueing time now averages $5\frac{1}{2}$ minutes. This represents a 37.5 per cent increase.

7-6 In case (i) ASPT $= 1/\mu - \lambda$ hours $= \frac{1}{30}$ hours or *2 minutes*, the probability of having to wait (call it $P(w)$) is $\lambda/\mu = 0.7$. In case (ii) the multi-server formula applies with $c = 2$. Note that $\rho = \lambda/c\mu = 70/(2 \times 50) = 0.7$.

$$P_0 = \frac{0.6}{1.96 + 0.6(1 + 1.4)} = \frac{0.6}{3.4}$$

Thus

$$\text{ASPT} = \frac{1.96}{2(0.09)2(50)} P_0 + \frac{1}{50} = 0.0392 \text{ hours or } 2.35 \text{ minutes.}$$

In this case the probability of having to wait is

$$P(w) = \frac{1.96}{2(1 - 0.7)} P_0 = 0.5765$$

In case (iii) assume that an arrival is equally likely to join either queue regardless of the lengths. So here ASPT $= 1/(50 - 35)$ hours $= 4$ minutes and $P(w) = 35/50 = 0.7$.

In case (iv) assume that there is no interference between the two stages and all customers go through both stages. So

$$\text{ASPT} = 2\left(\frac{1}{200 - 70}\right) \text{ hours} = 0.92 \text{ minutes.}$$

As regards the probability of having to wait, if this is interpreted as meaning waiting at the first service point then $P(w) = 0.35$. The probability of having to wait at *either* point is $1 - (0.65)^2 = 0.5775$.

7-7 First find the probability of having to wait, for the 2, 3, and 4 server alternatives. With the usual formula $P = 0.8; 0.382677;$ and 0.147621 respectively. In the 3-server case, the net hourly saving in comparison with two servers is

$$10(0.8 - 0.382677) - 3.80 = 0.37323$$

Now, with a 2750 hour year the annual saving is

$$0.37323(2750) = 1026.4$$

This value constitutes the annual 'return' on the investment of £3000 that is required in this case. Since the project is a perpetuity at 10 per cent the net present value is

$$\frac{1026.4}{0.1} - 3000 = 7264$$

In the 4-server case the net present value (in comparison with two servers) is

$$\frac{[10(0.8 - 0.147\,621) - 6]2750}{0.1} - 6000 = 8404$$

Since both present values are positive, both the 3 and 4 server alternatives are superior to the 2-server case. Since the 4-server alternative provides the better NPV, this will be the alternative selected. For further discussion of net present values and annuities see the Appendix to this volume and Samuels, Wilkes (1980).

7-8 (a) In the original circumstances, $\lambda = 16$, $\mu = 80$

$$\text{Average waiting (i.e., queueing time)} = \frac{\lambda}{\mu(\mu - \lambda)} = \frac{16}{20(20 - 16)} = 0.2 \text{ hours.}$$

When the second attendant is employed,

$$\rho = \frac{16}{2(20)} = 0.4, \qquad P_0 = \frac{1.2}{2.8}$$

and the average queueing time is

$$\frac{0.64}{2(0.36)2(20)} \frac{1.2}{2.8} = 0.009\,524 \text{ hours}$$

Thus the reduction in waiting time (per arrival) is 0.190 476 hours. With 16 arrivals per hour and 2000 hours per year at a saving of £1.60 per hour the annual saving is

$$£0.190\,476(16)(2000)1.60 = £9752.37$$

So, with the attendants' wages of £3000 deducted there is a net 'return' of £6752.37 per annum for 10 years. The initial outlay required to secure this is 2000. The net present value at 15 per cent (using annuity tables) is

$$6752.37(5.0188) - 2000 = 31\,889$$

The huge positive net present value means that the additional attendant should certainly be employed.

(b) Analytical methods can still be used if some other simple distribution of times (e.g., Erlang) obtains. Otherwise simulation could be used. The reader should describe this approach.

7-10 (a) The original ASPT $= \dfrac{1}{24-20}$ hour or 15 minutes.

(b) The original average cost per hour $= 20 \times 3 = 60$ with two channels it is £100; therefore, with 20 enquiries per hour an extra £2 per enquiry is needed. With three channels the additional cost is £125 − £60, i.e., £3.25 extra per enquiry.

(c) An actual value of customers' time cannot be calculated, only a *lower bound* can be given. The ASPT in the two-channel case is 7.2 minutes. If customers prefer this situation they must value their time at at least $(£5-£3)/(15-7.2)$ per minute or £15.38 per hour.

7-11 (a) With $\lambda = 8$:

larger service channel

cost to company $= 120 + 7(8) = £176$ per hour

extra small channel:

cost to company $= 50 + 60 + 8(8) = £174$ per hour.

Thus in the current year, the extra small service channel has a marginal advantage.

With $\lambda = 15$:

larger service channel

cost to company $= 120 + 7(15) = £225$ per hour

extra small channel:

cost to company $= 50 + 60 + 8(15) = £230$ per hour.

So in this case the single, larger channel has the edge.

(b) Larger channel

$$\text{ASPT} = \frac{1}{20-15} = 0.2 \text{ hours}$$

∴ value of customers' time per hour $= 0.2(15)(25) = £75$ per hour

Extra small channel

$$= 0.75, \quad P_0 = \tfrac{1}{7}, \quad \text{ASPT} = 0.228\,57 \text{ hours}$$

∴ value of customers' time per hour $= 0.228\,57(15)(25) = £85.71$

(c) The larger service channel is selected since both the company's and the customers' costs are lower with this arrangement.

8-2 (i) $F_1 = 10$; $F_2 = 20.5$; $F_3 = 52.025$; $F_4 = 57.151\,25$; $F_5 = 55.685$.

(ii) Mean life = 3.9 months. Mean no. of failures $= 200/3.9 = 51.2821 =$ cost of individual policy (∞ interval between group replacements). Group replacement intervals: costs 1 month £80 per month; 2 months £45 per month; 3 months £36.83 per month; 4 months £40.63 per month; 5 months £43.94 per month; 6 months £45.89 per month. Thus the 3-month interval is optimal.

8-3 The failure tree is shown in Fig. A8-3.

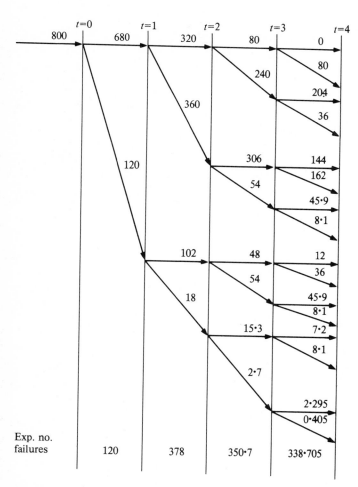

Figure **A8-3**

The mean life is 2.35 months, found as follows:

life	f_t	$f_t \times$ life
0	0	0
1	0.15	0.15
2	0.45	0.90
3	0.30	0.90
4	0.10	0.40
		2.35

So that the mean no. of failures is $800 \div 2.35 = 340.426$ per month. Thus attending to individual failures only would cost £3404.26 per month. For the finite intervals between group replacements the workings are:

		Individual costs in month					Monthly
Interval	Group cost	1	2	3	4	Total	average
1	5000					5 000	5000
2	5000	1200				6 200	3100
3	5000	1200	3780			9 980	$3326.\overline{66}$
4	5000	1200	3780	3507		13 487	3371.75
5	5000	1200	3780	3507	3387.05	16 874.05	3374.81

From which it is concluded that the best interval between group replacements is two months.

   (ii) If the individual replacement cost is £R then we have:

Interval	Monthly average cost
1	5000
2	$2500 + 60R$
3	$1666.\overline{66} + 166R$
4	$1250 + 212.175R$
5	$1000 + 237.481R$
∞	$340.426R$

So that

$$2500 + 60R \leqslant 5000 \qquad \rightarrow R \leqslant 41.\overline{66}$$
$$2500 + 60R \leqslant 1666.\overline{66} + 166R \rightarrow R \geqslant 7.86$$
$$2500 + 60R \leqslant 1250 + 212.175R \rightarrow R \geqslant 8.21$$
$$2500 + 60R \leqslant 1000 + 237.481R \rightarrow R \geqslant 8.45$$
$$2500 + 60R \leqslant 340.426R \qquad \rightarrow R \geqslant 8.92$$

So that the range for R alone is $8.92 \leqslant R \leqslant 41.\overline{66}$.

(iii) With the group replacement cost as G, the two-month policy costs $0.5G + 60R$. So in comparison with the other intervals:

$$0.5G + 60R \leqslant G \qquad\qquad \rightarrow G \geqslant 120R$$
$$0.5G + 60R \leqslant 0.3\overline{3}G + 166R \quad \rightarrow G \leqslant 636R$$
$$0.5G + 60R \leqslant 0.25G + 212.175R \rightarrow G \leqslant 608.70R$$
$$0.5G + 60R \leqslant 0.2G + 237.481R \;\rightarrow G \leqslant 591.60R$$
$$0.5G + 60R \leqslant 340.426R \qquad \rightarrow G \leqslant 560.85R$$

$$\therefore \quad 120R \leqslant G \leqslant 560.85R$$

(iv) The monthly saving is $5000 - 3100 = 1900$ which is 22 800 per annum in perpetuity. The net present value of the changeover is then

$$\frac{22\,800}{0.2} - 20\,000 = 94\,000$$

8-4 (i) 144 after three years, 161 after four years (160.9).
(ii) The mean length of stay is 1.6 years as worked out below:

t	f_t	tf_t
0	0	0
1	0.6	0.6
2	0.3	0.6
3	0.0	0
4	0.1	0.4
		1.6

Thus the mean number of resignations per year is $250 \div 1.6 = 156.25$.
(iii) With the improved facilities the mean stay becomes 1.8 years giving an average leaving rate of 138.89 per year. The annual saving in recruitment costs is then £20$(156.25 - 138.89) = $ £347.20 which, being less than the extra expenditure of £400 p.a., means that the improvements are not worth while.

8-5 (a) The failure tree (rounded workings) is shown in Figure A8-5(a).
(b) 2.3 years.
(c) To maintain the total, the number of new rentals must equal the average number of hirings terminated $= 200 \div 2.3 = 87$.
(d) With the new probabilities the expected length of hire becomes 2.85 years, therefore, average number of new renters per year $= 200 \div 2.85 = 70$.

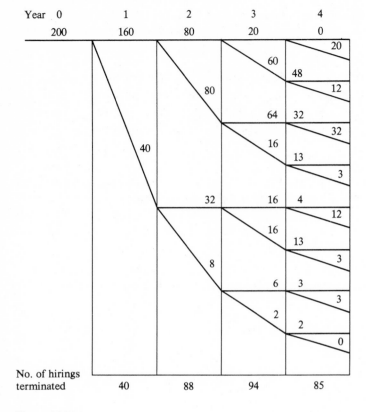

Year   0   1   2   3   4

Figure A8-5(a)

The saving in administrative costs is $(87 - 70)20 = 340$ per year. This is the upper limit on costs for the advertising campaign.

9-5 (i) The workings are:

X	Y	$X - \bar{X}$	$Y - \bar{Y}$	$(X - \bar{X})(Y - \bar{Y})$	$(X - \bar{X})^2$	$(Y - \bar{Y})^2$
106	155	+6	+15	+90	36	225
90	110	−10	−30	+300	100	900
92	130	−8	−10	+80	64	100
100	145	0	+5	0	0	25
112	160	+12	+20	+240	144	400
500	700			+710	344	1650

$$\bar{X} = \frac{\Sigma X}{n} = \frac{500}{5} = 100; \quad \bar{Y} = \frac{\Sigma Y}{n} = \frac{700}{5} = 140$$

The required equation is $Y = a + bX$

$$b = \frac{(X - \bar{X})(Y - \bar{Y})}{(X - \bar{X})^2} = \frac{710}{344} = 2.064$$

$$a = \bar{Y} - b\bar{X} = 140 - 2.064(100) = -66.4$$

∴ equation is $\qquad Y = -66.4 + 2.064X$

(ii) For $X = 120$ the prediction for Y is 181.28.

(iii) $r = \dfrac{(X - \bar{X})(Y - \bar{Y})}{\sqrt{(X - \bar{X})^2 (Y - \bar{Y})^2}} = \dfrac{710}{\sqrt{(344)(1650)}} = 0.9424$

This value measures the degree of *linear* relationship between the variables. It is a measure of the goodness of fit of the regression line.

(iv) The coefficient of determination is the square of the correlation coefficient. This value gives the proportion of variation in Y that is accounted for by variation in X. In the present case $r^2 = 0.8881$.

9-6 (i) The workings are:

X	Y	$X - \bar{X}$	$Y - \bar{Y}$	$(X - \bar{X})(Y - \bar{Y})$	$(X - \bar{X})^2$	$(Y - \bar{Y})^2$
129	33	-21	0.33	-6.93	441	0.11
126	33	-24	0.33	-7.92	576	0.11
124	29	-26	-3.67	95.42	676	13.47
121	25	-29	-7.67	222.43	841	58.83
138	31	-12	-1.67	20.04	144	2.79
153	32	3	-0.67	-2.01	9	0.45
160	34	10	1.33	13.30	100	1.77
169	35	19	2.33	44.27	361	5.43
179	36	29	3.33	96.57	841	11.09
185	36	35	3.33	116.55	1225	11.09
161	34	11	1.33	14.63	121	1.77
155	34	5	1.33	6.65	25	1.77
1800	392			613	5360	108.68

$$\bar{X} = \frac{\Sigma X}{n} = \frac{1800}{12} = 150; \quad \bar{Y} = \frac{\Sigma Y}{n} = \frac{392}{12} = 32.67$$

In $Y = a + bX$, $b = \dfrac{613}{5360} = 0.114$

$$a = 32.67 - 0.114(150) = 15.57$$

∴ regression equation is

$$Y = 15.57 + 0.114X$$

The correlation coefficient is $r = \dfrac{613}{\sqrt{(5360)(108.68)}} = 0.803$

$$\therefore \quad r^2 = 0.645$$

(ii) First we need to find the sample based estimate of the variance of the error term, $\hat{\sigma}^2$. With Y^* representing the regression equation values of Y for the sample X values we have

$$\hat{\sigma}^2 = \frac{\Sigma(Y_i - Y^*)^2}{n-2}$$

where $n-2$ is the number of degrees of freedom, i.e., 10. The workings for $\hat{\sigma}$ are

X	Y	Y^*	$Y - Y^*$	$(Y - Y^*)^2$
129	33	30.28	2.72	7.40
126	33	29.93	3.07	9.42
124	29	29.71	−0.71	0.50
121	25	29.36	−4.36	19.01
138	31	31.30	−0.30	0.09
153	32	33.01	−1.01	1.02
160	34	33.81	0.19	0.04
169	35	34.84	0.16	0.03
179	36	35.98	0.02	0.00
185	36	36.66	−0.66	0.44
161	34	33.92	0.08	0.01
155	34	33.24	0.76	0.58
				38.54

So that $\hat{\sigma} = \sqrt{\dfrac{38.54}{12-2}} = 1.963$

Now with 10 degrees of freedom, Table 9-2 gives the relevant t value of 2.228. So using formula (6) we obtain

$$\text{for } X^* = 150, \ Y^* = 32.67; \text{range} = 32.67 \pm 2.228(1.963)\sqrt{1+\frac{1}{12}}$$

(since in this case $X^* = \bar{X}$).

Thus the 95 per cent confidence interval is

$$32.67 \pm 4.55$$

For $X^* = 190, \ Y^* = 37.23;$

$$\text{range} = 37.23 \pm 2.228(1.963)\sqrt{1+\frac{1}{12}+\frac{(190-150)^2}{5360}}$$

$\therefore$ range $= 37.23 \pm 5.14$

For $X^* = 220, \ Y^* = 40.65;$

$$\text{range} = 40.65 \pm 2.228(1.963)\sqrt{1+\frac{1}{12}+\frac{(220-150)^2}{5360}}$$

$\therefore$ range $= 40.65 \pm 6.18$

9-7 The workings for $\hat{\sigma}$ are:

X	Y	Y^*	$Y - Y^*$	$(Y - Y^*)^2$
106	155	152.38	2.62	6.86
90	110	119.36	-9.36	87.61
92	130	123.49	6.51	42.38
100	145	140.00	5.00	25.00
112	160	164.77	-4.77	22.75
				184.60

So that $\hat{\sigma} = \sqrt{\dfrac{184.6}{3}} = 7.84$

The 95 per cent confidence interval will then be

$$181.28 \pm 3.182(7.84)\sqrt{1 + \frac{1}{5} + \frac{(120-100)^2}{344}} = 181.28 \pm 38.35$$

(Note: the width of the interval is very large. This is partly due to the very small number of observations which fact results in a high t value. For instance, if there had been 60 observations with prediction errors on the same scale as above, the $\hat{\sigma}$ value would have come down to about 6.2 and the t value would be about 2. The square root term would also be reduced (examine its components to see why) resulting in a range of about 181.28 ± 13.09 which is only one-third as wide.)

9-8 (i) The deseasonalized data are shown in the last column of workings below. Trend data are sum 2 data divided by eight. The deseasonalized data are the original Y values minus the quarterly averages.

Quarter	Y	Sum 4	Sum 2	Trend (T)	$Y - T$	Deseasonalized
1977 Q$_1$	269					255.75
Q$_2$	280	1046				264.75
Q$_3$	256	1054	2100	262.50	-6.50	263.25
Q$_4$	241	1054	2108	263.50	-22.50	262.25
1978 Q$_1$	277	1056	2110	263.75	$+13.25$	263.75
Q$_2$	280	1062	2118	264.75	$+15.25$	264.75
Q$_3$	258	1066	2128	266.00	-8.00	265.25
Q$_4$	247	1070	2136	267.00	-20.00	268.25
1979 Q$_1$	281	1072	2142	267.75	$+13.25$	267.75
Q$_2$	284	1078	2150	268.75	$+15.25$	268.75
Q$_3$	260					267.25
Q$_4$	253					274.25

The averaging for the quarters is as follows:

	Q$_1$	Q$_2$	Q$_3$	Q$_4$	
	+13.25	+15.25	−6.50	−22.50	
	+13.25	+15.25	−8.00	−20.00	
Average	+13.25	+15.25	−7.25	−21.25	[Σ = 0]

for which no adjustments are necessary.

(ii) The crudest moving average-based forecast for the first quarter of 1980 would be simply $1078 \div 4 = 269.5$. A somewhat more subtle approach would be to make some 'allowance' for trend and seasonal variation. Using the Trend column (T) the sum of the first four entries is 1054.5 which divided by four gives 263.625. This is the average value of 'trend' in the first half of the trend data. In the second half the average value is 267.375. The difference between these two figures is 3.75. Over a one-year period the average value of trend has risen by 3.75. This is itself an average rate of 0.9375 per quarter. We are going to estimate the 1980 Q$_1$ figure by first estimating what the trend figure would be corresponding to that year and then adding the seasonal factor. Thus if we suppose the trend figure to increase on average by 0.9375 per quarter, the trend figure opposite 1980 Q$_1$ will be $268.75 + 3(0.9375) = 271.5625$. Adding the seasonal factor for this quarter of 13.25 gives the estimate of $284.8125 \simeq 285$. Thus our estimate would be 285. This is a plausible result if the data is examined carefully.

9-9. (i)

Quarter	X	Y	X^2	XY	$(\hat{Y})$	$100\left(\dfrac{Y}{T}\right)$	Deseasonalized
1978 Q$_1$	1	82	1	82	78.36	104.65	84.39
Q$_2$	2	79	4	158	83.17	94.99	80.99
Q$_3$	3	90	9	270	87.98	102.30	88.32
Q$_4$	4	96	16	384	92.79	103.46	92.85
1979 Q$_1$	5	87	25	435	97.60	89.14	89.53
Q$_2$	6	103	36	618	102.41	100.58	105.60
Q$_3$	7	110	49	770	107.22	102.59	107.95
Q$_4$	8	117	64	936	112.03	104.44	113.16
1980 Q$_1$	9	116	81	1044	116.84	99.28	119.38
Q$_2$	10	120	100	1200	121.65	98.64	123.03
	55	1000	385	5897			

$$\bar{X} = 5.5; \quad \bar{Y} = 100$$

$$b = \frac{n\Sigma XY - \Sigma X \Sigma Y}{n\Sigma X^2 - (\Sigma X)^2} = \frac{58\,970 - 55\,000}{3850 - 3025} = \frac{3970}{825} = 4.81$$

So that

$$a = 100 - (4.81)5.5 = 73.55.$$

The regression equation is then

$$Y = 73.55 + 4.81X$$

For the quarterly averaging:

	Q_1	Q_2	Q_3	Q_4	
	104.65	94.99	102.30	103.46	
	89.14	100.58	102.59	104.44	
	99.28	98.64			
Unadjusted	97.69	98.07	102.45	103.95	$\Sigma = 402.16$
Adjusted	97.17	97.54	101.90	103.39	

(ii) The forecast is the trend value (using the regression equation with the higher X values) multiplied by the seasonal index. The final column gives the rounded values.

	X	Trend	Seasonal factor	Forecast	Rounded
1980 Q_3	11	126.46	0.9717	122.88	123
Q_4	12	131.27	0.9754	128.04	128
1981 Q_1	13	136.08	1.0190	138.67	139
Q_2	14	140.89	1.0339	145.67	146

9-10 The 'next forecast' column in the table below is the exponentially smoothed series. The last entry, 298.94 (rounded in the forecast column) is the forecast for June of 1980.

Month	Actual production	Forecast	Forecasting error	$X = 0.4$ correction	Next forecast
June	304	300	+4.00	+1.60	301.60
July	302	301.60	+0.40	+0.16	301.76
Aug.	306	301.76	+4.24	+1.70	303.46
Sept.	300	303.46	−3.46	−1.38	302.08
Oct.	296	302.08	−6.08	−2.43	299.65
Nov.	298	299.65	−1.65	−0.66	298.99
Dec.	298	298.99	−0.99	−0.40	298.59
Jan.	302	298.59	+3.41	+1.36	299.95
Feb.	300	299.95	+0.05	+0.02	299.97
Mar.	296	299.97	−3.97	−1.59	298.38
Apr.	298	298.38	−0.38	−0.15	298.23
May	300	298.23	+1.77	+0.71	298.94
June	299				

9-12 (a) We are required to estimate the regression equation of total overhead (y) against direct labour hours (x). The formula for slope

$$b = \frac{n\Sigma XY - \Sigma X\Sigma Y}{n\Sigma X^2 - (\Sigma X)^2}$$

will be used. Total overhead data will be expressed in units of one thousand. The workings are:

Month	Total overhead Y	DLH X	XY	X^2	Y^2
Jan.	15.00	736	11 040	541 696	225.0
Feb.	14.50	800	11 600	640 000	210.25
Mar.	15.75	1008	15 876	1 016 064	248.0625
Apr.	15.25	880	13 420	774 400	232.5625
May	16.25	1056	17 160	1 115 136	264.0625
June	15.00	840	12 600	705 600	225.0
	91.75	5320	81 696	4 792 896	1404.9375

$$\bar{Y} = 15.2917; \quad \bar{X} = 886.7$$

$$b = \frac{6 \times 81\ 696 - 91.75 \times 5320}{6 \times 4\ 792\ 896 - (5320)^2}$$

$$= \frac{2066}{454\ 976} = 0.00454$$

Intercept $a = \bar{Y} - b\bar{X}$

$$= 15.2917 - 0.004\ 54 \times 886.7$$

$$= 11.266$$

So: $y = 11.266 + 0.004\ 54X$

Since total overhead is measured in thousands of pounds the relationship is

$$\text{Total overhead} = 11\ 266 + 4.54 \times \text{DLH}$$

(b) The coefficient of determination, r^2, can be expressed as

$$r^2 = \frac{(N\Sigma XY - \Sigma X\Sigma Y)^2}{[n\Sigma X^2 - (\Sigma X)^2][n\Sigma Y^2 - (\Sigma Y)^2]}$$

$$= \frac{(2066)^2}{454\ 976 \times [6 \times 1404.9375 - (91.75)^2]}$$

$$= 0.8114$$

(c) In the multiple regression equation, the appearance of plant hours has more than halved the intercept term while the DLH coefficient is hardly changed. The inclusion of PH has explained much that was originally lumped into the intercept term. The fact that the DLH regression coefficient is virtually unchanged suggests that PH and DLH are unrelated. As an exercise the reader may verify that the correlation between PH and DLH is only -0.08. The coefficient of determination gives the proportion of the variation in the dependent variable (overhead) that is explained by changes in the independent variable(s). With DLH alone in the equation, 81.14 per cent of the variation in overhead was accounted for. With both DLH and PH in, the proportion of explained variation rises to 98.73 per cent.

The question might arise as to which of DLH and PH has the more important effect on overhead. The size of regression coefficients is nothing to go by as these can be scaled up or down depending on the units of measure of the independent variables. The high explained variation with DLH alone in the regression equation (81 per cent) might lead us to expect that this is the more important influence. This can be confirmed using *beta weights*. The beta (β) weight for DLH is the ratio of the standard deviations of DLH and overhead multiplied by the DLH regression coefficient. Thus

$$\beta(\text{DLH}) = \frac{123.15}{620.82} \times 4.7 = 0.932$$

while for PH

$$\beta(\text{PH}) = \frac{8.39}{620.82} \times 31 = 0.419$$

where 8.39 is the standard deviation of plant hours. So DLH are seen to be the more important factor.

(d) Inserting the values given into the equation

$$\text{Total overhead} = 5758 + 4.7(1000) + 31(168) = 15\,666.$$

9-13 (a) For a cost–volume relationship to be useful, the costs involved should be directly comparable. Substantial changes in prices of resources can make a nonsense of the relationship which is intended—as the name implies—to relate cost to output level alone. In this example, it is most convenient to work in year (5) prices (as whole numbers result). To deal with the materials price change we inflate the materials cost figures in year (1) and (2) by 25 per cent. Similarly the labour costs in the first three years are increased by $33\frac{1}{3}$ per cent to bring them into year (5) terms. So, in terms of year (5) values (in units of £1000) we have:

Year:	1	2	3	4	5
Costs: Materials	25	35	42	37	48
Labour	36	48	52	48	54
Overheads	24	24	28	33	32
Total	85	107	122	118	134

With the revised data, the regression workings are shown below. Sales data are in units of one hundred.

Year	Sales X	Total cost Y	$(X-\bar{X})$	$(Y-\bar{Y})$	$(X-\bar{X})^2$	$(X-\bar{X})(Y-\bar{Y})$
1	21	85	−9.8	−28.2	96.04	276.36
2	28	107	−2.8	−6.2	7.84	17.36
3	34	122	3.2	8.8	10.24	28.16
4	31	118	0.2	4.8	0.04	0.96
5	40	134	9.2	20.8	84.64	191.36
Totals	154	566			198.80	514.20

$$\bar{X} = \frac{\Sigma X}{n} = \frac{154}{5} = 30.8 \quad \text{and} \quad \bar{Y} = \frac{\Sigma Y}{n} = \frac{566}{5} = 113.2$$

$$b = \frac{\Sigma(X-\bar{X})(Y-\bar{Y})}{\Sigma(X-\bar{X})^2} = \frac{514.20}{198.80} = 2.5865$$

$$a = \bar{Y} - b\bar{X} = 113.2 - 2.5865(30.8) = 33.535$$

So the full regression equation is

$$Y = 33.535 - 2.587X$$

The interpretation of this equation is that total fixed cost is £33 535 and unit variable cost is £25.87. Now, using the regression equation to forecast costs for the possible volumes, and where revenue is price times volume, the greatest excess of revenue over costs is seen to result from a price of £40.

Volume	Cost (C)	Price	Revenue (R)	R − C
4500	149 950	37	166 500	16 550
4000	137 015	40	160 000	22 985
3400	121 493	42	142 800	21 307

(b) The main advantage of linear regression analysis is that in comparison to other methods of fitting straight lines it produces the 'best, linear, unbiased' estimates. There are plenty of computer packages if these are needed and many calculators have regression programmes for the smaller scale work. Regression is a well-worked-through method and properties and dangers are well understood. There are a number of limitations (some of which apply to other methods too). Usually, rather more than five observations would be desirable (as we saw in Q 9-7) so that we may be dealing with a long period of time over which many important factors (specifically the firm's technology) may have changed. The line may be a poor fit, and predictions based on poorly fitting lines can be very misleading. The fit may be good only close to the range of outputs sampled. The relationship between cost and output may not be linear: there may be economies (or diseconomies beyond a certain point) of scale.

10-2 The first step in the simulation procedure is to allocate blocks of two-digit numbers to the alternative outcomes. This is done in the table below.

Probability	Return	Nos. allocated
0.06	1500	00–05
0.17	2000	06–22
0.22	4500	23–44
0.29	6000	45–73
0.16	7500	74–89
0.10	9400	90–99

Of course, the digits *could* have been allocated in any other way that gave 6 per cent of the total to correspond to the 1500 return, 17 per cent to correspond to the 2000 return and so on. Although the particular details will differ depending upon how the allocation is done, in practice there should be a sufficiently large number of runs so that these differences cancel out on average.

Now using the digits given, in pairs from left to right to generate return data for the first run, we obtain the results

Random no.	Return
87	7500
05	1500
69	6000

Thus the NPV will be given by

$$-12\,000 + \frac{7500}{(1.1)} + \frac{1500}{(1.21)} + \frac{6000}{(1.331)} = 565.74$$

The data for the full five runs are given in the table below.

	Cash flow (returns)			NPV
Run no. 1	7500	1500	6000	565.74
2	1500	7500	9400	2624.34
3	4500	2000	2000	−4753.57
4	7500	7500	9400	8078.89
5	4500	6000	1500	−1823.44
			$\Sigma =$	4691.96

where, in run (2), the numbers used are 05, 81, 94. For the remaining runs the digits are used in a similar fashion beginning with 27. The total NPV for the five runs is 4691.96 which gives an average of 938.39. This is the simulation estimate of ENPV.

Having obtained the estimate of ENPV we can go on to estimate the variance and hence standard deviation and coefficient of variation. The variance will be

$$\frac{\Sigma(NPV - ENPV)^2}{4}$$

The workings are:

NPV	(NPV – ENPV)	(NPV – ENPV)^2
565.74	– 372.65	138 868
2624.34	1685.95	2 842 427
– 4753.57	– 5691.96	32 398 409
8078.89	7140.50	50 986 740
– 1823.44	– 2761.83	7 627 705
		93 994 149

Thus variance is

$$\sigma^2 = \frac{93\,994\,149}{4} = 23\,498\,537$$

so that the coefficient of variation, c, is given by

$$c = \frac{\sqrt{23\,498\,537}}{938.39} = 5.17$$

10-3

Supply	Prob.	Nos. allocated	Demand	Prob.	Nos. allocated
50	0.2	0,1	50	0.2	0,1
100	0.3	2,3,4	100	0.2	2,3
150	0.3	5,6,7	150	0.5	4,5,6,7,8
200	0.2	8,9	200	0.1	9

Note that only single-digit random numbers are needed here.

Day	No.	Supply	Cost	No.	Demand	Sales	Revenue	Sh. loss	Profit
1	8	200	1200	4	150	150	1500	—	300
2	8	200	1200	0	50	50	500	—	−700
3	3	100	600	3	100	100	1000	—	400
4	4	100	600	7	150	100	1000	100	300
5	9	200	1200	6	150	150	1500	—	300
6	1	50	300	5	150	50	500	200	0
									600

(i) Estimated annual profit = 600(50) = £30 000.

(ii) The first six columns above remain unchanged. We now have:

Sales	Revenue	Sh. loss	Σstore	Profit
150	1500	—	50	300
50	500	—	200	−700
100	1000	—	200	400
150	1500	—	150	900
150	1500	—	200	300
150	1500	—	100	1200
				2400

Thus the storage facilities would increase weekly profit in the simulation exercise by £1800. This is no less than £90 000 per annum!

(iii) A confidence interval for annual profit could be obtained which would be more useful than a single-figure estimate. The simulation could be re-worked for changes other than the installation of storage, for instance, a sale-or-return arrangement with the supplier. Part of the value of simulation is in its ability to evaluate structural changes. Of course, six runs is not enough to give a basis from which firm conclusions can be drawn. Otherwise, the usual caveats about the use of the procedure apply.

10-5 (a) The 'breakeven volume' is the level of output at which costs are just covered. This means that revenue equals costs. Revenue is selling price (p) times volume (v). Total costs are unit variable costs (c) times volume (v) plus fixed costs (F), i.e., breakeven means that $pv = cv + F$. Another way of expressing this is

$$v = \frac{F}{p - c}$$

So in expected value terms in the present case

$$v = \frac{580\,000}{300 - 175} = 4640$$

The expected profit, Π, is given by

$$\Pi = v(p-c)-F$$
$$= 5000(300-175)-580\,000 = £45\,000$$

(b) The procedure in any one run of the simulation would be that for each component of the profit equation a random number is selected; the table given is then used to identify the number of standard deviations the variable is away from its mean value. Since the standard deviations are known, this procedure identifies a particular value of the variable. For instance, using the numbers given in the question:

Variable	Expected value	Standard deviation	Random number	Deviation from mean	Value of variable
v	5 000	400	20	-0.8	4 680
p	300	5	96	$+1.8$	309
F	580 000	10 000	68	$+0.4$	584 000
c	175	7.5	59	$+0.2$	176.5

Taking the variables in the order given in the question, the first random number 20, means that v is 0.8 standard deviations below its mean value, $\therefore v = 5000 - 0.8(400) = 4680$. The second random number 96 means that p is 1.8 of its standard deviations above its mean, i.e., $p = 300 + 1.8(5) = 309$. Thus profit in the first run of the simulation is

$$\Pi = 4680(309 - 176.5) - 584\,000 = +36\,100$$

This procedure would be repeated many times—ideally over a hundred—though 30 or so runs would give fairly reliable results. The mean and variance of this simulated sample of profit values can then be determined.

(c) Once the parameters (mean and variance) of the profit distribution have been obtained from the simulation, confidence intervals can be ascertained, and the probability of making a profit can be found. In practice, however, a rather more complicated model might be used as it is unlikely that sales volume and price vary independently.

10-6 (a) Before setting up a simulation exercise it is often useful to perform a few crude calculations with what data is to hand. This may give some useful clues as to the features of the system. First, the mean 'service time' seems to be 4.9 days $(= 2(0.1) + 5(0.8) + 7(0.1))$. With a 5-day week there is an arrival, on average, every 2.5 days. So, unless there is more than one 'service point' or simultaneous service of several clients the queue length will expand indefinitely (perhaps this accounts for some of the concern mentioned in the question!). In the simulation outlined below we shall thus assume that *two* customers can be served simultaneously (this would take the physical form of two 'attendants' each serving one customer or the same attendant serving two—it does not matter which in this case). For the problem to be of any interest there had better be some random elements. We shall assume that the customers arrive Poisson-fashion at the mean rate of 2 per 5 days. We shall, however, assume that the 'service' times are fixed at 2, 5, or 7 days as implied by the question.

Now consider a possible format for the simulation. The queueing theory experiment of Sec. 10.4 provides one arrangement. Getting the data on a daily basis, the mean rate of arrivals is $\lambda = 0.4$ per day, so that the inter-arrival time in days (T) is given by

$$f(T) = \lambda e^{-\lambda T} = 0.4 e^{-0.4T}$$

for which the cumulative distribution is

$$F(T) = 1 - e^{-0.4T}$$

Let us now use the first set of random digits in Sec. 10.5 to generate observations on arrivals. The digits were:

$$4\,7\,1\,0\,5\,1\,4\,9\,1\,2\,7\,9\,6\,1\,3\,1\,5\,2\,5\,3\,9\,8\,0\,8\,7\,6\,4\,9\,7\,5$$

To generate values of T, use these in triplets (as before, although two at a time would be sufficiently accurate here). Thus the first value of T is the solution to

$$0.471 = 1 - e^{-0.4T}$$

which solves for $T = 1.59$ which we shall round to the nearest whole number, so $T = 2$. The next observation on inter-arrival time is given by

$$0.051 = 1 - e^{-0.4T}$$

giving $T = 0.13$, rounded to *zero*. The full list of values is contained in the following table:

Digits (D)	$1 - D$	T	T (rounded)
.471	.529	1.59	2
.051	.949	0.13	0
.491	.509	1.69	2
.279	.721	0.82	1
.613	.387	2.37	2
.152	.848	0.41	0
.539	.461	1.93	2
.808	.192	4.12	4
.764	.236	3.61	4
.975	.025	9.22	9

Now the rounded T data can be used in the format of Sec. 10.4. In the table below, the urgent (u) or non-urgent (N) status of an arrival is determined (randomly) by the first of the digits in the triplets above. A zero would give a u classification—anything else would give an N classification. Thus the first arrival is N (from the 4 in the .471), the second is u (from the 0 in .051) and so on.

(1) Arrival no.	1	2	3	4	5	6	7	8	9	10	
(2) Inter-time	2	0	2	1	2	0	2	4	4	9	
(3) Type	N	u	N	N	N	N	N	N	N	N	
(4) Arrival time	2	2	4	5	7	7	9	13	17	26	
(5) Service time	5	2	5	5	5	5	5	5	5	5	
(6) Into time	2	2	4	7	9	12	14	17	19	26	
(7) From time	7	4	9	12	14	17	19	22	24	31	= total time
(8) Q time	0	0	0	2	2	5	5	4	2	0	$\Sigma = 20$
(9) System time	5	2	5	7	7	10	10	9	7	5	

It turns out that the one urgent case in this simulation can be dealt with at once. Arrival (1) goes straight into service at $t = 2$, arrival (2) (sometime later that same day) can be served at once (he goes 'into' at $t = 2$) since the service point can, by our assumption, handle two customers at once. Arrival (3) can be served as soon as *either* (1) or (2) emerge. This is at $t = 4$. And so on. Various system parameters can then be estimated. For instance, the average queueing time for non-urgent cases is 20/9 days (total time that N cases spend queueing divided by the number of N cases in the simulation) The ASPT (non-urgent) is 65/9 days. These values are low and reflect the fact that we started the exercise with an empty queue. Different initial conditions could have been employed. However, the queue length would (on average) reduce slowly as time goes on in the conditions assumed.

(b) Re-run the exercise with the non-urgent (b) cases now treated as urgent. Say 0 or 1 as the first digit in a triplet would now indicate an urgent case. More complex arrangements could also be tried involving different classes of urgency.

(c) If a very large number of runs are performed in each case (say several hundreds) there is little possibility of any significant chance differences remaining. Otherwise the same set of random numbers could be used in each alternative system, thus ensuring that comparisons are made under the same arrival conditions.

10-7 It would be helpful if certain features of the problem could be quantified before the simulation began. Phrases such as 'the yearly total can however vary slightly from that figure' are unlikely to be found in contracts. Presumably a 5 per cent shortfall would not be excessive, so it would be helpful if the simulation could give the probabilities of producing at least 950 000 units in each of the years. We should certainly want to obtain the probability of producing 3 000 000 units over the three-year period. Any contract would stipulate what the 'substantial penalty' was, so that the different probabilities of achieving the figure with the X equipment or the Y equipment could be used in an expected value calculation involving the initial costs.

The simulation would have to be performed by computer since 900 days are required per run and several runs would be required. The assignation of the random numbers would be as follows. For company X we should first need a two-digit table for the probability of breakdown on any day, viz.:

Random nos	Outcome
00–95	No breakdown
96–99	Breakdown

(once again we should point out that it does not matter *which* four two-digit numbers are used to correspond to breakdown). This table would be used for all three machines. For the downtime separate tables are required for each machine:

A	B	C	Down time (days)
00–39	00–39	00–34	1
40–74	40–69	35–74	2
75–99	70–99	75–99	3

The simulation could then proceed for company X's machines. A possible layout is shown below. On day (1) there are no breakdowns on any machines according to the random numbers turning up so that no random numbers are needed for the downtime (these would be shown in the columns headed D_A, D_B, D_C) and output is 4500. On day (2) there are no breakdowns and output is again 4500. On day (3), however, machine A breaks down (but B and C do not). Use of the downtime random number table shows that 41 falls in the two-day range for machine A. So there will be zero output on days (3) and (4). And so on. If two breakdowns occurred on one day the longer down time duration would apply. Output would be summed for days 1–300, 301–600, 601–900. Each sum would give the simulated observation on yearly output (for comparison with 950 000). The sum for the whole 900 days would give one observation on three-yearly output. The simulation would then be repeated. One hundred runs would be no problem even for a small computer.

Similar procedures would then be followed for company Y's equipment. Note that a three-digit table would be required for the breakdowns. Comparisons between the machines could then be undertaken.

Day	A	B	C	D_A	D_B	D_C	Downtime	Output
1	63	88	06	—	—	—	0	4500
2	24	51	79	—	—	—	0	4500
3	96	20	13	41	—	—	2	0
4								0
5	81	34	42	—	—	—	0	4500

11-2-1 (i) The profit per item sold is £20. The loss per item unsold is £10. In tabular form the results are:

	Units purchased					
Demand (X)	1	2	3	4	$P(X)$	$P(X, ADVT)$
1	20	10	0	−10	0.1	0.1
2	20	40	30	20	0.4	0.1
3	20	40	60	50	0.3	0.4
4	20	40	60	80	0.2	0.4
EXP Π	20	37	42*	38		
EXP Π($ADVT$)	20	37	51	53*		

Thus in the original circumstances
     (i) three units should be ordered.
     (ii) This is £37.50. The expected profit on three units bought is given by:

$$0.1[(p-35)-20]+0.4[2(p-35)-10]+0.3[3(p-35)]+0.2[3(p-35)]$$

Equating this expression to zero and solving for p gives $p = 37.50$.
     (iii) Yes, provided that the store now orders four units per day. As can be seen from the table above, expected profit on four units is £53. After paying £10 for the advertisement, an increase of £1 remains.
     (iv) Yes. As can be seen from the table below, a profit of £47.50 could be made.

	Units purchased				
Demand X	1	2	3	4	$P(X)$
1	15	5	−5	−15	0
2	15	30	20	10	0.1
3	15	30	45	35	0.3
4	15	30	45	60	0.6
EXP Π (PRICE CUT)	15	30	42.5	47.5*	

11-2-2 (a) It is not convenient to work in units of 100 kg/cartons. Thus 'one unit' will mean 100 kg and one batch of 100 cartons. First consider the costs per unit.

Source of Cost	Cost (£)	When incurred
Buying in price	30	$t = 0$
Processing & packaging	70	$t = 0$
Storage	25	$t = 1$

and on the revenue side:

Selling price	200	$t = 1$

Now construct a table of revenues. This will enable expected revenue to be calculated for each possible level of purchases.

In the 2500 column of Table A11-2-2(ai) if 2500 units are purchased and demand is for 2000 units then 2000 will be sold producing revenue of 400 000. If demand is for 2500 units, this will be the level of sales, and revenue of 500 000 is produced.

Finally, if demand is for 3000 units only, 2500 will be sold (since sales are purchases or demand, whichever is the smaller) again giving revenue of 500 000. Each of these possible levels of revenue is multiplied by the chance of it arising (the corresponding figure in the probability column). After summing up, the result is an expected revenue of £480 000 at the end of the year if 2500 units are purchased at the beginning of the year.

Now we are asked to maximize 'the expected value of cash flows from the year's operations'. With the *timing* of each cash flow then being given explicit mention in the earlier part of the question as well as a cost of capital figure being provided it seems likely that it is expected *present* value that is the criterion. With such a high cost of capital figure a company in practice would be unlikely to ignore differences in timing of one year. However, an alternative

Table A11-2-(ai)

	Units purchased			Demand probability
Demand	2 000	2 500	3 000	
2000	400 000	400 000	400 000	0.2
2500	400 000	500 000	500 000	0.5
3000	400 000	500 000	600 000	0.3
Expected value	400 000	480 000	510 000	

interpretation of the questions is possible and although we shall start with present value workings a 'non-present value' calculation will be given subsequently.

First consider the expected cash flow resulting from 2000 units being purchased initially. At time $t = 0$ there is a cash flow out of 200 000 resulting from purchase expenses of 60 000 ($= 2000 \times 30$) and processing and packaging costs of 140 000 ($= 2000 \times 70$). At $t = 1$ there is an expected net cash flow in of £280 000 being composed of expected revenue of £400 000 less the storage costs of £50 000 ($= 2000 \times 25$) and less the fixed costs of £70 000 which are payable at this time. The expected net present value that results is $+£24 000$ which is obtained thus

$$- 200\,000 + \frac{280\,000}{(1.25)} = +24\,000$$

These results and those for the other possible levels of purchase are shown in Table A11-2-2(aii).

Table A11-2-2(aii)

	Net cash flow		
Purchased	$t = 0$	$t = 1$	ENPV at 25%
2000	− 200 000	280 000	+ 24 000
2500	− 250 000	347 500	+ 28 000
3000	− 300 000	365 000	− 8 000

where, in Table A11-2-2(aii): $347\,500 = 480\,000 - (62\,500 + 70\,000)$
and $365\,000 = 510\,000 - (75\,000 + 70\,000)$

Thus the level of purchases which maximizes expected net present value is 2500 units.

An alternative construction on question (a) would be to assume that interest at 25 per cent is charged on the cash flow out at $t = 0$, and that interest due on the storage costs comes to £6.25. This would produce the following results:

200 units purchased:
$$- 200\,000(1.25) - 70\,000 - 2000(1.25)25 + 400\,000 = +17\,500$$

2500 units purchased:
$$- 250\,000(1.25) - 70\,000 - 2500(1.25)25 + 480\,000 = +19\,375$$

3000 units purchased:
$$- 300\,000(1.25) - 70\,000 - 3000(1.25)25 + 510\,000 = -28\,750$$

Thus the optimal number to be purchased, as it happens, is still 2500 units.

(b) In simply choosing the course of action that maximizes expected value no explicit account is taken of risk. For example with 2500 units purchased there is a 0.8 probability that revenue will be 500 000 and a 0.2 chance that revenue will be only 400 000. Thus, in terms of the present value approach, there are two possible figures for NPV: +44 000 with probability 0.8 and −36 000 with probability 0.2 (note that 28 000 = 0.8 × 44 000 − 0.2 × 36 000). In other words there is a one in five chance of a substantial loss. Table A11-2-2(b) gives for each level of purchases the possible values of NPV and the associated probabilities.

Table A11-2-2(b)

No. purchased	NPV	Probability
2000	+24 000	1.0
2500	+44 000	0.8
	−36 000	0.2
3000	−96 000	0.2
	−16 000	0.5
	+64 000	0.3

Few companies would opt for the 3000 level of purchases since it has the largest spread of possible outcome and the lowest, indeed negative, expected figure. The real choice is between the first two possibilities. Investment decisions under conditions of risk cannot be discussed in detail here, but the situation of more expected return being obtainable only at the price of greater diversity of return figures is typical. The investor has to decide whether the greater risk is compensated for by the increased expected return. Quite possibly, purchase of 2000 units with its guaranteed return of +24 000 would be selected.

11-2-3 (a)

Order level

		Q 0	1	2	3
X					
Demand level	0	0	−1.0	−2.0	−3.0
	1	0	1.8	0.8	−0.2
	2	0	1.8	3.6	2.6
	3	0	1.8	3.6	5.4

(b), (c) This is simply a roundabout way of saying calculate the expected profits. In previous questions we have adopted the form of putting the probabilities on the right of the table and the expected profits below. The expected profits emerge as 0, 1.52, 1.92, 1.48. The maximum daily profit is £1.92 when the order level is two units. In matrix form we could write

$$PA = (0.1 \quad 0.4 \quad 0.3 \quad 0.2) \begin{pmatrix} 0 & -1.0 & -2.0 & -3.0 \\ 0 & 1.8 & 0.8 & -0.2 \\ 0 & 1.8 & 3.6 & 2.6 \\ 0 & 1.8 & 3.6 & 5.4 \end{pmatrix}$$

$$PA = (0 \quad 1.52 \quad 1.92 \quad 1.48)$$

(d) The changes to be made to the profit table, A, are

$$\begin{pmatrix} 0 & 0 & 0 & 0 \\ 0 & 0.8 & 0.8 & 0.8 \\ 0 & 0.8 & 1.6 & 1.6 \\ 0 & 0.8 & 1.6 & 2.4 \end{pmatrix}$$

This array is subtracted, element from corresponding element from the original profit table/matrix to give the new profit table/matrix:

$$\begin{pmatrix} 0 & -1.0 & -2.0 & -3.0 \\ 0 & 1.0 & 0 & -1.0 \\ 0 & 1.0 & 2.0 & 1.0 \\ 0 & 1.0 & 2.0 & 3.0 \end{pmatrix}$$

The new expected profits are

$$0 \quad 0.8 \quad 0.8 \quad 0.2$$

so that the optimum order level is either one unit or two units.

11-2-4 (a) The workings here are as follows:

	Sales (000)	Probability	Expected value (000)
Year 1	5	0.2	1.0
	10	0.5	5.0
	20	0.3	6.0
			12.0
Year 2	5	0.4	2.0
	10	0.6	6.0
			8.0
Year 3	5	0.8	4.0
	10	0.2	2.0
			6.0

so that the expected sales each year are:

Year	Expected sales
1	12 000
2	8 000
3	6 000
Total expected sales	26 000

(b) Three-figure discount factors were given in the question. Workings are:

Year end	Expected sales (000)	Profit contribution (£)	Expected contribution for year (£000's)	Discount factor	Present value (£000's)
1	12	8	96	0.909	87.26
2	8	7	56	0.826	46.26
3	6	6	36	0.751	27.04
					160.56

So that the expected value of contributions is £160 560.

(c) For the expected sales of softback version of book, the workings are:

	Sales (000)	Probability	Expected value (£000's)
Year 2	20	0.5	10
	30	0.5	15
			25
Year 3	10	0.8	8
	20	0.2	4
			12
Year 4	5	0.9	4.5
	10	0.1	1.0
			5.5

For the expected present value of the softback alternative the workings are:

Year end	Expected sales (000)	Contribution (£)	Expected contribution for year (£000)	Discount factor	Present value (£000)
1	12	8	96	0.909	87.26
2	25	4	100	0.826	82.60
3	12	3	36	0.751	27.04
4	5.5	2	11	0.683	7.51
					204.41

This option, therefore, has an expected present value of contribution of £204 410. Note that the first-year sales and contribution of the hardback version are included.

We have now to advise on which option is preferable. No mention is made of the size of initial outlays necessary in the two schemes. Let K_H represent the outlay required for the hardback project and K_S be the further outlay on the softback. We then have the following:

Expected NPV (hardback only) $= £160\,560 - K_H$

Expected NPV (softback alternative) $= £204\,410 - (K_H + K_S)$

So, for the softback alternative to be preferable:

$$204\,410 - (K_H + K_S) > 160\,560 - K_H$$

i.e.,
$$K_S < 43\,850$$

That is, the outlay on the softback project must be less than £43 850. One last point: we have made no measures of the *spread* of possible NPV values. This would normally be considered in respect of sizeable projects.

11-3-3 Row two, column three (3); row five, column five (0).

11-3-4 A's probabilities must be such that no matter what B's actions A's expected gain is the same. If player B plays the first column, A's expected gain is E_1 where

$$E_1 = -p + (1-p)$$

This must be equated to the expected gain when B plays his second column

$$E_2 = 2p + 0(1-p)$$

Solving $E_1 = E_2$ gives $p = \frac{1}{4}, 1-p = \frac{3}{4}$

The value of the game to player A is given by either E_1 or E_2 when the optimal value of p is inserted. Thus the value of the game is 0.5. This is what A can expect to gain on average.

11-3-5 (i) (1,1); (ii) (1,1); (iii) (1,1); (iv) (1,1); (v) (3,3); (vi) (3,3) (each attempts to maximize the other's minimum payoff); (vii) (3,3) (under either assumption).

11-3-6 Note that variety D is dominated by variety B, so that D can be omitted.

    (i) (a) Variety B
        (b) Variety A
        (c) The Hurwicz numbers (H) will be 0.6 (best profit) $+0.4$ (worst profit) as shown below.

Variety	H
A	9 520
B	10 640
C	9 200

Thus variety B would be planted.
    (d) In the Laplace criterion we assume that each of the rainfall patterns is equally likely and the Laplace number (L) for a variety will be 1/3 (low rainfall profit) + 1/3 (medium rainfall profit) + 1/3 (high rainfall profit). So we obtain:

Variety	L
A	9100
B	9900
C	8300

Thus variety B would be selected in this case.
    (e) The regret matrix is:

	Low	Medium	High
A	0	4900	300
B	1100	0	1700
C	4400	3200	0

Thus variety B with maximum 'regrets' of only 1700 is clearly indicated.

11-4-2 (ii) 3, 5, 10, 7, 4, 8, 9, 2, 1, 6. The solution is non-unique as the positions of jobs 10 and 7 could be interchanged.

11-4-3 (ii) Reducing the problem to a two-machine case (as condition (b) for Johnson's method is satisfied). Let D_i be the combined machine A and B times and let E_i be the combined times on machines B and C. We obtain:

Job	D_i	E_i
(1)	42	37
(2)	34	35
(3)	36	39
(4)	33	42
(5)	27	35
(6)	36	34
(7)	35	38
(8)	30	44

which leads to the optimal sequence:

$$5, 8, 4, 2, 7, 3, 1, 6.$$

11-4-4 (i) Given the conditions stated, there are only eight alternative arrangements. The total times are given in the table.

Arrangement	Time (hours)
4 3 1 2 5	15.1
4 3 2 1 5	16.6
4 1 3 2 5	13.8
4 2 3 1 5	13.6
1 4 3 2 5	13.6
2 4 3 1 5	13.7
3 4 1 2 5	16.3
3 4 2 1 5	17.2

Thus there are two optimal sequences.
  (ii) 2.7 hours ($= 16.3 - 13.6$).

11-5-2 (i) The network with cost calculations is:

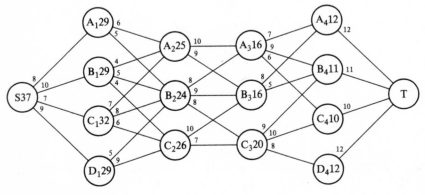

Figure A11-5-2(i)

The lowest overall cost is 37 and the cheapest is S, A_1, B_2, A_3, C_4, T.

(ii) The number of paths from S to each 'station' is shown in the circles below. There are 62 paths all told.

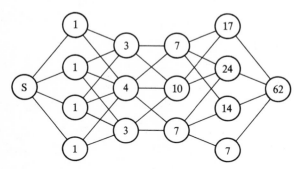

Figure A11-5-2(ii)

11-5-3 Let v_t = sales, month t; q_t = purchases, month t; I_t = stock at start of month t, then: $I_t = I_{t-1} + q_{t-1} - v_{t-1}$. The first stage concerns June ($t = 6$) and the problem is to

$$\text{Maximize} \quad \Pi_1 = 43v_6 - 39q_6$$

$$\text{subject to} \quad v_6 \leqslant I_6$$
$$q_6 \leqslant 500 - I_6 + v_6$$
$$q_6 \geqslant 0, v_6 \geqslant 0$$

Clearly $q_6 = 0$, $v_6 = I_6$ and maximum $\Pi_1 = 43I_6$. Now in stage two we

$$\text{Maximize} \quad \Pi_2 = 46v_5 - 34q_5 + \text{Max } \Pi_1$$
$$= 46v_5 - 34q_5 + 43I_6$$
$$= 46v_5 - 34q_5 + 43(I_5 + q_5 - v_5)$$
$$= 3v_5 + 9q_5 + 43I_5$$

$$\text{subject to} \quad v_5 \leqslant I_5$$
$$q_5 \leqslant 500 - I_5 + v_5$$
$$q_5 \geqslant 0, v_5 \geqslant 0$$

As will be apparent from a diagram, in the linear programming problem at each stage, the basic solution that will be optimal will be either $v_t = 0$, $q_t = 500 - I_t$ if the objective function contours (q_t on vertical axis) have slope $> +1$ or $v_t = I_t$, $q = 500$ if the objective function contours have slope $< +1$. The solution is non-unique if the contours have slope $+1$. In the case of the stage two problem the contours have negative slope $(-3/9)$ so that

$$\boxed{v_5 = I_5, q_5 = 500, \text{Max } \Pi_2 = 46I_5 + 4500}$$

In stage three we have

$$\text{Maximize} \quad \Pi_3 = 36v_4 - 38q_4 + \text{Max} \, \Pi_2$$
$$= 36v_4 - 38q_4 + 46I_5 + 4500$$
$$= 36v_4 - 38q_4 + 46(I_4 + q_4 - v_4) + 4500$$
$$= -10v_4 + 8q_4 + 46I_4 + 4500$$

The slope of the contours is $+1.25 \, (= 10/8)$ so that

$$\boxed{v_4 = 0, \, q_4 = 500 - I_4, \, \text{Max} \, \Pi_3 = 38I_4 + 8500}$$

In stage four

$$\text{Maximize} \quad \Pi_4 = 41v_3 - 36q_3 + 38(I_3 + q_3 - v_3) + 8500$$
$$= 3v_3 + 2q_3 + 38I_3 + 8500$$

The slope of the contours is $-3/2$, so $\boxed{\begin{array}{l} v_3 = I_3, q_3 = 500, \\ \text{Max} \, \Pi_4 = 41I_3 + 9500 \end{array}}$

In stage five

$$\text{Maximize} \quad \Pi_5 = -6v_2 + 4q_2 + 41I_2 + 9500$$

so that $\boxed{v_2 = 0, q_2 = 500 - I_2, \, \text{Max} \, \Pi_5 = 37I_2 + 11\,500}$

In stage six

$$\text{Maximize} \quad \Pi_6 = 8v_1 + 2q_1 + 37I_1 + 11\,500$$

so $\boxed{v_1 = I_1, q_1 = 500, \, \text{Max} \, \Pi_6 = 45I_1 + 12\,500}$

Now since I_1 (January stocks) $= 250$ we have $v_1 = 250$ and Max $\Pi_6 = 23\,750$. This is the maximum overall profit that can be attained. Now, beginning the unrolling process, in stage five since

$$I_2 = I_1 + q_1 - v_1 \text{ so } I_2 = 250 + 500 - 250 = 500, \quad \therefore \, q_2 = 0.$$

And so on. The fully unrolled outcome is:

$$v_1 = 250$$
$$q_1 = 500$$
$$I_2 = 500$$
$$v_2 = 0$$
$$q_2 = 0$$
$$I_3 = 500$$
$$v_3 = 500$$
$$q_3 = 500$$
$$I_4 = 500$$

$$v_4 = 0$$
$$q_4 = 0$$
$$I_5 = 500$$
$$v_5 = 500$$
$$q_5 = 500$$
$$I_6 = 500$$
$$v_6 = 500$$
$$q_6 = 0$$

Although the total profit is 23 750, it varies greatly between the months. The cash flow is

January	−6 250
February	0
March	+2 500
April	0
May	+6 000
June	+21 500
	23 750

11-5-4 First note that the £3000 expenditure alternative on Top-Pop is not feasible given the budget and the necessity to promote each product. Let stage (1) consider only Slim-Fizz expenditures. We have

State	Π_1
1.0	20
1.5	25
2.0	27.5
2.5	30

For stage (2) consider Slim-Fizz and Top-Pop together

State	Composition		Π_2
	Top-Pop	Stage 1 state	
2.0	1.0	1.0	35
2.5	1.0	1.5	40
3.0	2.0	1.0	40
	1.0	2.0	42.5
3.5	2.0	1.5	45
	1.0	2.5	45

Note that no decision has yet been taken—all is revealed at the unrolling stage. Now for stage (3) (Slim-Fizz + Top-Pop + Perraigne):

| State | Composition | | |
	Perraigne	Stage 2 state	Π_3
3.0	1.0	2.0	50
3.5	1.5	2.0	60
	1.0	2.5	55
4.0	2.0	2.0	65
	1.5	2.5	65
	1.0	3.0	57.5
4.5	2.0	2.5	70
	1.5	3.0	67.5
	1.0	3.5	60

The best entry in the Π_3 column is 70 which means that the Perraigne investment must be 2.0 and the stage (2) state must be 2.5. So, returning to the stage (2) table the only form of the 2.5 state is for Top-Pop to be 1.0 and for the state of 1.5 to hold at stage one. This means an investment of 1.5 in Slim-Fizz. In the present example we have considered 19 combinations of 3-, 2-, and 1-product expenditures. After deleting the 3.0 Top-Pop alternative there are only 24 combinations of expenditures remaining (some of which are unfeasible). Thus the method is not a great improvement on enumeration in this case. However, as the number of possibilities increases, dynamic programming evaluates a decreasing percentage of the number of possible combinations and can work well on problems for which complete enumeration is quite unfeasible.

SELECTED BIBLIOGRAPHY

Bellman, R. E. (1957), 'Dynamic Programming,' Princeton University Press.

Churchman, C. W., R. L. Ackoff, and E. L. Arnoff (1957), 'Introduction to Operations Research,' Wiley.

Daellenbach, H. G., and J. A. George (1978), 'Introduction to Operations Research Techniques,' Allyn and Bacon.

Littlechild, S. C. (1977), 'Operational Research for Managers,' Philip Allan.

Makower, M. S., and E. Williamson (1967), 'Teach Yourself Operational Research,' E.U.P.

Metzger, R. W. (1958), 'Elementary Mathematical Programming,' Wiley.

Morrel, J. (1972), 'Management Decisions and the Role of Forecasting,' Penguin Books.

Murdoch, J. (1978), 'Queueing Theory,' Macmillan.

Phillips, D. T., A. Ravindran, and J. Solberg (1976), 'Operations Research: Principles and Practice,' Wiley.

Samuels, J. M., and F. M. Wilkes (1980a), 'Management of Company Finance' (3rd edn) Nelsons.

——— and ——— (1980b) 'Company Finance Workbook,' Nelsons.

Sasieni, M., A. Yaspan, and M. Friedman (1959), 'Operations Research: Methods and Problems,' Wiley.

Shamblin, J. E., and G. T. Stevens (1978), 'Operations Research: A Fundamental Approach,' McGraw-Hill.

Taha, H. A. (1976), 'Operations Research: An Introduction' (2nd edn), Collier Macmillan.

Theierauf, R. J., and R. C. Keklamp (1975), 'Decision Making Through Operations Research' (2nd edn), Wiley.

Wagner, H. M. (1972), 'Principles of Operations Research,' Prentice Hall.

Wheelwright, S. C., and S. Makridakis (1977), 'Forecasting Methods for Management' (2nd edn), Wiley.

Wild, R. (1971), 'The Techniques of Production Management,' Holt, Rinehart and Winston.

Wilkes, F. M. (1977), 'Capital Budgeting Techniques,' Wiley.

INDEX